ANIMAL STORIES

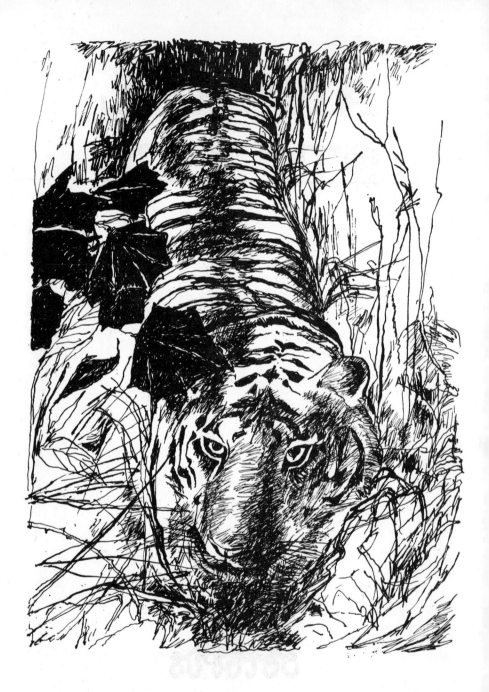

ANIMAL STORIES

Edited by
Anthea Ridett
Illustrated by
Sally Stiff

Contents

First published 1980 by
Octopus Books Limited
59 Grosvenor Street
London W 1
Reprinted 1981, 1982, 1983, 1984, 1986, 1987

ISBN 0 7064 1173 0

Printed in Czechoslovakia
50397/8

THE NIGHTINGALE AND THE ROSE

Oscar Wilde

'She said that she would dance with me if I brought her red roses,' cried the young Student, 'but in all my garden there is no red rose.'

From her nest in the holm-oak tree the Nightingale heard him, and she looked out through the leaves and wondered.

'No red rose in all my garden!' he cried, and his beautiful eyes filled with tears. 'Ah, on what little things does happiness depend! I have read all that the wise men have written, and all the secrets of philosophy are mine, yet for want of a red rose is my life made wretched.'

'Here at last is a true lover,' said the Nightingale. 'Night after night have I sung of him though I knew him not: night after night have I told his story to the stars and now I see him. His hair is dark as the hyacinth-blossom, and his lips are red as the rose of his desire, but passion has made his face like pale ivory and sorrow has set her seal upon his brow.'

'The Prince gives a ball tomorrow night,' murmured the young Student, 'and my love will be of the company. If I bring her a red rose she will dance with me till dawn. If I bring her a red rose, I shall hold her in my arms, and she will lean her head upon my shoulder and her hand will be clasped in mine. But there is no red rose in my garden, so

I shall sit lonely and she will pass me by. She will have no heed of me, and my heart will break.'

'Here, indeed, is the true lover,' said the Nightingale. 'What I sing of, he suffers: what is joy to me, to him is pain. Surely love is a wonderful thing. It is more precious than emeralds and dearer than fine opals. Pearls and pomegranates cannot buy it, nor is it set forth in the market-place. It may not be purchased of the merchants, nor can it be weighed out in the balance for gold.'

'The musicians will sit in their gallery,' said the young Student, 'and play upon their stringed instruments, and my love will dance to the sound of the harp and the violin. She will dance so lightly that her feet will not touch the floor, and the courtiers in their gay dresses will throng round her. But with me she will not dance, for I have no red rose to give her'; and he flung himself down on the grass, and buried his face in his hands, and wept.

'Why is he weeping?' asked a little Green Lizard, as he ran past him with his tail in the air.

'Why, indeed?' said the Butterfly, who was fluttering about after a sunbeam.

'Why, indeed?' whispered a Daisy to his neighbour, in a soft, low voice.

'He is weeping for a red rose,' said the Nightingale.

'For a red rose?' they cried; 'how very ridiculous!' and the little Lizard, who was something of a cynic, laughed outright.

But the Nightingale understood the secret of the Student's sorrow, and she sat silent in the oak-tree, and thought about the mystery of Love.

Suddenly she spread her brown wings for flight, and soared into the air. She passed through the grove like a shadow and like a shadow she sailed across the garden.

In the centre of the grass-plot was standing a beautiful rose-tree, and when she saw it she flew over to it, and lit upon a spray.

'Give me a red rose,' she cried, 'and I will sing you my sweetest song.'

But the Tree shook its head.

'My roses are white,' it answered; 'as white as the foam of the sea, and whiter than the snow on the mountain. But go to my brother who grows round the old sun-dial, and perhaps he will give you what you want.'

So the Nightingale flew over to the Rose-tree that was growing round the old sun-dial.

'Give me a red rose,' she cried, 'and I will sing you my sweetest song.'

But the Tree shook its head.

'My roses are yellow,' it answered; 'as yellow as the hair of the mermaiden who sits upon an amber throne, and yellower than the daffodil that blooms in the meadow before the mower comes with his scythe. But go to my brother who grows beneath the Student's window, and perhaps he will give you what you want.'

So the Nightingale flew over to the Rose-tree that was growing beneath the Student's window.

'Give me a red rose,' she cried, 'and I will sing you my sweetest song.'

But the Tree shook its head.

'My roses are red,' it answered; 'as red as the feet of the dove, and redder than the great fans of coral that wave and wave in the ocean-cavern. But the winter has chilled my veins, and the frost has nipped my buds, and the storm has broken my branches, and I shall have no roses at all this year.'

'One red rose is all I want,' cried the Nightingale, 'only one red rose! Is there no way by which I can get it?'

'There is a way,' answered the Tree, 'but it is so terrible that I dare not tell it to you.'

'Tell it to me,' said the Nightingale, 'I am not afraid.'

'If you want a red rose,' said the Tree, 'you must build it out of music by moonlight, and stain it with your own heart's-blood. You must sing to me with your breast against a thorn. All night long you must sing to me, and the thorn must pierce your heart, and your life-blood must flow into my veins, and become mine.'

'Death is a great price to pay for a red rose,' cried the Nightingale, 'and Life is very dear to all. It is pleasant to sit in the green wood, and to watch the Sun in his chariot of gold, and the Moon in her chariot of pearl. Sweet is the scent of the hawthorn, and sweet are the bluebells that hide in the valley, and the heather that blows on the hill. Yet Love is better than Life, and what is the heart of a bird compared to the heart of a man?'

So she spread her brown wings for flight, and soared into the air. She swept over the garden like a shadow, and like a shadow she sailed through the grove.

The young Student was still lying on the grass, where she had left him, and the tears were not yet dry in his beautiful eyes.

'Be happy,' cried the Nightingale, 'be happy; you shall have your red rose. I will build it out of music by moonlight, and stain it with my own heart's-blood. All that I ask of you in return is that you will be a true lover, for Love is wiser than Philosophy, though he is wise, and mightier than Power, though he is mighty. Flame-coloured are his wings, and coloured like flame is his body. His lips are sweet as honey, and his breath is like frankincense.'

The Student looked up from the grass, and listened, but he could not understand what the Nightingale was saying to him, for he only knew the things that are written down in books.

But the Oak-tree understood, and felt sad, for he was very fond of the little Nightingale who had built her nest in his branches.

'Sing me one last song,' he whispered; 'I shall feel lonely when you are gone.'

So the Nightingale sang to the Oak-tree, and her voice was like water bubbling from a silver jar.

When she had finished her song, the Student got up, and pulled a note-book and a lead-pencil out of his pocket.

'She has form,' he said to himself, as he walked away through the grove—'that cannot be denied to her; but has she got feeling? I am afraid not. In fact, she is like most artists; she is all style without any sincerity. She would not sacrifice herself for others. She thinks merely of music, and everybody knows that the arts are selfish. Still, it must be admitted that she has some beautiful notes in her voice. What a pity it is that they do not mean anything, or do any practical good!' And he went into his room, and lay down on his little pallet-bed, and began to think of his love; and, after a time, he fell asleep.

And when the moon shone in the heavens the Nightingale flew to the Rose-tree, and set her breast against the thorn. All night long she sang, with her breast against the thorn, and the cold crystal Moon leaned down and listened. All night long she sang, and the thorn went deeper and deeper into her breast, and her life-blood ebbed away from her.

And when the student opened his window he found the beautiful, red rose.

She sang first of the birth of love in the heart of a boy and a girl. And on the topmost spray of the Rose-tree there blossomed a marvellous rose, petal following petal, as song followed song. Pale was it, at first, as the mist that hangs over the river—pale as the feet of the morning, and silver as the wings of the dawn. As the shadow of a rose in a mirror of silver, as the shadow of a rose in a waterpool, so was the rose that blossomed on the topmost spray of the Tree.

But the Tree cried to the Nightingale to press closer against the thorn. 'Press closer, little Nightingale,' cried the Tree, 'or the Day will come before the rose is finished.'

So the Nightingale pressed closer against the thorn, and louder and louder grew her song, for she sang of the birth of passion in the soul of a man and a maid.

And a delicate flush of pink came into the leaves of the rose, like the flush in the face of the bridegroom when he kisses the lips of the bride. But the thorn had not yet reached her heart, so the rose's heart remained white, for only a Nightingale's heart's-blood can crimson the heart of a rose.

And the Tree cried to the Nightingale to press closer against the thorn. 'Press closer, little Nightingale,' cried the Tree, 'or the Day will come before the rose is finished.'

So the Nightingale pressed closer against the thorn, and the thorn touched her heart, and a fierce pang of pain shot through her. Bitter, bitter was the pain, and wilder and wilder grew her song, for she sang of the Love that is perfected by Death, of the Love that dies not in the tomb.

And the marvellous rose became crimson, like the rose of the eastern sky. Crimson was the girdle of petals, and crimson as a ruby was the heart.

But the Nightingale's voice grew fainter, and her little wings began to beat, and a film came over her eyes. Fainter and fainter grew her song, and she felt something choking in her throat.

Then she gave one last burst of music. The white Moon heard it, and she forgot the dawn, and lingered on in the sky. The red rose heard it, and it trembled all over with ecstasy, and opened its petals to the cold morning air. Echo bore it to her purple cavern in the hills, and woke the sleeping shepherds from their dreams. It floated through the reeds of the river, and they carried its message to the sea.

'Look, look!' cried the Tree, 'the rose is finished now'; but the Nightingale made no answer, for she was lying dead in the long grass, with the thorn in her heart.

And at noon the Student opened his window and looked out.

'Why, what a wonderful piece of luck!' he cried; 'here is a red rose! I have never seen any rose like it in all my life. It is so beautiful that I am sure it has a long Latin name'; and he leaned down and plucked it.

Then he put on his hat, and ran up to the Professor's house with the rose in his hand.

The daughter of the Professor was sitting in the door-way winding blue silk on a reel, and her little dog was lying at her feet.

'You said that you would dance with me if I brought you a red rose,' cried the Student. 'Here is the reddest rose in all the world. You will wear it tonight next your heart, and as we dance together it will tell you how I love you.'

But the girl frowned.

'I am afraid it will not go with my dress,' she answered; 'and, besides, the Chamberlain's nephew has sent me some real jewels, and everybody knows that jewels cost far more than flowers.'

'Well, upon my word, you are very ungrateful,' said the Student angrily; and he threw the rose into the street, where it fell into the gutter, and a cart-wheel went over it.

'Ungrateful!' said the girl. 'I tell you what, you are very rude; and, after all, who are you? Only a Student. Why, I don't believe you have even got silver buckles to your shoes as the Chamberlain's nephew has'; and she got up from her chair and went into the house.

'What a silly thing Love is!' said the Student as he walked away. 'It is not half as useful as Logic, for it does not prove anything, and it is always telling one of things that are not going to happen, and making one believe things that are not true. In fact, it is quite unpractical, and, as in this age to be practical is everything, I shall go back to Philosophy and study Metaphysics.'

So he returned to his room and pulled out a great dusty book, and began to read.

THE MIRACLE CLIMB

Gerald Durrell

The fauna of Australia is something that makes any self-respecting naturalist excited. It has been described by one person as 'the attic of the world', the place where all the old things are stored; this is quite an apt description but is not strictly accurate. The two most interesting orders in Australia are the monotremes and the marsupials. The monotremes are the most primitive of mammals and have retained many of the characteristics which prove how mammals are descended from the reptiles. Superficially, the monotremes resemble conventional mammals in the sense that they breathe air, they are covered with fur, and they are warm blooded, but their chief and most astonishing reptilian characteristic is the fact that they lay eggs, and then, when the young hatch from the eggs, the parents feed them on milk. Most famous of the monotremes, of course, is the Duck–Billed Platypus.

The marsupials are remarkable for a number of characteristics, best known of which is, of course, that the majority of them have a very short gestation period and give birth to their young in an almost embryonic condition. The baby then finds its way to the mother's pouch and continues its development from there. The marsupials are very primitive creatures and it is lucky for them that the land bridge over which they spread into Australia was destroyed, for the more conventional mammals (such as tigers, leopards, lions and so on) would have made short work of them. However, cut off as they were, with this great continent to themselves, they evolved along the most amazing lines—a sort of parallel evolution took place; instead of the great herds of hoofed animals that developed in Africa, Asia and America, you get the kangaroos and wallabies, who filled the same grazing niche. The places occupied by bushbabies or squirrels in other parts of the world were occupied in Australia by Possums and phalangers. A creature like the Badger has its equivalent in Australia in the Wombat, and the predators are represented by such things as the Tasmanian Wolf—not a true wolf, of course, but a marsupial, looking remarkably like its counterpart. So not only did the marsupials adapt themselves to the various niches but they came to resemble, in habits and sometimes in appearance, totally unrelated creatures that had evolved in other parts of the world: thus, the little Honey-Eaters look, at first glance, exactly like some of the smaller species of mouse; the Wombat resembles the Badger; the Tasmanian Wolf a member of the dog family, and there is even a Banded Anteater, to complete the picture. As an example of evolution the continent of Australia, with its monotremes and marsupials, is just as extraordinary as the Galapagos Islands, which so excited Darwin's imagination that he evolved the whole evolutionary thesis.

By and large, before the coming of man the marsupials had a pretty idyllic set-up. Then came the aborigines and with them (one suspects) came the Dingo, a very cunning predator who rapidly became, together with his owners, the aborigines, Public Enemy Number One to the fauna. Although the Dingoes multiplied and spread, they did not appear to upset the balance of nature very much; neither did the aborigines, for there were too few of them, but with the advent of white men, the picture became very much blacker for the marsupials. Not only were their numbers depleted by human beings, but their habitat was invaded by introduced creatures such as the European fox and rabbit, the fox on the one hand acting as predator and the rabbit acting as competition to the grazing marsupials for the food. Then came the sheep, and this is where the larger grazing marsupials started to acquire a bad reputation, for now they were in competition with the sheep and the sheep was more important to man. The farmers opened up whole new areas which, prior to this, had been arid and unsuitable country even for kangaroos and wallabies, and by driving wells and bore-holes they produced lush pastures for their sheep. They also found, to their annoyance, that the kangaroos and wallabies were deeply appreciative of this and poured into these new areas in numbers equalling, and in some cases exceeding, the sheep. So what is called the 'kangaroo menace' came into being.

Before you can control any wild animal, you have to know something about its basic biology; a simple policy of slaughter—quite apart from its threat to the survival of that particular species—is liable to do untold damage to the whole ecological structure of the country. An unbiological approach in different parts of the world to problems of this sort has, in the past, proved disastrous. So if an animal is becoming a pest you must set to work to learn everything you can about it; it is a case of 'knowing thine enemy'. The Wildlife Department of the CSIRO was set up with just this object in mind. As soon as an animal is proclaimed a pest, the CSIRO moves in and investigates the whole problem. They have to act, really, in the capacity of a High Court Judge, because in many cases a creature has been labelled a pest, and upon investigation, has proved to be considerably less of a pest than was thought. At Canberra, the CSIRO have a large laboratory where one of their major studies at the moment is the two species of kangaroo—the Great Red and the Great Grey—so it was here that we went to get first-hand information on what would be the ultimate fate of the two largest and most spectacular marsupials in the world.

The team is headed by Harry Frith, who is one of Australia's foremost biologists and, among other things, famous for his brilliant ecological studies of various Australian ducks and geese and the Mallee-Fowl. He is a stocky, curly-haired man, his face browned and seamed by the sun and wind, the possessor of the most cynically amused pair of eyes I have seen for a long time, and of a dry, caustic and deceptively laconic approach towards his work. When I suggested that we would like to do some film sequences of their work, Harry stared at me moodily.

'I'll take you down to the yards,' he said, 'and introduce you to the boys. I don't mind you doing some film sequences but it's up to the boys. They're all working hard and it would mean they would have to waste a certain amount of time with you, so the decision must rest with them. If they tell you to push off, I can't do anything about it.' Then he smiled encouragingly at me.

Hoping that 'the boys' were going to be a trifle less misanthropic, we followed him down to the yards, which were a series of paddocks in which various species of kangaroo and wallaby were kept and bred. Here we were introduced to Geoff Sharman, a tall and utterly charming Australian scientist who is probably one of the world's foremost authorities on the biology of the marsupial. Having, as it were, pushed us into the lion's den, Harry then retreated to get on with his work, leaving me to try to make my mark with Geoff Sharman. This, to my relief, proved far easier than I had been led to anticipate; not only was Geoff a charming person, but so enthusiastic over his work that anybody who evinced the slightest interest in it became somebody worth talking to.

'We're looking for information that can be used for assessing the wild animals we find in the field. In other words, we're measuring the young in the pouch to see how they grow, and from this we can build up growth curves, which can be used to tell the age of the wild-caught young ones,' Geoff explained to me. 'We're also looking at their teeth. This is very important because the eruption pattern of the teeth seems to be a good way of telling the age of a kangaroo. This will give us some idea of the actual age structure of any population we are dealing with in the wilds. Once we've found that out here, the next thing is to go out and get a wild population of kangaroos marked in some way so that we can identify them. Then we examine their teeth every time we capture them, and see if we get the same kind of eruption pattern in the wild animal.'

'What's the breeding potentiality of a female kangaroo?' I asked him.

'Terrific,' Geoff said. 'It's like a Ford production belt. She can have one growing inside her, one in the pouch fastened to a teat and another one out of the pouch but still feeding from her.'

I asked him about the actual birth of the kangaroo, a thing that had always fascinated me, and it was at this juncture that he dropped his bomb-shell.

'Oh, the *birth*,' he said casually, 'I've got a bit of film I can show you of that.'

I stood rooted to the spot and stared at him.

'You've actually filmed it?' I said incredulously, 'but I thought that very few people had ever witnessed a birth, let alone got it on film.'

'Well, I think we're the first to get it on film,' he said. 'But we've got it down to quite a fine art here. We can tell you to within a few hours when the female is going to give birth.'

Chris and Jacquie were further down the yards, making love through the wire to an enchanting and precious wallaby. I rushed down to Chris.

'Chris, do you know what Geoff Sharman's just told me?'

'What?' said Chris without interest, continuing his love-making with the wallaby.

'He's just told me that he's got some film of the actual birth of a kangaroo!'

'Oh?' said Chris, somewhat mystified by my obvious excitement, and appearing to be under the impression that to have a piece of film of a kangaroo birth was most commonplace. 'So what?'

'What do you mean, so what?' I said. 'You moron, don't you realize that very few people have ever *seen* a kangaroo birth, and I didn't think anyone had ever *filmed* it. In fact, I think that Geoff is probably the first person to do so.'

'Um,' said Chris, brightening a little, 'is it very interesting?'

'Well, of course it's interesting,' I said. 'The thing's only about the size of a hazlenut when it's born—it's virtually an embryo, in fact, and once it's born it then has to climb all the way up its mother and get into the pouch.'

'That sounds as though it would make a good sequence,' said Chris, displaying more enthusiasm. 'I wonder if Geoff would let us use his film?'

We went over to where Geoff had extracted a hairless and rather revolting-looking baby kangaroo from its mother's pouch and was solemnly weighing it in a cloth bag.

'Geoff,' I said wheedlingly, 'is there any chance of you letting us have that piece of film on the kangaroo birth?'

'Sure,' he said instantly, and then dampened my hopes by adding, 'but you'll have to check with Harry first.'

'Oh yes,' I said, 'I'll do that, but look, if the film for some reason is not suitable, is there a chance of our re-shooting it?'

'Oh yes,' said Geoff, 'that's easy enough, we've got several females that will be ready fairly soon, but again I can't let you do that without permission from Harry.'

'But,' I said, getting things quite clear, 'you'd have no objection to our doing it providing Harry says it's okay?'

'None at all,' said Geoff. 'I'd be glad to help.'

We had arranged to meet Harry for lunch and during it I cunningly kept off the subject of marsupial births until Harry had engulfed several lamb chops and a couple of pints of beer and was beginning to look a little bit benign round the edges. Then I took a deep breath, and started.

'Harry, Geoff Sharman tells me that you have some film of a kangaroo birth,' I said.

Harry eyed me inimically.

'Yes,' he said cautiously.

'I suppose it wouldn't be possible for us to have a print of that to include in the series?' I said.

'I don't see why not,' said Harry, 'but I'm afraid the decision must rest with Geoff.'

'Oh,' I said, 'well that's all right then, he has already said yes, but he had to have your confirmation.'

Harry ruminated on this and there was a faint twinkle in his eye.

'But supposing,' I said, hastily pouring him out another glass of beer, 'that the film is not entirely suitable for television?'

'Well,' said Harry, 'let's suppose it, what then?'

'Well, would it be possible to re-shoot it?'

'I presume,' said Harry dryly, 'that you've already got Geoff Sharman's permission for this?'

'Well, in a tentative sort of way,' I admitted, 'but he said that you'd have to give the final word.'

'I don't mind,' said Harry. 'If Geoff feels he can fit it in with his work and if he can organize it for you, I don't mind a bit.'

I heaved a deep sigh of relief and beamed at Christopher.

'This, dear boy,' I said, 'is going to be the climax of the series. If we get it!'

After lunch we went jubilantly back to Geoff Sharman to tell him that Harry had agreed. Geoff was delighted and had very soon fixed up a projector in his room in order to show us the coveted piece of film. This, however, proved disappointing, for although it showed the details that were of importance from Geoff's point of view as a scientist, it was unsuitable for television. This meant that we would have to put into operation Plan Two, which was to re-film the whole thing.

'I think Pamela is probably our best bet,' said Geoff, staring at a doe-eyed Grey Kangaroo who was busy picking up pieces of carrot in her monkey-like front paws and chewing them vigorously. 'She is due in about a week's time and, anyway, if we fail with her we can fall back on Marilyn or Marlene, who should be giving birth shortly afterwards.'

'What's the drill then?' I asked.

'Well, the first signs,' said Geoff, 'are that she starts to clean out the pouch. This generally happens a few hours before the birth itself. If you are somewhere within easy reach, we can 'phone you and it will give you time to set up the lights and the cameras.'

'Won't the camera and lights worry her?' asked Chris.

'I shouldn't think so for a moment,' said Geoff, 'she's a very placid creature.'

So began a period of waiting, while we hovered round Pamela like expectant fathers, filming her every move. But we wanted to try to show the full picture of the kangaroo problem as well as the birth, if we were lucky enough to get it, and so Harry, together with Bevan Bowan, took us out to a 'spread' not far from Canberra (a tiny little smallholding of some 200,000 acres) on which they were investigating another facet of the kangaroo's biology.

'We're endeavouring to find out a number of different things,' said Harry as we bumped our way over the sun-bleached grass in among the eucalyptus trees. 'Firstly, we want to know how the groups of kangaroos move—how much territory they cover in, say, a week or a month. This we can only do by catching them up and marking them, so that they are recognisable from a distance, through field-glasses. We do this by putting a coloured collar on them, with

She was slumped in the corner, oblivious to everything around her.

a number. You'll see how we do it presently. The other thing we are trying to find out is whether or not the kangaroo is a selective feeder. Now take East Africa; there's a country that supports vast quantities of game animals and the reason they haven't turned it into a gigantic dust bowl is because they are selective feeders, so that one species of antelope feeds on a certain series of plants and ignores others, which are, in turn, eaten by a different species of antelope. Where your undermining of the country and the creation of erosion comes in, is when you introduce a species that is an indiscriminate feeder. In East Africa the damage is largely done by the huge herds of skinny and totally unattractive cattle, and flocks of goats which just chew up everything in sight. It's possible that we might find a roughly similar situation here. It's possible that we might find that the kangaroo is a selective feeder and therefore, in fact, does less damage to the country than the rabbit or the sheep, although, of course, if this proves to be so, we are going to have the devil's own job persuading the sheep farmer that this is the case.'

He chuckled reminiscently.

'I remember up north,' he said, 'when I went about telling the rice farmers that the Magpie Goose was not the pest that they claimed, I nearly got lynched on several occasions, and once I was pulled out of my car by a giant of a man, who would have flattened me if it had not been for the fact that I luckily had Bevan with me.'

'I never knew conservation could be so bloodthirsty,' I said.

'You'd be surprised,' said Harry. 'No, but it's quite obvious that the kangaroo is a problem. I've known of farms where the kangaroo population has outnumbered the sheep population by about three to one. Obviously this is detrimental to the sheep farmers' interests and something must be done about it. What we hope to achieve is a control over the kangaroo so that we don't have to exterminate them. I see no reason why, if we can learn to control them successfully, we should not have both kangaroos and sheep.'

We had been driving for some considerable time along the edge of a barbed wire fence and we came now to a curious structure at one corner of this gigantic field. A sort of funnel had been built alongside the fence, using the fence as one wall and wire netting for the other. This funnel led into a small paddock some thirty feet square.

'This,' said Harry, 'is the trap. Now the art of catching the kangaroo is this; first you find your kangaroos and then you chivvy them gently until they're heading along the fence. Gradually you increase speed, but you have to do it very cautiously—if you are too quick, you'll panic them and they'll jump over the fence and get away. You must chivvy them at just the right speed to keep them on the go so they'll hop right down that fence, through the funnel and into that trap, and then you've got to run like hell to catch them before they jump out of the trap.'

He leant out of the window to shout some instructions to Bevan, who was driving the other Land-Rover, and then both vehicles were off, circling the paddock, searching for the kangaroos. Travelling at 35 miles an hour over that bumpy terrain, swerving in and out of the eucalyptus trees, was quite a hair-raising experience. The first creatures we disturbed were a flock of Emus, who behaved in a fairly typically stupid manner. Instead of breaking away from us, they seemed so panic-stricken and fascinated that they ran to try to cut across our bows. Having got just in front of us, they then appeared to become quite hysterical and incapable of running to one side, and thumped along in front of us, their great feet almost touching their chins in their efforts to out-run us. Presently we came to a fence and, to my astonishment, the Emus made no effort to stop, but just ran straight at it. One went through, leaving a cloud of feathers behind him, but the other one struck the barbed wire at an angle and bounced off. He staggered back and then took another run at it, and this time he was successful, although he, too, left enough feathers behind him to stuff a small cushion.

'That's why the farmers don't like Emus, either,' said Harry, 'they do the hell of a lot of damage to the fences.'

We progressed for about another quarter of an hour, then suddenly heard Bevan honking his horn. Looking over, we saw a flock of about ten Grey Kangaroos sitting stock-still at the edge of a little wood, staring at us with their ears pricked. Harry swerved violently round a tree to correct our course and we headed straight for the kangaroos, while Bevan drove out further to prevent them from breaking back. As we drew close to them they started hopping off in a rather nonchalant fashion, but as the vehicles accelerated the kangaroos panicked and started running away in real earnest. It was fascinating to watch them taking those prodigious leaps, using their tails purely as a balancing organ. Soon we had chivvied them round so that they were lolloping along the length of the fence towards the trap, and here both vehicles suddenly put on a burst of speed. I would not have thought it was possible to drive through that sort of country at 50 miles an hour, but we did it. The kangaroos were by now thoroughly panic-stricken, and although some of them stopped and made an attempt to leap the fence, we always managed to prevent them by putting on another burst of speed. At last, the trap came into sight. A final burst of speed from the two Land-Rovers and the panic-stricken kangaroos raced down the funnel and found themselves at a dead end. We clamped on our brakes, leapt out of the Land-Rover and raced down the fence into the trap amongst the milling mob of kangaroos. There is only one way to catch a kangaroo successfully and that is to avoid, at all costs, his massive and potentially lethal hind legs, and grasp him firmly by the tail. He then proceeds to bounce in front of you until he is exhausted or until someone else comes to your rescue and grabs other parts of his anatomy. This we proceeded to do until we had all the kangaroos firmly hogtied. Under the baking sun, the poor things were panting and sweating with the exertion and the heat. Carefully each one was dressed up in a neat, celluloid collar in different colours and with a different number on each, and we took them, one by one, outside the trap and let them go. Most of them hopped away rapidly and with obvious relief, but there was one small one who, when placed on the ground, remained standing stock-still, staring into space. Harry went up behind it and patted it gently on the rump, whereupon the kangaroo turned on him ferociously, and an extremely amusing boxing match took place, with Harry endeavouring to shoo the kangaroo away and the kangaroo endeavouring to get its own back on Harry. As the kangaroo only measured about three feet high and Harry was a good six feet, the marsupial's attacks on him had all the temerity of David's encounter with Goliath. At last, however, it decided that its desire to disembowel Harry was doomed to failure and so, with a certain amount of reluctance, it hopped off to join the others.

It was now getting near the time when we could expect the birth and so we took up residence in a Motel, conveniently situated about half a mile down the road from the laboratories. This was when Pamela decided that she was going to give us a run for our money. For three days she designed a series of false alarms for us, and she timed these so cleverly that they did the maximum amount of damage to our nervous systems. Suddenly, as we were in the middle of lunch, or in the bath, or just drifting cosily off to sleep, there would be a frantic telephone message from Geoff to say he thought, from Pamela's behaviour, that the birth was imminent. If we happened to be bathing or sleeping it meant a frantic scramble into our clothes, a wild gallop into the courtyard with our equipment, and we would pile into the Land-Rover and drive off with a deafening roar. Every time we got down to the yards, however, Pamela would be munching some delicacy and would look up with a faintly surprised air that we should have bothered to pay her yet another visit.

Then came the evening when, in the middle of dinner, the Motel proprietor came galloping into the dining-room and informed us that Geoff Sharman had just 'phoned and said that *quite definitely* Pamela was going to give birth at any minute. Knocking over a bottle of wine and leaving our napkins strewn across the floor like autumn leaves, we fled from the dining-room, pursued by cheers and shouts of 'Good luck' from our fellow guests. Chris, in his eagerness, started the Land-Rover so quickly that I was left with one foot inside and one on the ground when he was changing into top; with a fearful effort that almost dislocated my spine, I managed to scramble in, and we zoomed down the road to the laboratories.

'She's definitely going to do it this time,' said Geoff. 'I'm quite certain of it.'

She couldn't have picked a better time. It was pitch dark, bitterly cold, and everything was drenched in dew. Hastily we rigged up the arc lights and got the cameras in position. Pamela was sitting, leaning against a fence and getting on with the good work of cleaning out her pouch. This she did very fastidiously, using her front paws. The pouch, when untenanted, tends to exude a waxy substance similar to the wax in a human ear, and it was this that she was cleaning out, carefully combing the furry interior of the pouch with her claws. We filmed her doing this and then sat and gazed at her expectantly. She continued cleaning her pouch out for about half an hour, stared round moodily, then hopped down to the far end of the paddock and started to eat.

'I think we've got a little time to wait,' said Geoff.

'Are you quite sure that this isn't another of her false alarms?' I asked.

'Oh no,' said Geoff, 'this is the real thing; she wouldn't clean out her pouch as thoroughly as that if she wasn't going to give birth.'

We sat in the freezing cold and stared at Pamela and she stared back at us, her jaws moving rhythmically.

'Let's go into the hut while we're waiting,' said Geoff, 'it will be a little bit warmer. If your hands get too cold, you won't be able to manipulate your equipment.'

We crowded into the tiny shed, where I produced, to the delight of the assembled company, a bottle of whisky that I had had the foresight to bring with me. We took it in turns, between drinks, to go out and peer hopefully in Pamela's direction.

It came as somewhat of a relief when one of Geoff's assistants appeared in the doorway of the hut and said, 'Action stations, I think we're off.'

We scrambled out of the hut and took up our positions. Pamela was moving about, looking rather uncomfortable. Presently, against the fence of the paddock, she dug a shallow hole in the ground and then took up a position in it, with her tail sticking out between her hind legs and her back resting against the fence. She sat like this for a few minutes and then obviously started feeling uncomfortable again, for she lay down on her side for a few seconds and then stood up and moved around for a bit. Then she went back to the hole she had dug and again sat with her tail sticking out between her legs and her back against the fence. She was completely unperturbed by the fact that arc lights, two cine cameras and the eyes of about a dozen people were fixed on her.

'You'd better start the cameras now,' said Geoff.

The cameras started to whirr and, as if on cue, the baby was born. It dropped out on to Pamela's tail and lay there, a pinky-white, glistening blob no longer than the first joint of my little finger.

Although I knew roughly what to expect, the whole performance was one of the most miraculous and incredible things that I have ever seen in all the years that I have been watching animals. The baby was, to all intents and purposes, an embryo—it had, in fact, been born after a gestation period of only 33 days; it was blind and its hind legs, neatly crossed over each other, were powerless; yet in this condition it had been expelled into the world. As if this was not enough of a handicap, it now had to climb up through the fur on Pamela's stomach until it found the entrance to the pouch. This was really the equivalent of a blind man, with both legs broken, crawling through thick forest to the top of Mount Everest, for the baby got absolutely no assistance from Pamela at all. We noticed (and we have it on film to prove it) that the mother does *not* help the baby by licking a path through the fur, as is so commonly reported. The baby, as soon as it was born, with a curious, almost fish-like wiggle, left the mother's tail and started to struggle up through the fur. Pamela ignored it. She bent over and licked her nether regions and her tail clean and then proceeded to clean her fur *behind* the baby as it was climbing, for it was obviously leaving a trail of moisture through her hair. Occasionally her tongue passed over the baby, but I am certain that this was more by accident than design. Slowly and valiantly the pulsating little pink blob struggled on through the thick fur. From the moment it was born to the moment it found the rim of the pouch took some ten minutes. That a creature weighing only a gramme (the weight of five or six pins) could have achieved this climb was a miracle in itself, but, having got to the rim of the pouch, it had another task ahead of it. The pouch is approximately the size of a large, woman's handbag. Into this the Lilliputian kangaroo had to crawl and then search the vast, furry area in order to find the teat; this search might have taken him anything up to twenty minutes. Having found the teat, he would then fasten on to it, whereupon it would swell in his mouth, thus making him adhere to it firmly—so firmly, indeed, that if you try to pull a baby kangaroo off its mother's teat, you will tear the soft mouth parts and cause bleeding. This has given rise to the entirely erroneous idea that baby kangaroos are born on the teat, i.e. develop from the teat itself, like a sort of bud.

Finally the baby hauled itself over the edge of the rim of the pouch and disappeared into the interior, and we could switch off the cameras and the lights. We had got some remarkable and unique film. For me it had been an unforgettable experience, and I am sure that even the most hardened anti-kangaroo sheep farmer would have been impressed by the baby's grim determination to perform its herculean task.

After being cast out into the world only half-formed, and being made to undertake this prodigious climb, I felt that the baby kangaroo thoroughly deserved his life in his fur-lined, centrally-heated pram with its built-in milk bar. I hoped very sincerely, that the work that was being done by Harry Frith, Geoff Sharman and the other members of the team would find a way to preserve the largest of the marsupials from complete eradication.

THE GREAT FEAR

'BB'

Rufus was hungry. His hunting the night before had been unsuccessful and his belly rumbled for food. So he went on down to the brook and across to Coldhangar, sending a flock of sheep by the side of the stream running and bunching, for they thought he was a red dog. Jackman, coming across from Hazelbeech in his milk-float, saw the sheep at graze and stopped the cart. He caught a glimpse of a red slinking form under the far hedge, and he thought of his raided hen-house with its scattered mangled corpses, and swore softly. His mind travelled back to the farm, to the shelf in the cow house, where he kept a tin, and he vowed to lay Rufus by the heels ere the winter was out. Rufus, all unheeding of this small tea-cupful of grey matter that was reasoning to bring about his downfall, continued up the crab-strewn ditch, his eyes slits in the grey afternoon light as he set his mask for Coldhangar.

He had returned from the fastnesses of Summermoon and Badby, for the love of his old haunts was strong upon him and he yearned for his vixen. But he searched the bare woods and thickets without finding her, and he quested over the old haunts where they used to hunt together, but he never saw her again. The clicketing season was beginning to heat the blood in his veins and he was thinking of another mate. It was now early February and every ditch was full of water to its brim. The brook, so short a time ago dead low, was now running breast-high between its banks, clotting the dead flotsam of winter on the rusty strands of wire stretched across the brook to keep the sheep from straying when the water was at summer level.

Rufus had been lucky to have escaped the Great Fear for so long, and maybe this gave him a sense of false security. However that may be, he took to kennelling, not below ground, but in the reeds of Lamport ponds. A fox likes a dry bed and a warm one, and one might have thought the reeds would have been too damp for him in the marsh, but this was not so. In places they grew so thick, and had done so for years, that they had formed a thick platform whereon he could lie over a foot above the damp ground, and here, screened by thick willow thickets and high spreading reeds, he was secure.

One Monday, in the first week of February, there came the Great Fear, and it found Rufus off his guard. It may be, as I say, that he had grown careless, for an unhunted fox deteriorates in fitness and cunning if left to himself. He had gone to the reeds after killing a chicken at the crossing gate-keeper's pen, and had dined well, which made him sleep soundly. The faint wind, rustling the reeds, lulled him, and he lay curled round like a tired dog, safe from prying eyes. Not even the sneaking jay could see him, so he slept like the dead. A little wren hunting the dead reed jungles hopped past, but she did not notice him, so still he lay; only a very faint heaving moved his red sides as he breathed as gently as a sleeping babe. A rabbit came hopping down a damp trodden run and paused with ears in a V. Its eyes were dilated and the nose worked up and down as it caught the reek of fox. Then it turned back and disappeared. Rufus slept on, full fed and warm. At times his hind legs moved in little jerks as he happily pounced on his game in the woods of dreamland, for a fox dreams like a dog. His heart pumped slowly in his sleeping body, and so sound and deep was he drowned in sleep, that the sentries of his life dozed at their posts though the heavy penalty was death.

*   *   *   *

Crossing-keeper Herbert Smith had lost many a chicken during the past fortnight and Jackman had also seen the fox about his fields. So maybe a note or a passing word to the Hunt had set matters moving, and already, through the soft winter morning, the hounds were jogging to the Meet at Houghton, the little village that looked over the flashing valley floods. It was not a very big meet, for the Monday country is not a fashionable district, and not more than sixty riders at the most were gathered under the tall elms on the green . . .

In the morning hounds tried the park and Scaldwell spinney, and drew a blank in both. Then they came pouring down the pretty village street of Lamport and went slowly down the fold of the green valley to Lamport ponds. The field was gathered on the hill top, and some in the road, as the Huntsman took his heart's delight down to the marsh, quietly and without fuss . . .

A moment or two, as hounds and pink vanished behind the trees and the waving sterns went feathering through the dead docks of the upper marsh. Then, to the watching field on the hill, there came a fierce burst of sudden music, halloing, and the horn. In a moment the little valley was full of sound and the black and pink of the field began to wheel and move, uncertain yet which way the fox had gone . . .

The first thing that Rufus knew was a big hound pushing through the reeds not a foot away. Rufus was on his lithe feet in an instant, every nerve alive with sudden fear, for, as we know, the sentries had slept and he was betrayed. The hound saw him and winded him at the same time and lunged forward, crying out. Rufus went straight over the embankment of the middle pool and, seeing the whipper-in sitting his horse on the slope of the field below the road, turned swiftly as a stoat under the rails of the lower pool, emerging in a field below the last willow thickets and making for the railway.

His mind was working with the lightning speed of a seasoned fox, and he knew where he was to go. Coldhangar first . . . and then he would see. The hounds were only a field away, screaming to a breast-high scent with their heads well up, and there was not a moment to lose. The whole hillside down to the pools was alive with galloping horsemen, and many were pouring through the gate by Tyrell's house on the station hill. Two platelayers dropped their spades and ran when they heard the hounds, and they saw Rufus cross the metals and turn up the line for fifty yards before going through the hedge on the other side. He went over the stream, not going through, but springing like a deer from bank to bank, where it swept round a sharp bend by a leaning ash. A green woodpecker swooped away, calling, but Rufus went unheeding up to Hopping Hill. Through the gorse bushes, over the road, and down to the valley and Maidwell Dales.

Cars, travelling along the road, stopped to watch the hunt, but they had not seen Rufus slip like a weasel across the road. Now the field was jumping the brook by the railway, some were thundering up the turf margin of the road and pouring through the gate at the foot of Hopping Hill. Rufus had three fields in hand, but he was not running well because of his orgy of the night before, and several times he was viewed by the huntsman. He passed Maidwell Dales and went straight to Coldhangar, and found, perhaps well for him that day, that the earth was stopped. Jim Corfield had done his work well and thoroughly.

Sitting in his upturned barrow by the side of the Hazelbeech road the old roadmender was having a satisfying pipe of shag. For some time he had been watching a little robin that was hopping about his feet, picking up his luncheon crumbs. It hopped along in the sandy flints and sodden leaves, cocking an eye at the old man in the barrow. Then, finding no more crumbs, it flew up into the hedge, and, perching on a spray of red berries that matched its waistcoat, trilled a sad little song.

The old man dozed, the pipe slipping sideways in his mouth. For fifty years he had worked on the roads, grubbing like an old badger in ditch and drain; skilful, too, at laying a hedge. When he won the hedge-laying competition twelve years ago it was the most wonderful day of his life, that, and when he married his wife—now gone out of the world . . .

He awoke suddenly, and pulled out his big turnip watch. 'Coo, he musta dropped right off, this wouldn't do, be Gor.' . . . At that moment Rufus, a terrible sight, staggered across the narrow lane, not twenty feet away from the roadmender. The old man was so startled at this sudden apparition that the barrow upset and tipped him out on to the grass verge among his turf peelings. When he got painfully up, with many grunts, to his feet, the road lay empty, and the robin had flitted away.

Soon came the cry of the hounds from the direction of Talli Ho! and the narrow road resounded with the cloppings of horses' hooves. The old man stood waving his hat to all and sundry, and then, on bow legs, went staggering uncertainly down the road. Soon the hounds trickled through the hedge like a flood of white yellow-lipped water. With loose strides they crossed the road in twos and threes, and plunged into the little belt of trees opposite.

Down across the park went Rufus, every yard becoming more of an effort. When he had seen the old roadmender he had straightened his back and lifted his brush, and the extra spurt had used him ill. Mercifully, it sometimes happens that a beaten fox does not give off so powerful a scent, and this especially so after some extra fright or exertion. Certain it was that hounds were hunting more slowly, and though they were only a matter of a few fields behind, Rufus, for a time, held his ground. His last hope, Hieaway, stood dark-crested on its hill over the railway two miles away, on the other side of the valley. He ran through some sheep below the wooded park, and, nearly spent, he reached the railway line. Only another mile now, over the brook, up the little hill, and there was sanctuary and the low hustling of the gentle pines.

Hounds checked at the sheep, but it was obvious where Rufus was making for, and a quick cast brought hounds on to the line. Down from the wooded ridge came the field, turf flying and with drumming hooves. There was plenty of light yet, and Rufus, unless a miracle happened, was nearly done.

He struggled through the stream and the cold water refreshed him. Then he turned to face the climb to the firs. Those last few yards were agony. With brush right low and arched back, his feet were of lead, and always the cruel grass was before his eyes. Now he could see the dark crest of firs, and with a final effort he entered the wood with the first hound not more than half a field behind. . . .

He went up the steep mound to the earth under the pines. It was blocked. . . .

★   ★   ★   ★

Jackman, digging a fence hole just below the farm, had heard the cry of the hounds. He put down the long narrow tool and straightened his back, gazing towards the crest of Hieaway. He could see horsemen cantering over the valley floor two miles away, and the pink coats of the huntsmen bobbing along by the side of the line. The hounds he could not see, for they were already up the hill and entering the wood.

A flock of pigeons left the firs and circled away, and two carrions went flagging out from the lower end, cawing hoarsely, and wheeling. Then he saw the pink coats streaming up to the wood, and black coats mingled. From the heights of Hazelbeech a single rider in black was cantering down, far behind all others. . . . On the Hazelbeech road the old roadman was the recounting his experience to a fellow rustic.

'Cor! I was sittin' in me barrer, when the blurry old fox went right across the road, near knocked me over, 'er did! Looked a game 'un though, bless ye. . . .'

All at once Jackman saw a red, draggled slip of a fox coming along the high headland from Hieaway. It was making directly for the farm and Jackman began to run up the hill. It was a spent fox, and was moving slowly; as Jackman ran, he could see the hounds just coming over the ridge with two men in pink cantering on the slope of the field below. With them, but thirty yards behind, rode several of the field and a girl riding side-saddle. When Jackman came panting up the slope, red of face, and gasping as if he had run a mile, he saw Rufus slip under the muddy gate of the farmyard and go straight into the cow byre at the end of the farm.

'They'll have him, be God!' he swore, still running up the hill. He reached the byre before the first hounds had topped the rise, and entered gingerly, scanning the trampled smelly straw in the corners. Leading out of the byre was a little tumble-down stable where the grey mare was housed, and at one end of this was a manger half full of hay. Standing in one corner was a bundle of planks and poles laid up against the wall, and above this the roof sloped down to the white, stained, plaster.

The fox did not seem to be in the byre, so Jackman went into the stable, scanning the poles in the corner and running his eye along the top of the wall. . . .

With a mighty effort Rufus had gained the byre, and gone straight into the stable. He had climbed the stack of wood and now lay stretched out like a hiding moorhen, right under the sloping eaves, among the cobwebs. About three feet from his nose was the dried cup of a swallow's nest, with the blue scurf of the babies still in the bottom among the draggled hen feathers. Droppings were still caked on the plaster ledge below. Those swallows were now far, far away, in a land of sand and sun, where white egrets stalked the rice fields by the Nile. . . . His flanks were heaving and his teeth were unclenched, but his eyes and ears were all alive. He heard Jackman come into the byre, and then come below him, treading on the straw and breathing heavily from his run, but he did not move.

He could almost feel the man's eyes scanning the ledge where he lay. . . . A large black spider bustled out of a crack and in again, and in the silence he could hear the sparrows chirp-chirping on the farm buildings outside. . . .

Jackman had seen the tip of Rufus's brush just showing over the edge of the plaster, but he did nothing for a moment. Then with a smile that was meant to be cunning, he went out of the stable into the midden of the yard. The hounds were now all about, sending the white chickens into an ecstasy of terror, and the great gobbler forgot his dignity and ran under the yard gate, head well forward and red wattles swinging. Soon the huntsman came riding up to the gate and Jackman shouted to him. ''E's in 'ere, seen 'im run into my byre. He's lying top o' the wall! . . .'

The first whipper-in swung himself down from his horse, gathering up the thong of his whip in one hand and handing his horse to another servant. He strode into the byre, calling hounds to him and they gathered round, whimpering for blood. . . .

By now most of the field had come up and were grouped below the farm, their horses steaming from the gallop over the valley, and white lather smeared on velvet skin and top boots. . . .

Rufus, lying on top of the wall, heard the man come through the byre until he stood on the straw below. The sound and smell of the Great Fear was nauseating, but Rufus did not move. He was lying tense and ready for his last spring, and within boiled a fury and a fear. Soon the little stable was full of hounds, and they were making the confined space hideous with their cries. Some were trying to scramble up the poles in the corner, for the reek of fox told them plainly where their prey had gone.

The man let fly with his lash on the white plaster, but the curling

Staggering with exhaustion, Rufus crossed not twenty feet from the old man.

thong could not reach the high ledge; only a slab of plaster fell, leaving a sandy stain on the wall. At the slash of the thong Rufus tried to squeeze lower against the rafters, his trembling body pressing against the slates.

Jackman, standing and peering in the doorway, grasped a stout stick. He meant murder, if by some chance the fox got away from the hounds. On the face of things, nothing short of a miracle could save Rufus now. At the end of the ledge stood a rusty golden syrup tin, and in that tin was stored the poison that had killed Rufus's parents. Such is the queer twist of chance.

Unable to move the crouching fox from below, the man called for a box to stand upon, and Jackman soon returned, not with a box, but a short ladder which he used for gathering apples in his orchard. He smiled as he came in, the same cunning smile, for he thought of the tin at the end of the ledge and how it had accounted for many a red robber—how little the Hunt knew!

Meanwhile, the whipper-in had tried to clamber up the planks in the corner, but had only covered his white breeches with dirt and dust, and he slipped back among his clamouring hounds. Several of the Hunt had dismounted now, and were looking in at the open doorway. Rufus still lay there motionless, just the tip of his brush showing at the end of the ledge with a cobweb over it. The ladder was brought and the man climbed up three rungs. He could reach the fox now with his thong, and he might have drawn Rufus out. But the floor below was a seething mass of hounds, all watching for the red bolt dropping to their jaws, just as the corpse of a fox is tossed down to the waiting pack in an open kill.

The whipper-in, on higher level now, could see the top of Rufus's back over the edge of the white plaster, and he drew back his whip and sent the lash across under the cobwebs. Things happened so quickly that it was difficult to follow. From the end of the shelf bounded the rusty tin, and the tense-strung pack surged upwards like a wave as it fell. But Rufus, his brain working with lightning speed, turned on the narrow ledge, and, at the same moment the tin was sent flying by the lash, leapt backwards over the man's head and down the sloping planks. Only ten hounds saw him, the others were scrambling in the corner where the tin had rolled. He ran in under their legs, by some miracle escaped death by the slashing haste of clicking jaws, scrambled over the back of two hounds and ran between Mr Jackman's legs. That worthy let fly with his ash plant and Beauty went howling against the wall.

Shouting men, boots, a confused jumble of legs and hooves, and Rufus was out under the gate and went like a red wire along the foot of the yard wall, among the dead stinging nettles. . . .

Within the byre, all was confusion. The man never saw Rufus slip down behind him, for in that second his eyes, like those of his hounds, had been on the bounding tin. But the baffled ten had turned and went streaming out into the yard, calling the others to them. One of the field halloed Rufus away, and in a flash the pack streamed out of the yard, and went singing down the wall.

There was a scramble for mounts, shouts, and the thud of hooves, the squeal of a kicked horse . . . a man's shout. . . .

Mr Jackman stood by his wife at the entrance to the yard, watching the hunt stream down the slope. 'Well, I be . . . the VARMINT!' Jackman was speechless. He went slowly back into the byre and picked up the tin. Luckily the lid was still on and he picked it up and looked at it. 'Well, I be. . . .'

The short respite had put new life into Rufus, and he went away down the hill at a great pace, towards the railway, and there, puffing slowly up the line towards Northampton, was a long, rumbling goods train. The driver was leaning out and, together with his fireman, watched the Hunt streaming down the hill. The whipper-in saw the danger and rode like a madman to head his hounds. He won, by a bare forty yards, and with great skill turned the racing pack. His whip cracked like a gun—hounds' lives were at stake.

When the long train of wagons had passed, Rufus had gained five fields, and was making for the crossing spinney. Dusk was falling and the Master gave a reluctant order for home. And so, by the merest thread, the bright life of Rufus was saved. Coincidence, Chance, Pre-ordination, call it what you will, but over the darkling fields went Rufus, slowly now because the sounds of pursuit had died with the rumbling of the train, and he came to Talli Ho! just as the moon was climbing, a great silver plate, above the vaulted trees.

He lay down at the root of an ash, still panting, and deadly weary.

High above him rose the moonlit branches, every twig shining in the greenish light, right up and up, until the very topmost twig was reached, a picture of majestic and eerie beauty. . . . Far away a little owl was hooting for its mate, and a lonely peewit called from the moon-drenched wilderness of Penny plain. He had run a great race and won. . . .

The tip of his right ear was gone, nipped by Ruby in the byre, and from now on he was branded for all men to see.

THE WILD GOOSE CHASE
AT THE KINGDOM OF THE BIRDS

G.K.Chesterton

G. K. Chesterton, later famous as the author of the Father Brown detective stories, wrote this story in 1892 at the age of eighteen, while he was still at school.

Once upon a time there lived in a certain village a little boy who was so dreamy and gentle by nature that it was the general opinion of the villagers that he couldn't, as they figuratively expressed it, 'say boo to a goose'. Why this ceremony should be selected as a test of the average minimum of personal courage, he never could make out, and nor can I. But, being resolved to show that he was not unfit for this perilous venture, he went one evening to the village green at sunset, where a number of geese were congregated, to pronounce the mysterious monosyllable.

'Boo,' observed the Little Boy, addressing the first biped, with all the earnestness of scientific enquiry. The goose received it in dignified silence, and the Little Boy went on to the next and said, 'Boo,' but no effects followed. When, however, he came to the third, who was a wilder and shyer bird than the others, and tried the experiment on him, he fluttered, flapped his wings and flew away in a straight line towards the setting sun. The white geese looked superciliously after it and then at each other and waddled back over the village green, observing that it was only a wild goose and perhaps one could expect no better. But the Little Boy was already far away.

What impulse led him to chase the wild goose he never knew, but with the persistence of scientific enquiry he scampered through the streets in pursuit of the bird that fluttered on before him. Nothing could stop his course. He cleared the stile, he climbed over the palings, he upset three vestrymen and a beadle (though that, of course, was quite right), he ran out of the town gates and out into the fields and lanes, lonely in the evening. As he paused for a moment to take breath under an elm-tree, he saw a titmouse just fluttering into its nest among its fat little family. 'It is evening,' observed the titmouse, 'and I and my family go to rest. It is very comfortable here. Where are you going, little boy?' And the Little Boy sighed as he answered, 'Yes, a home is very comfortable, but now I have no home. I am seeking the wild goose that has flown westward towards the sunset.' And after bowing to the maternal titmouse and patting the little ones on the head, he ran westward once more. And now as the sun went down through rose-red fire to bury itself in violet mist, he reached a wonderful place where the gorgeous light of sunset glittered on the plumage of gorgeous birds, moving proudly about spaces of green park. Here peacocks spread their green-eyed fantails before him, golden pheasants bowed their necks under his hand and the air above him glittered with the emerald and ruby-throated humming-birds, whirring round in ceaseless movement. Pausing under a magnificent flowering fruit-tree, he asked a Bird of Paradise if she had seen a wild goose pass there lately. The 'Paradisia Apoda' rustled through all its flaming feathery appanage and observed gravely and severely, 'If you are seeking a wild goose, sir, I can assure you that he has not been here. We do not visit them.' And the royal lady closed her eyes and looked as if she only wanted a pair of eye-glasses to make her complete.

A pea-hen swept up to her and said smiling, 'Oh, pray excuse me, but the band is going to commence; and I know you dote on music.' 'Oh yes,' said the Bird of Paradise, closing her eyes again. 'Frivolous creature,' she muttered as the pea-hen swept away. 'Supercilious old owl,' snapped the pea-hen under her breath. Meanwhile the Little Boy had moved forward, anxious to know what was meant by 'the band'. He found it impersonated by one shabby little brown nightingale, who every evening gave a musical performance to the rapture of the assembled company. After the performance the Little Boy got a word with the poor little nightingale.

'Whence have you come?' said the poor musician. 'Have you come from the calm woods and the fields and the sweet country lanes? I can remember when I too was free in the free forests and sang my songs as the free gift of God. But now I have these grand patrons and the beauty of the woods has died out of me till you for a moment brought it back. In God's name do not linger here. Flee westward to seek your wild goose and do not lose your work as I have done.' And so sorrowful was the look in the eyes of the little old songster that the Little Boy broke into tears as he said farewell and ran from the place. All he could gather about the object of his search was that he had better go and ask the Owl that dwelt in the Forest of Dead Leaves in a deep twilight of meditation. An hour after he had emerged from the Park he came to the Forest of Dead Leaves, a weird brown twilight of thick trees, amid which the ground was heaped and littered with drifts of dry leaves, through which he waded and struggled waist-deep for hours before he came to the great mystic oak in the dark shadow of whose branches he could dimly see the solemn round eyes of the gigantic owl. When she saw the Little Boy, she blinked several times and enquired in a muffled voice what he wanted. 'I came to you for some information,' replied the Little Boy 'as I heard you were very wise.'

'Too whoo! and you heard right. Do you see these brown leaves heaped thick throughout the forest? They are the leaves that have fallen from this Tree of Knowledge, and I am waiting till they are withered and worth touching. Too whoo; they may think themselves very fine with their bright crests and plumage, but they will never know what I do. What do you want to know?'

'I am seeking the wild goose,' replied the Little Boy, 'that fled westward towards the sunset.'

The Owl blinked, coughed a little and said, 'The wild goose, or Anserferus, as it is scientifically termed, is an inhabitant of many parts of the globe. It was of the plumes of this animal that the archers of the Middle Ages. . . .'

'Yes, yes,' said the Little Boy, impatiently, 'but I want to know where it can be found. It fled westward half an hour before sunset.'

'Sunset,' replied the Owl, smoothing down her feathers, 'is caused by the orb of the earth moving in its revolution. . . .'

'Confound its revolution,' said the naughty Little Boy. 'Cannot you tell me where the thing I want is?'

'Well, what *do* you want?' asked the Owl with a stare.

And all the Little Boy could answer was, 'I want the beautiful wild goose that flew towards the sunset.'

'And what do you want with a wild goose?'

'Well, I want it,' began the Little Boy, 'because—because it was so wild and natural.'

'Was not the titmouse you left behind natural?'

'Yes,' said the Little Boy, puzzled. 'But I followed it because it was beautiful.'

'Were not the Bird of Paradise and the Peacock as beautiful?' asked the Owl.

'I think,' said the Little Boy at last in a brown study, 'I seem to have followed because I couldn't get it.'

'Logical,' sniffed the Owl.

'No,' replied the Boy, 'not logical, only natural. I looked at the white bird flapping far away against the fiery sunset and I seemed to long to spend my whole life in seeking for it in the strange sunset lands. I longed to follow it and find where it lived and all about it simply because it seemed as if the chase might last for ever.'

The Little Boy paused for a reply, stared, shook the tree and woke up the owl from a sound nap which she had indulged in during the mystical explanation above. 'What do you want?' asked the owl sleepily. 'Don't disturb me. I'm thinking. Don't you know I'm the wisest person in the world?'

'You are the most useless rubbish in the world,' said the rude Little Boy. 'I come to you for simple directions and you give me extracts from dictionaries. I come to you in search of my vanished ideal and you tell me I am not logical. I tell you the feelings of my nature and you go to sleep while I am speaking. Oh, it were better to be the little titmouse that hops and twitters its happy little life and dies than this miserable old spirit of darkness.' And with that he turned and strode away, leaving behind him the Owl of Learning and the Forest of Dead Leaves. Just, however, as the indignant hootings of the old owl had died away in the distance he heard another loud 'too whoo!' close to his ear. 'What,' he cried, 'is there another owl here?'

'No,' said a shrill voice from the same direction, with a caricature of his childish accent. 'No. No owls here. Except you.'

Looking round the tree behind him, he beheld a thin black bird with a kind of furtive grin and a cruel look in his eyes.

'Who—who are you?' asked the Little Boy falteringly.

'I—, I am—a—the Mocking Bird,' replied the bird, imitating him once more. 'You have been talking to that unconscionable old imbecile, the owl. Too whoo! Too whoo! I'm the wisest person in the world. What did you want with her?'

'I am looking for a wild goose,' replied the Little Boy, beginning to be a trifle tired of the answer, 'that has fled towards the sunset.'

'Cackle, cackle,' said the Mocking Bird. 'Birds of a feather flock together. I don't wonder you want to flock with a goose.'

The Little Boy flushed scarlet. 'I don't know why you should speak to me—'

'Go it,' grinned the Mocking Bird. 'Do the virtuous indignant business. It pays nowadays. About the only thing to be said for it. Go it. Charge, Chester, charge, etc. Ha, ha.'

'Who are you to speak to me in this way?' asked the Boy fiercely.

'I'm a cynic,' chuckled the Mocking Bird, 'and cynics are allowed to say anything. I suppose it is a kind of recognition that they are the only people who speak the truth. I'll prove we speak the truth. You're a fool.'

'Hold your tongue!' shouted the Little Boy, clenching his fists.

'Can't be done. Heroic style won't do for you,' said the Mocking Bird placidly. 'Your voice, my dear boy, is too juvenile.'

'My voice may be juvenile,' retorted the Little Boy, 'but it is my own. I have something of my own to say and my natural voice to say it in. I am not like the miserable misanthrope who can do nothing but pick holes in his own versions of other people's voices. I would as soon be the echo on a blank garden wall.'

Not having anything particular to answer to this and being irritated and a trifle confused, the Mocking Bird only said excitedly, 'Too whoo, cockadoodledoomeowcackle-bowwow, confound it,' and ran into a hole in the tree, while the Little Boy continued his onward march. He had emerged from the outskirts of the wood and come out on a broad, bleak upland, beyond which the sunset was fading in level clouds. He had not walked far when he heard a scream and there sidled up to him, in a semi-tipsy manner, a disreputable-looking large bird with a crooked beak, a long bare neck with a ruff of dirty white feathers, a smart red crest and a leering eye.

'How de do,' he observed hoarsely.

'How do you do,' said the Little Boy meekly, but not much liking his company.

'Coming my way?' asked the Vulture, taking out a cigar. 'See *our* tree. Better job than those,' and he jerked his thumb-claw in the direction of the forest. 'Come with me. Introduce you to the fellers— There they are!' And he nodded in the direction of the sunset against which there now rose dark and grim the outline of a gibbet, almost obscured by the crowds of vultures that flocked round it. 'Here we are,' said the Vulture. 'Lots of fellers. Writing fellers. Doosid original fellers. I'm a doosid original feller.'

The Little Boy thought he was.

'Yes,' said the vulture. 'This is where I hang out,' though the last expression would have more properly applied to another part of his establishment. 'Won't you come in?'

'N-no thank you,' said the Little Boy hurriedly. 'I think this is my way,' which was not strictly true, as he ran three miles and a half out of his way in order to give a wide berth to the Tree of the Vultures.

And as the moon came slowly up over the moor he wandered among the ruins of an old building in which no living thing stirred, save flocks of lugubrious looking ravens that darkly flapped and croaked round the turrets. After wandering about for some time he fell into conversation with a large, gaunt, disappointed-looking bird, of whom he asked his question in the formula of which the reader has probably got as tired as he had.

'Wild goose?' replied the Raven wearily. 'I don't know. There's nothing worth going after nowadays. Look at this abbey. Its all tumbling down. What can the world be coming to? Take my advice, little boy, leave things alone. There's nothing worth touching in these days. Croak, croak.'

And shaking his large head mournfully, he blinked and went to sleep. 'Croak, croak,' cried all the ravens fretfully as the Little Boy passed slowly out of the ruins and struck westwards once more.

For years and years he wandered over the earth, past rivers and cities and mountain-ranges, until one day he found himself on the wild slopes of a mountain, above which incline a line of dark cliffs jutted, overshadowing the base of the hill.

After wandering about disconsolately for some time he was attracted by the low moaning and sobbing of a living thing. Stooping down he found it was a starling, fluttering close to the ground.

'What is the matter, poor little bird?' he asked, and forgot even to ask after the wild goose; and the starling told him that his brother had just been carried off by a ferocious eagle, who had swooped down from his nest upon the cliff's edge. 'There he is,' cried the starling, and looking up he saw a large bird flapping on the cliff with a smaller one struggling in his grasp. The Little Boy, not being acquainted with the law of the success of the fittest in Nature, rushed forward, wildly clambered up the cliff and continued at the imminent risk of his neck to get onto the ledge with the oppressor and his victim. Seizing the eagle by the throat and claw, he forced it back against the rock, while the starling flew joyfully to join his companion, and the eagle flapped sulkily back to his nest. Just then, as the Little Boy hung clinging to the edge of the cliff and wondering how he should get down again, he saw with a start that almost loosed his hold, gleaming for a moment amid the rock-rooted brake and thicket above his head, the white wings of the wild goose. In a moment he was on the ground above, just in time to see the wild goose disappear over the next swell of ground. When he had passed this, he saw spread before him a mighty valley, watered by broad rivers and clothed with deep forests, and beyond it a range of mountains in the distance, culminating in one central, snow-crested peak, upon which he could see perched the white shining bird that he sought. And after it he set forth across the mighty valley.

Years passed and he had grown to a strong man, who might have won the hands of ladies or tilted in the tournaments of Kings, but that he was still upon the quest of his life, when he arrived at the mountain of the wild goose. Bare-headed, with a staff in his hand, with a wild hope in his eyes, he climbed the rocky slopes, until late upon a summer evening he clambered close beneath the topmost crag whereon sat the wild goose. And even as he stretched out his hand to touch it, it started

The little boy, clinging to the edge, saw the wild goose above him.

and flew far from him, vanishing over the twilight sea, and he stood on the lonely crest, with a sheer precipice beneath him. And he gave a great groan and sank with his face buried in his hands.

'It is gone,' he murmured. 'Gone for ever. And my youth is gone, which I wasted, and my strength which I exhausted for it. The graves are green on all the friends I loved. I am alone in a strange land, where all are strangers. My hope is gone, for which I gave up everything. Heaven has had no pity on me.' And then all was silence.

'Yes,' said a strange voice above him. 'Heaven has pitied you, and for your sake time itself shall be defied. I am the Spirit of the Past. I am come to give you back everything and to wipe out all your sorrows. I am come to tear the page of all your toils and wanderings out of the very book of what has been, and make you once more a little boy playing upon a village green and not thinking of a wild goose.'

The wanderer lifted his head and gazed dreamily over the sea and a strange light grew in his eyes.

'No, spirit, no,' he said quickly. 'It is better as it is. I will not have it so.'

And with that the dim spirit of the Past moved slowly towards the far-off hills of his home.

But over the darkening sea there came a sudden, strange, wordless song as of a flight of wild birds, and a glimmer of white wings seemed floating towards him. He gave a great cry and leapt forward; and no man ever saw him again on earth.

★　　★　　★　　★

And I have not said whether he ever found the wild goose, and the story ends abruptly. And must not all stories of brave lives and long endeavours and weary watching for the ideal so end, until all be ended?

I cannot tell you whether he found what he sought. I have told you that he sought it.

THE CHIMPS COME TO CAMP

Jane van Lawick-Goodall

In 1961 Jane Goodall returned from a six-month visit to England to the Gombe Stream Reserve in Tanzania, where she had been studying the behaviour of chimpanzees. Some of them, including William; the handsome David Greybeard and the athletic Goliath, had become used to her presence, and she wondered whether they would have forgotten her.

I need not have worried; when I got back to the Gombe Stream it seemed that the chimps were, if anything, *more* tolerant of my presence than before. I resumed my work in the mountains as though I had never been away.

One evening I returned to camp and found Dominic and Hassan (my African cook and helper) very excited. A large male chimpanzee, they told me, had walked right into camp and spent an hour feeding from the palm tree that shaded my tent. The following evening I learned that the same chimp paid another visit. I determined to stay down the next day to see if he came again.

It seemed strange to lie in my bed and watch the dawn break, to have breakfast in camp, to sit in my tent in the *daylight* to type out my previous day's notes on the typewriter I had brought back from England. And it seemed quite unbelievable when, at about ten o'clock, David Greybeard strolled calmly past the front of my tent and climbed the palm tree. I peeped out and heard him giving low-pitched grunts of pleasure as he poked the first red fruit from its horny case. An hour later he climbed down, paused to look, quite deliberately, into the

49

tent, and wandered off. After all those months of despair, when the chimpanzees had fled at the mere sight of me five hundred yards away, here was one making himself at home in my very camp. No wonder I found it hard to believe.

David Greybeard paid regular visits until the palm tree's fruit was finished, and then he stopped coming. These oil nut palms do not all fruit at the same time, however, and so, a few weeks later, the hard nut-like fruits on another of the camp palms became red and ripe. David Greybeard resumed his daily visits. I did not often stay to watch him for there was a limit to the amount of information I could gain from watching a lone male guzzling palm nuts—sometimes, though, I waited for him to come just for the intense pleasure of seeing him so close and so unafraid. One day, as I sat on the veranda of the tent, David climbed down from his tree and then, in his deliberate way, walked straight towards me. When he was about five feet from me he stopped and, slowly, his hair began to stand on end until he looked enormous and very fierce. A chimpanzee may erect his hair when he is angry, frustrated or nervous: why, I wondered somewhat apprehensively, had David put his hair out? All at once he ran straight at me, snatched up a banana from my table, and hurried off to eat it farther away. Gradually his hair returned to its normal sleeked position.

After that incident I asked Dominic to leave bananas out whenever he saw David, and so, even when there were no ripe palm nuts, the chimp still wandered into camp sometimes, looking for bananas. But his visits were irregular and unpredictable, and I no longer waited in my tent for him to come.

About eight weeks after my return to the Gombe I had a slight attack of malaria. I stayed in bed and, hoping that David Greybeard might pass by, asked Dominic to set out some bananas. Late that morning David walked up to my tent and helped himself to the fruit. As he walked back towards the bushes I suddenly saw that a second chimpanzee was standing there, half hidden in the vegetation. Quickly I reached for my binoculars—it was Goliath. As David sat down to eat, Goliath went close to him, peering into his face. As David rolled a banana skin wedge around in his lower lip, squeezing out the last juices and occasionally pushing it forward to look down at it over his nose, Goliath reached out one hand to his friend's mouth, begging for the wadge. Presently David responded by spitting out the well-chewed mass into Goliath's hand, and then Goliath sucked on it in turn.

The next day Goliath followed David to camp again. I kept hidden right inside my tent, with the flap down, and peeped out through a small hole. This time Goliath, with much hesitation and with all his hair on end, followed David to the tent and seized some bananas for himself.

The following few weeks were momentous. I sent Hassan off to the village of Mwamgongo, to the north of the Reserve, to buy a supply of bananas, and each day I put out a pile near my tent. The figs in the home valley were ripe again so that large groups of chimps were constantly passing near camp. I spent part of my time up near the fig trees, and the remainder waiting for David in camp. He came nearly every day, and not only did Goliath sometimes accompany him, but William also, and, occasionally, a youngster.

One day, when David came by himself, I held a banana out to him in my hand. He approached, put his hair out and gave a quick soft exhalation, rather like a cough, whilst at the same time he jerked his chin up. He was mildly threatening me. Suddenly he stood upright, swaggered slightly from foot to foot, slapped the trunk of a palm tree beside him with one hand, and then, very gently, took the banana from me.

The first time I offered Goliath a banana from my hand was very different. He, too, put his hair out, then seized a chair and charged past me, almost knocking me over. Then he sat and glowered from the bushes. It was a long time before he behaved as calmly in my presence as David; if I made a sudden movement and startled him he often threatened me quite vigorously, uttering a soft barking sound whilst rapidly raising one arm or swaying branches with quick rather jerky movements.

It was exciting to be able to make fairly regular observations on the same individuals, for previously I had found this almost impossible. Chimpanzees follow no set route on their daily wanderings and so, except when a good fruit tree had been ripe, it had only been by chance that I had observed the same chimpanzee more than a few times in any one month. In camp, however, I was able to make detailed observations on social interactions between David, Goliath and

William several times a week. Often, too, I saw incidents involving one of the three when I was watching the chimpanzee groups feeding on figs in the home valley.

It was at this point that I began to suspect that Goliath might be the highest-ranking male chimpanzee in the area—and later I found that this was indeed the case. If William and Goliath started to move towards the same banana at the same time, it was William who gave way and Goliath who took the fruit. If Goliath met another adult male along a narrow forest track he continued—the other stepped aside. Goliath was nearly always the first to be greeted when a newcomer climbed into a fig tree to join a feeding group of chimpanzees. One day I actually saw him driving another chimp from her nest in order to take it over for himself. It was nearly dark when I observed this from the Peak. The young female had constructed a large leafy nest and was peacefully lying there, curled up for the night. Suddenly Goliath swung up on to the branch beside her and, after a moment, stood upright, seized an overhead branch and began to sway it violently back and forth over her head. With a loud scream she leapt out of bed and vanished into the darkening undergrowth below; Goliath calmed instantly, climbed on to her vacated nest, bent over a new branch, and lay down. Five minutes later the ousted female was still constructing a new bed in the last glimmers of dusk.

William, with his long scarred upper lip and his drooping lower lip, was one of the more subordinate males in his relationships with the other chimpanzees. If another adult male showed signs of aggression towards him, William was quick to approach with gestures of appeasement and submission, reaching out to lay his hand on the other, crouching with soft panting grunts in front of the higher-ranking individuals. During such an encounter he would often pull back the corners of his lips and expose his teeth in a nervous grin. Initially William was timid in camp also. When I offered him a banana in my hand for the first time he stared at it for several moments, gently shook a branch in his frustration, and then sat, uttering soft whimpering sounds, until I relented and put the fruit on the ground.

It took me much longer to determine David Greybeard's position in the dominance hierarchy. In those early days I only knew that he had a very calm and gentle disposition: if William or some youngster approached him with submissive gestures David was always quick to respond with a reassuring gesture, laying his hand on the other's body or head, or briefly grooming him. Often, too, if Goliath showed signs of excitement in camp—if I approached too closely, for instance— David would reach out and lay his hand gently in his companion's groin or make a few brief grooming strokes on Goliath's arm. Such gestures nearly always seemed to calm the more dominant male.

★   ★   ★   ★

It was during these weeks that Hugo arrived at the Gombe Stream. I had, at last, agreed that a professional photographer be allowed to come and photograph the chimpanzees, and Louis had recommended Hugo. The National Geographic Society had accepted the advice and given Hugo funds for filming me and the chimpanzees—partly to obtain a documentary film record of as much behaviour as possible, and partly in the hope of being able to prepare a lecture film for their members.

I felt some apprehensions as to how the chimpanzees would tolerate a man with a load of photographic equipment, but I realized the importance of getting a documentary film record of the chimpanzees' behaviour. Also there was David Greybeard—I did not anticipate that David would be too upset by the arrival of a stranger.

On Hugo's first morning at the Gombe Stream, David Greybeard arrived very early in the camp, for he had nested nearby. I had decided that it might be best if David first got used to the new tent, and then to its occupant; so whilst David ate his bananas, Hugo remained inside, peering out through the flaps. David scarcely glanced at the tent until his meal was finished: then he walked deliberately over, pulled back one of the flaps, stared at Hugo, grunted and plodded away in his usual leisurely manner.

To my surprise Goliath, and even timid William, who arrived together a short while afterwards, also accepted Hugo with very little fuss. It was as though they regarded him as merely part of the furniture of the camp. And so, on his first day, Hugo was able to get some excellent film of interactions—greetings, grooming and begging for food—between the three males. And on his second day, Hugo was able to get some even more remarkable film—shots of chimpanzees eating a monkey.

Since that memorable day when I first watched David Greybeard feeding on the carcass of a young bushpig, I had only once seen meat-eating again. On that occasion the prey had been a young bushbuck—but, again, I could not be sure that the chimps had caught it themselves. But on this third occasion Hugo and I actually witnessed the kill.

It happened most unexpectedly. I had taken Hugo up to show him the Peak, and we were watching four red colobus monkeys that were, it seemed, separated from their troop. Suddenly an adolescent male chimpanzee climbed cautiously up the tree next to the monkeys and moved slowly along a branch. Then he sat down. Three of the monkeys, after a moment, jumped away—quite calmly it seemed. The fourth remained, his head turned towards the chimp. A second later another adolescent male chimp climbed out of the thick vegetation surrounding the tree, rushed along the branch on which the last monkey was sitting, and grabbed it. Instantly several other chimps climbed up into the tree and, screaming and barking in excitement, tore their victim into several pieces. It was all over within a minute from the time of capture.

We were too far away for Hugo to film the hunt—and anyway, it happened so suddenly that he could hardly have expected to do so even had we been close enough. But he did get some film of the chimpanzees eating their share of the kill, though from very far away to be sure.

After such a startlingly auspicious beginning, however, Hugo's luck changed. True, he was able to get a great deal of excellent ciné film and still photographs of David, William and Goliath. But he needed, for his documentary record, more than that. He needed film of as many aspects of the chimpanzees' life as possible—their life in the mountains and forests. And most of them fled from Hugo just as, two years earlier, they had fled from me; even Goliath and William distrusted him when they met him in the forest.

As I had done prior to Judy's visit, I had constructed a few ramshackle hides for Hugo, close to trees that I expected would bear fruit. I had even stuck empty bottles through the walls to try to get the chimps used to the sight of camera lenses. Somehow, though, they instantly detected the difference when they spied real lenses and, if they did arrive in the tree, they usually stared intently towards the hide and vanished silently. Poor Hugo—he lugged most of his camera equipment up and down the steep slopes himself so as not to create the added disturbance of taking an African porter with him. He spent long hours perched on steep rocky hillsides or down on the softer earth of the valley floors that always seemed to harbour biting ants. Frequently no chimps came at all: when they did they often left before he could get even a foot of film.

However, it seemed that the chimps, having very slowly got used to one white-skinned ape in the area, and having then had the chance to study a second, very similar-looking ape in the person of my sister, took a relatively short time to accept a third. And David Greybeard hastened the process. Occasionally, when he saw Hugo or me, he would leave his group and come to see whether, by any chance, we had a banana: the other chimps, of course, watched intently.

When David, William and Goliath had started visiting camp I had soon discovered that they loved chewing on cloth and cardboard—sweaty garments, presumably because of their salty flavour, were the most sought after. One day, when Hugo was crouched in a small hide by a large fruiting tree, a group of chimps climbed up and began to feed. They did not, it appeared, notice him at all. Just as he was beginning to film he felt his camera being pulled away from him. For a moment he couldn't imagine what was going on—then he suddenly saw a black hairy hand pulling at the old shirt which he had wrapped around his camera to try to camouflage the shiny surfaces of the lenses. Of course it was David Greybeard—he had walked along the valley path behind Hugo and then, when he got level with the hide, spied the tempting material. Hugo grabbed hold of one end and engaged in a frenzied tug-of-war until the shirt finally split and David plodded off to join the group in the tree with his spoils in one hand. The other chimps had watched these proceedings with apparent interest, and after that they tolerated Hugo's filming even though, during the struggle with David, most of the hide had collapsed.

In fact, it was only a month after he arrived before most of the chimpanzees accepted not only Hugo, but also his clicking, whirring cameras—provided he kept still and did not move around. But the rains, once again, started early, and just as the weather had consistently ruined Judy's few photographic opportunities the year before, so it was with Hugo. Day after day he sat in his hides, the sun shining, the lighting perfect—but with no chimpanzees to film. Then a group arrived, everything was just right—and, almost as though pre-arranged, it began to rain.

Nevertheless, Hugo did, over the weeks, get some first-rate material on chimpanzee behaviour in the mountains: also, of course, he continued to film interactions between David, Goliath and William in camp.

One of my problems, from the time when I first tried to tempt David and the others to my camp with bananas, had been that of the baboons. There was never a day when the troop did not pass through camp, and some of the males often hung around on their own, as old Shaitani had done, in the hope that bananas would appear. One day, when David, William and Goliath were sitting around a large pile of bananas, a particularly aggressive male baboon suddenly ran at them. William retired from the fray almost at once, his lips wobbling in his agitation, and, with the few bananas he had managed to seize, watched the ensuing battle from a safe distance. David also ran from the baboon when first it threatened him, but he then approached Goliath (who was calmly ignoring the commotion and finishing his bananas) and flung his arms around his friend. Then, as though made brave by the contact, he turned to scream and wave his arms at the baboon. Again the baboon threatened him, lunging forward, and again David rushed to embrace Goliath. This time Goliath responded; he got up, ran a few steps towards the baboon, and then leapt time and time again into the air, in an upright posture, waving his arms and uttering his fierce *waa* or threat bark. David Greybeard joined in, but it was noticeable that he kept a few feet behind Goliath from the start. The baboon retreated, but a moment later, avoiding Goliath, it rushed to lunge and slap at David.

This happened again and again. Goliath leapt at the baboon and the baboon, avoiding him with ease, managed each time to hit out at David, no matter how the latter tried to hide behind his friend. Eventually it was David and Goliath who retreated, leaving the baboon

Suddenly David stood upright and, very gently, took the banana from me.

to grab the spoils of victory and rush off to a safer distance. Hugo managed to film the entire incident and, to this day, it remains one of the best records of an aggressive encounter between chimpanzees and baboons.

★   ★   ★   ★

The National Geographic Society had agreed to finance Hugo's work at the Gombe Stream until the end of November so that he would be able to film the chimpanzees using tools during the termite season. I expected this to start, as in previous years, during October. But, although Hugo and I daily examined different termite mounds, we saw no signs of any activity until early November. Then, when Hugo had only just two weeks longer at the Gombe, the termites finally began to co-operate. One day, when Hugo made his pilgrimage to his favourite nest near camp, he saw a few moist spots. He scratched away the newly sealed-over passages, poked a grass down and, to his delight, felt the insects grip on. But the chimpanzees, perversely, showed no desire to eat termites. During the following week David, William and Goliath passed the heap frequently but never paused to examine it. Hugo grew desperate. He even led David Greybeard to the termite nest one day, walking along ahead of him with a banana in one hand and, whilst the chimp sat there eating the fruit, offered him a strawfull of clinging termites. David glanced at them and then hit the straw from Hugo's hand with a soft threat bark.

However, during Hugo's last ten days, the chimpanzees finally demonstrated their skill in tool-using and tool-making. Hugo was able to film and take still photographs of David, William and Goliath working at the camp termite heap. It was exciting material, and Hugo hoped that it would help him to persuade the Geographic Society to let him return the following year and continue filming the chimpanzees.

When Hugo left at the end of November I was alone again. I still was not lonely, yet I was not as completely happy in my aloneness as I had been before he came. For I had found Hugo a companion with whom I could share not only the joys and frustrations of my work, but also my love of the chimpanzees, of the forests and mountains, of life in the wilderness. He had been with me into some of the wild, secret places where, I had thought, no other white person would ever tread. Together we had roasted in the sun and shivered under polythene in the rain. In Hugo I knew I had found a kindred spirit—one whose appreciation and understanding of animals was on a level with my own. Small wonder that I missed him when he was gone.

I shall always remember Christmas at the Gombe Stream that year. I bought an extra large supply of bananas and put them around a little tree which I had decorated with silver paper and cotton wool. Goliath and William arrived together on Christmas morning and gave loud screams of excitement when they saw the huge pile of fruit. They flung their arms around one another and Goliath patted William again and again on his wide-open screaming mouth, whilst William laid one arm over Goliath's back. Finally they calmed down and began their feast, still uttering small squeaks and grunts of pleasure, somewhat muffled and sticky through their mouthfuls of banana.

David arrived much later, on his own. I sat close beside him as he ate his bananas. He seemed extra calm, and after a while I very slowly moved my hand towards his shoulder and made a grooming movement. He brushed me away—but so casually that, after a moment, I ventured to try again. And that time he actually allowed me to groom him for at least a minute. Then he gently pushed my hand away once more. But he had let me touch him, tolerated physical contact with a human—and he was a fully adult male chimpanzee who had lived all of his life in the wild. It was a Christmas gift which I shall always treasure.

Shortly after Christmas I had to leave the Gombe Stream myself for another term at Cambridge. My last two weeks were sad, for William fell ill. His nose ran, his eyes watered and he constantly coughed—a dry hacking cough that shook his entire body. The first day of William's illness I followed him when he left camp for, by that time, I was able to move about the forests with both William and David, although Goliath still threatened me if I tried to follow him. William went a few hundred yards along the valley, climbed into a tree, and made himself a large and leafy nest. There he lay until about three in the afternoon, wheezing and coughing and sometimes, apparently, dozing. Several times he actually urinated whilst lying in his bed—behaviour so unusual that I knew he must be feeling very bad indeed. When he finally got up he fed on a few bits and pieces of leaf and vine, wandered slowly back to camp, ate a couple of bananas, and then climbed into a tree just beside my tent and made another nest.

That night I stayed out for there was a moon. At about one o'clock heavy clouds invaded the sky from the East; soon it began to rain. I was crouched some way up the steep slope of the mountain at a slightly higher level than William's nest, and when I shone my powerful torch in his direction I could just make out his huddled figure, sitting up on his wet bed with his knees up to his chin and his arms round his legs. For the rest of the night it rained on and off, and the silences between the pattering of the raindrops were punctuated by William's hacking cough. Once at the start of a really heavy deluge William gave a few rather tremulous pant-hoots and then was silent.

When he climbed down in the morning I saw that, every few moments, his body shook with violent spasms of shivering. As he shivered his long slack lips wobbled, but it was no longer funny. I longed to be able to wrap a warm blanket around him and give him a steaming hot toddy, but all I could offer were a few chilly bananas.

I was with William almost all the time for a week. He spent his days in the vicinity of camp, and many hours lying in different nests. Several times he joined David or Goliath for a while, but when they moved off up the mountain-side he turned back as though he couldn't face a long journey.

One morning I was sitting near William a little way up the mountain above camp when a boat arrived with some visitors from Kigoma for, by then, David Greybeard's fame had spread and people sometimes came for a Sunday picnic in the hope of seeing him. I should, of course, have gone down to say hallo, but I had become so attuned to William that I almost felt myself the chimps' instinctive distrust of strangers. When William moved down towards the tents I followed him: when he sat in the bushes opposite my camp I sat beside him. Together we watched the visitors: they had coffee and chatted for a while and then, since there was no sign of David, they left. I often wondered what they would have thought if they had known that I was sitting there, with William, peering at them as though they had been alien creatures from an unknown world.

One morning, two days before I had to leave, William stole a blanket from Dominic's tent. He had been sitting chewing on it for a while when David Greybeard arrived and, after eating some bananas, joined William at the blanket, For half an hour or so the two sat peacefully side by side, each sucking noisily and contentedly on different corners. But then William, like the clown he so often appeared to be, put part of the blanket right over his head and made groping movements with his hands as he tried to touch David from within the strange darkness he had created. David stared for a moment, and then patted William's hand. Presently the two wandered off into the forest together, leaving me with the echo of a dry hacking cough and the blanket lying on the ground. I never saw William again.

THE WART'S LESSON

T.H. White

T. H. White's novel The Sword in the Stone, *from which this episode is taken, tells the story of the boyhood of King Arthur—'the Wart', as he was called as a boy—and his education by the magician, Merlyn. It was an unusual education, to say the least of it. . . .*

'Shall we go out?' asked Merlyn. 'I think it is about time we began our lessons.'

The Wart's heart sank at this. His tutor had been there a month, and it was now August, but they had done no lessons so far. Now he suddenly remembered that this was what Merlyn was for, and he thought with dread of Summulae Logicales and the filthy astrolabe. He knew that it had to be borne, however, and got up obediently enough, after giving Cavall a last reluctant pat. He thought that it might not be so bad with Merlyn, who might be able to make even the Old Organon interesting, particularly if he would do some magic.

They went out into the courtyard, into a sun so burning that the heat of haymaking seemed to have been nothing. It was baking. The thunder-clouds which usually go with hot weather were there, high columns of cumulus with glaring edges, but there was not going to be any thunder. It was too hot even for that. 'If only,' thought the Wart, 'I did not have to go into a stuffy classroom, but could take off my clothes and swim in the moat.'

They crossed the courtyard, having almost to take deep breaths before they darted across it, as if they were going quickly through an oven. The shade of the gatehouse was cool, but the barbican, with its close walls, was hottest of all. In one last dash across the desert they had achieved the draw-bridge—could Merlyn have guessed what he was thinking about?—and were staring down into the moat.

It was the season of water-lilies. If Sir Ector had not kept one section free of them for the boys' bathing, all the water would have been covered. As it was, about twenty yards on each side of the bridge were cut each year, and you could dive in from the bridge itself. The moat was quite deep. It was used as a stew, so that the inhabitants of the castle could have fish on Fridays, and for this reason the architects had been careful not to let the drains and sewers run into it. It was stocked with fish every year.

'I wish I was a fish,' said the Wart.

'What sort of fish?'

It was almost too hot to think about this, but the Wart stared down into the cool amber depths where a school of small perch were aimlessly hanging about.

'I think I should like to be a perch,' he said. 'They are braver than the silly roach, and not quite so slaughterous as the pike.'

Merlyn took off his hat, raised his staff of lignum vitae politely in the air, and said slowly, 'Snylrem stnemilpmoc ot enutpen dna lliw eh yldnik tpecca siht yob sa a hsif?'

Immediately there was a loud blowing of sea-shells, conches and so forth, and a stout, jolly-looking gentleman appeared seated on a well-blown-up cloud above the battlements. He had an anchor tattooed on his tummy and a handsome mermaid with Mabel written under her on his chest. He ejected a quid of tobacco, nodded affably to Merlyn and pointed his trident at the Wart. The Wart found he had no clothes on. He found that he had tumbled off the draw-bridge, landing with a smack on his side in the water. He found that the moat and the bridge had grown hundreds of times bigger. He knew that he was turning into a fish.

'Oh, Merlyn,' cried the Wart. 'Please come too.'

'Just for this once,' said a large and solemn tench beside his ear, 'I will come. But in future you will have to go by yourself. Education is experience, and the essence of experience is self-reliance.'

The Wart found it difficult to be a fish. It was no good trying to swim like a human being, for it made him go corkscrew and much too slowly. He did not know how to swim like a fish.

'Not like that,' said the tench in ponderous tones. 'Put your chin on your left shoulder and do jack-knives. Never mind about the fins to begin with.'

The Wart's legs had fused together into his backbone and his feet and toes had become a tail fin. His arms had become two more fins—also of a delicate pinkish colour—and he had sprouted some more somewhere about his tummy. His head faced over his shoulder, so that when he bent in the middle his toes were moving towards his ear instead of towards his forehead. He was a beautiful olive-green colour with rather scratchy plate-armour all over him, and dark bands down his sides. He was not sure which were his sides and which were his back and front, but what now appeared to be his tummy had an attractive whitish colour, while his back was armed with a splendid great fin that could be erected for war and had spikes in it. He did jack-knives as the tench directed and found that he was swimming vertically downwards into the mud.

'Use your feet to turn to left or right with,' said the tench, 'and spread those fins on your tummy to keep level. You are living in two planes now, not one.'

The Wart found that he could keep more or less level by altering the inclination of his arm fins and the ones on his stomach. He swam feebly off, enjoying himself very much.

'Come back,' said the tench solemnly. 'You must learn to swim before you can dart.'

The Wart turned to his tutor in a series of zigzags and remarked, 'I don't seem to keep quite straight.'

'The trouble with you is that you don't swim from the shoulder. You swim as if you were a boy just bending at the hips. Try doing your jack-knives right from the neck downwards, and move your body exactly the same amount to the right as you are going to move it to the left. Put your back into it.'

Wart gave two terrific kicks and vanished altogether in a clump of mare's tail several yards away.

'That's better,' said the tench, now quite out of sight in the murky olive water, and the Wart backed himself out of his tangle with infinite trouble, by wriggling his arm fins. He undulated back towards the voice in one terrific shove, to show off.

'Good,' said the tench, as they collided end to end, 'but discretion is the better part of valour.'

'Try if you can do this one,' said the tench.

Without apparent exertion of any kind he swam off backwards under a water-lily. Without apparent exertion; but the Wart, who was an enterprising learner, had been watching the slightest movement of his fins. He moved his own fins anti-clockwise, gave the very tip of his own tail a cunning flick, and was lying alongside the tench.

'Splendid,' said Merlyn. 'Let's go for a little swim.'

The Wart was on an even keel now, and reasonably able to move about. He had leisure to observe the extraordinary universe into which the tattooed gentleman's trident had plunged him. It was very different from the universe to which he had hitherto been accustomed. For one thing, the heaven or sky above him was now a perfect circle poised a few inches above his head. The horizon had closed in to this. In order to imagine yourself into the Wart's position, you will have to picture a round horizon, a few inches above your head, instead of the flat horizon which you have usually seen. Under this horizon of air you will have to imagine another horizon of under water, spherical and practically upside down—for the surface of the water acted partly as a mirror to what was below it. It is difficult to imagine. What makes it a great deal more difficult to imagine is that everything which human beings would consider to be above the water level was fringed with all the colours of the spectrum. For instance, if you had happened to be fishing for the Wart, he would have seen you, at the rim of the tea saucer which was the upper air to him, not as one person waving a fishing-rod, but as seven people, whose outlines were red, orange, yellow, green, blue, indigo and violet, all waving the same rod whose colours were as varied. In fact, you would have been a rainbow man to him, a beacon of flashing and radiating colours, which ran into one another and had rays all about. You would have been burned upon the water like Cleopatra in the poem by Herédia. The reference may possibly be to Shakespeare.

The next most lovely thing was that the Wart had no weight. He was not earth-bound any more and did not have to plod along on a flat surface, pressed down by gravity and the weight of the atmosphere. He could do what men have always wanted to do, that is, fly. There is practically no difference between flying in the water and flying in the air. The best of it was that he did not have to fly in a machine, by pulling levers and sitting still, but could do it with his own body. It was like the dreams people have.

Just as they were going to swim off on their tour of inspection, a timid young roach appeared from between two waving bottle brushes of mare's tail and hung about, looking quite pale with agitation. It looked at them with big apprehensive eyes and evidently wanted something, but could not make up its mind.

'Approach,' said Merlyn gravely.

At this the roach rushed up like a hen, burst into tears and began stammering its message.

'If you p-p-p-please, Doctor,' stammered the poor creature, gabbling so that they could scarcely understand what it said, 'we have such a d-dretful case of s-s-s-something or other in our family, and we w-w-w-wondered if you could s-s-s-spare the time? It's our d-d-d-dear Mama, who w-w-w-will swim a-a-a-all the time upside d-d-d-down, and she d-d-d-does look so horrible and s-s-s-speaks so strange, that we r-r-r-really thought she ought to have a d-d-d-doctor, if it w-w-w-wouldn't be too much? C-C-C-Clara says to say so sir, if you s-s-s-see w-w-w-what I m-m-m-mean?'

Here the little roach began fizzing so much, what with its stammer and its tearful disposition, that it became perfectly inarticulate and could only stare at Merlyn with big mournful eyes.

'Never mind, my little man,' said Merlyn. 'There, there, lead me to your poor Mamma, and we shall see what we can do.'

They all three swam off into the murk under the draw-bridge upon their errand of mercy.

'Very Russian, these roach,' whispered Merlyn to the Wart, behind his fin. 'It's probably only a case of nervous hysteria, a matter for the psychologist rather than the physician.'

The roach's Mamma was lying on her back as he had described. She was squinting horribly, had folded her fins upon her chest, and every now and then she blew a bubble. All her children were gathered

Transformed, Merlyn and the Wart plunged into the murky olived water.

round her in a circle, and every time she blew a bubble they all nudged each other and gasped. She had a seraphic smile upon her face.

'Well, well, well,' said Merlyn, putting on his best bedside manner, 'and how is Mrs Roach today?'

He patted all the young roaches on the head and advanced with stately motions towards his patient. It should perhaps be mentioned that Merlyn was a ponderous, deep-beamed fish of about five pounds, red-leather coloured, with small scales, adipose in his fins, rather slimy, and having a bright marigold eye—a respectable figure.

Mrs Roach held out a languid fin, sighed emphatically and said, 'Ah, doctor, so you've come at last?'

'Hum,' said Merlyn, in his deepest tones.

Then he told everybody to close their eyes—the Wart peeped—and began to swim round the invalid in a slow and stately dance. As he danced he sang. His song was this:

> Therapeutic,
> Elephantic,
> Diagnosis,
>   Boom!
> Pancreatic,
> Microstatic,
> Anti-toxic,
>   Doom!
> With normal catabolism,
>   Gabbleism and babbleism.
> Snip, Snap, Snorum
> Cut out his abdonorum.
> Dyspepsia,
> Anaemia,
> Toxaemia,
> One, two, three,
> And out goes He,
> With a fol-de-rol-derido for the Five Guinea Fee.

At the end of his song he was swimming round his patient so close that he actually touched her, stroking his brown smooth-scaled flanks against her more rattly pale ones. Perhaps he was healing her with his slime—for all fishes are said to go to the Tench for medicine —or perhaps it was by touch or massage or hypnotism. In any case, Mrs Roach suddenly stopped squinting, turned the right way up, and said, 'Oh, doctor, dear doctor, I feel I could eat a little lob-worm now.'

'No lob-worm,' said Merlyn, 'not for two days. I shall give you a prescription for a strong broth of algae every two hours, Mrs Roach. We must build up your strength you know. After all, Rome wasn't built in a day.'

Then he patted all the little roaches once more, told them to grow up into brave little fish, and swam off with an air of great importance into the gloom. As he swam, he puffed his mouth in and out.

'What did you mean by that about Rome?' asked the Wart, when they were out of earshot.

'Heaven knows,' said the tench.

They swam along, Merlyn occasionally advising him to put his back into it when he forgot, and all the strange under-water world began to dawn about them, deliciously cool after the heat of the upper air. The great forests of the weed were delicately traced, and in them there hung motionless many schools of sticklebacks learning to do their physical exercises in strict unison. On the word One they all lay still: at Two they faced about: at Three they all shot together into a cone, whose apex was a bit of something to eat. Water snails slowly ambled about on the stems of the lilies or under their leaves, while fresh-water mussels lay on the bottom doing nothing in particular. Their flesh was salmon pink, like a very good strawberry cream ice. The small congregations of perch—it was a strange thing, but all the bigger fish seemed to have hidden themselves—had delicate circulations, so that they blushed or grew pale as easily as a lady in a Victorian novel. Only their blush was a deep olive colour, and it was the blush of rage. Whenever Merlyn and his companion swam past them, they raised their spiky dorsal fins in menace, and only lowered them when they saw that Merlyn was a tench. The black bars on their sides made them look as if they had been grilled; and these also could become darker or lighter. Once the two travellers passed under a swan. The white creature floated above like a zeppelin, all indistinct except what was under the water. The latter part was quite clear and showed that the swan was floating slightly on one side with one leg cocked up over its back.

'Look,' said the Wart, 'it's the poor swan with the deformed leg. It can only paddle with one leg, and the other side of it is all hunched.'

'Nonsense,' said the swan snappily, putting its head into the water and giving them a frown with its black nares. 'Swans like to rest in this position, and you can keep your fishy sympathy to yourself, so there.' It continued to glare at them from up above, like a white snake suddenly let down through the ceiling, until they were out of sight.

'You swim along,' said the tench in gloomy tones, 'as if there was nothing to be afraid of in the world. Don't you see that this place is exactly like the forest you had to come through to find me?'

'Is it?'

'Look over there.'

The Wart looked, and at first saw nothing. Then he saw a little translucent shape hanging motionless near the surface. It was just outside the shadow of a water lily and was evidently enjoying the sun. It was a baby pike, absolutely rigid and probably asleep, and it looked like a pipe stem or a sea horse stretched out flat. It would be a brigand when it grew up.

'I am taking you to see one of those,' said the tench, 'the Emperor of all these purlieus. As a doctor I have immunity, and I daresay he will respect you as my companion as well. But you had better keep your tail bent in case he is feeling tyrannical.'

'Is he the King of the Moat?'

'He is the King of the Moat. Old Jack they call him, and some Black Peter, but for the most part they don't mention him by name at all. They just call him Mr M. You will see what it is to be a king.'

The Wart began to hang behind his conductor a little, and perhaps it was as well that he did, for they were almost on top of their destination before he noticed it. When he did see the old despot he started back in horror for Mr M was four feet long, his weight incalculable. The great body, shadowy and almost invisible among the stems, ended in a face which had been ravaged by all the passions of an absolute monarch, by cruelty, sorrow, age, pride, selfishness, loneliness and thoughts too strong for individual brains. There he hung or hoved, his vast ironic mouth permanently drawn downwards in a kind of melancholy, his lean clean-shaven chops giving him an American expression, like that of Uncle Sam. He was remorseless, disillusioned, logical, predatory, fierce, pitiless: but his great jewel of an eye was that of a stricken deer, large, fearful, sensitive and full of griefs. He made no movement whatever, but looked upon them with this bitter eye.

The Wart thought to himself that he did not care for Mr M.

'Lord,' said Merlyn, not paying any attention to his nervousness. 'I have brought a young professor who would learn to profess.'

'To profess what?' inquired the King of the Moat slowly, hardly opening his jaws and speaking through his nose.

'Power,' said the tench.

'Let him speak for himself.'

'Please,' said the Wart, 'I don't know what I ought to ask.'

'There is nothing,' said the monarch, 'except the power that you profess to seek: power to grind and power to digest, power to seek and power to find, power to await and power to claim, all power and pitilessness springing from the nape of the neck.'

'Thank you,' said the Wart.

'Love is a trick played on us by the forces of evolution,' continued the monster monotonously. 'Pleasure is the bait laid down by the same. There is only power. Power is of the individual mind, but the mind's power alone is not enough. The power of strength decides everything in the end, and only Might is right.

'Now I think it is time that you should go away, young master, for I find this conversation excessively exhausting. I think you ought to go away really almost at once, in case my great disillusioned mouth should suddenly determine to introduce you to my great gills, which have teeth in them also. Yes, I really think you ought to go away this moment. Indeed, I think you ought to put your back into it. And so, a long farewell to all my greatness.'

The Wart had found himself quite hypnotised by all these long words, and hardly noticed that the thin-lipped tight mouth was coming closer and closer to him all the time. It came imperceptibly, as the cold suave words distracted his attention, and suddenly it was looming within an inch of his nose. On the last sentence it opened, horrible and vast, the thin skin stretching ravenously from bone to bone and tooth to tooth. Inside there seemed to be nothing but teeth, sharp teeth like thorns in rows and ridges everywhere, like the nails in labourers' boots, and it was only at the very last second that he was able to regain his own will, to pull himself together, recollect his instructions and to escape. All those teeth clashed behind him at the tip of his tail, as he gave the heartiest jack-knife he had ever given.

In a second he was on dry land once more, standing beside Merlyn on the piping draw-bridge, panting in all his clothes.

TYTO AND BRILA

Glyn Frewer

Tyto, a young barn owl, has been chased from home by his parents, to make way for their next brood. He has been learning to live on his own and fend for himself.

The following dusk Tyto glided from the pines, eager for food. His flight had used up a lot of energy and he was ravenous. He had not reached the foot of the hill before he heard the challenging cry of another male barn owl. Startled, Tyto turned towards the sound. Never in the previous time he had spent in the area had his sovereignty been put to the test by another of his species. Tyto swept around the hill with his facial disc feathers puffed out to give him his most fearsome look. As he rounded the fir trees in the half light, a barn owl crossed the gap on the hillside. Tyto veered towards it, then turned and circled, puzzled. The owl was a female and not the owl that had voiced the challenge. This put the situation in a different light. Far from being sovereign of the area, Tyto was the trespasser, for a pair of his own kind had settled here. Tyto glided towards the tree where he could see the female perched. So far, he had not glimpsed the male.

The female was a yearling like himself, with prominent dark flecks on her breast feathers giving her a speckled look more like that of a tawny owl. Her head swivelled to look at him, her eyes luminescent in the shadow. Tyto flew to the branch above her and her head flexed around so that she was looking directly behind her. Tyto's grunts were answered by a soft mewing that sent a strange, unfamiliar tremble through his body. In that second of time, Tyto's maleness asserted itself in every cell of his body, and his purpose in life was never again that of a young owl seeking only to hunt and survive.

When the challenging cry of the male rang through the pine-black shadows, it was a different Tyto who screeched his answer. No longer trespasser, no longer immature, no longer undecided, Tyto flew out to combat for a mate as well as territory.

★   ★   ★   ★

The two owls knew each other instantly. Tyto recognized the bright orange facial colouring and the thick tarsal tufts of the owl he had fought on the boathouse roof. And Gar recognized the young owl he had already chased and dismissed. With a confident screech, he swept towards Tyto, eager to repeat his earlier success.

The initial confrontation was a testing. Both birds, now well matched in size, flew headlong on a straight collision course, stalling within inches of each other at the last split second so that only their wing tips met. But the second stoop was in deadly earnest, and they collided in mid-air, judging the impact to a nicety, each seeking with claw and beak to injure the other. The air was filled with the thudding of wing-beats, harsh angry cries and a storm-burst of feathers. Locked in combat, the two birds tumbled over and over in the night air down to the long wet grass where they rolled and squawked, stabbed and scratched, sending up a spray of silver dew.

Then, as suddenly as the fight began, it was over. Tyto's flailing claw found a hold on the flank of his enemy and Gar's skin was lacerated deeply. Letting out a croak of pain and chattering with rage and defeat, Gar broke free of Tyto and, blood running down his leg, the older owl beat a hasty retreat over the field. Relentlessly Tyto pursued him, but his aerial buffeting was mocking more than damaging. Behind him, a silent witness to the rout, the female, Brila, flew on a wavering course, anxious to keep both owls within sight and sound.

Once again the river was the boundary. Gar, diving and swooping to avoid Tyto's stronger pursuit, flew low over the rushes seeking cover under the hanging willows on the far bank. With a final sharp screech of victory, Tyto turned away and winged slowly back to the wheeling Brila. When he reached her he acknowledged her with a low cry, then both birds returned to the pines. Tyto landed heavily, exhausted but unhurt, while Brila swooped below the tree to snatch an incautious shrew. She took it to the next tree to devour it.

For two hours Tyto did not move, except to preen his ruffled feathers. Then his hunger drove him out again across the field. The sight of the river earlier had sparked a memory of successful hunting, and he headed there again, registering familiar landmarks. He reached the willows and the reeds. There was no sign of Gar. Two male water voles squeaked in angry combat as they fought, writhing in the water-filled cattle hoofprints on the mud-bank. Tyto dived and lifted both animals in his talons. One, struggling, fell back into midstream, where it dived immediately. Tyto landed on the water tower and smashed the skull of the other with his beak. He swallowed it partially and sat with the tail limp from his mouth. Minutes later, it was gone. A lift of his wings and he was off again, sealing the fate of a field mouse at the foot of the tower.

Long before dawn, Tyto's hunger was appeased. His last catch, a young rabbit, was left half eaten in the lane. Brila had already returned to the roost in the water tower which she had shared for several nights with Gar. Although the two had shared, the season had not been ripe, the winter cold too recent, for Brila to have responded to Gar's half-hearted attempts at courtship. No doubt, if Tyto's arrival had not disturbed things, she and Gar would have mated.

For Brila and Tyto, the mating urge which grew stronger as the spring nights passed was outside their experience. Both birds being young, their courtship owed nothing to mimicry or imitation of their elders. The unfamiliar urgings awakening in Tyto were from the dawn of Time. Through him, Nature took its course, haltingly experimental, unhelped by confidence.

His awkward posturings whenever he approached Brila were rebuffed with sharp pecks, and her feathers rose aggressively. Yet Tyto would not accept these signs of antagonism from her as he would have done from any other barn owl. When on one occasion he approached her and she retaliated by fluttering and sparring with her talons, he did not retreat. Instead, he responded by acting aggressively himself, lowering his head, dilating his facial feathers and thrusting at her with his bill. Since Brila was an inch or so bigger than he was, he would have come off badly had a real combat developed, but apart from angry clacking of her mandibles as she parried his thrusts, the hen bird made no attempt to attack.

The two owls shared several roosts, sometimes the tower, sometimes the hole Tyto had used before in the dead Scots pine, and one very warm night they roosted in the canopy of ivy in the fork of a giant elm. Each night they quartered the countryside within a two-mile radius. There was no need to seek further since the food supply was plentiful. Gradually, it seemed to Tyto that Brila's rejection of his attention was becoming less determined.

Tyto persevered in his immature courtship. In the peak of condition, he was handsome, though his first real adult molt was yet to come. His breast, exceptionally pale even as a fledgling, was now snowy white with none of the usual buff shading. His wings and back, amber-yellow shaded with ash grey, were flecked with a striking pattern of brown and white markings. His broken pinion feather had fallen away, soon to be replaced by a perfect one, but the small dislocation would be with him for life and the gap was still there between the feathers. The broad soft feathers of his tail were again more white than yellow, barred with tawny brown. Grey and yellow featherlets formed a heart shape around the startlingly white down of his face, and his black eyes contrasted dramatically. He spent more time preening now, and was clearly conscious of his fine appearance, for his posturings in front of Brila took on a swagger of natural pride.

Brila, in contrast, was by nature less handsome. She was bigger than Tyto, but her plumage lacked the sheen of the male bird. The whiteness was much less apparent, and her pale cream breast was edged by noticeable black flecks. Her back and wings were deeper in colour, too, a rich buff with darker grey. To Tyto she was everything desirable, but already he had noticed her strange hunched posture and the fits of violent trembling to which she was subject.

Then on a night when the air was rich with the scent of pine and insects danced in frenetic clouds over field and river, the youthful courtship took another turn.

The quarter moon had risen when Tyto returned to the pine with a water vole in his bill. Brila was in the hole, huddled and silent. She gave a low cry as Tyto arrived. Tyto approached her step by step, and this time she made no move of rejection. Motionless, she waited until Tyto was beside her. His head made quick bowing motions and he shook himself, ruffling his feathers. He turned his face and rubbed it against the side of her head. She responded, bowing with him so that their faces stayed pressed together. Brila made a halfhearted peck at the vole but did not take it. Side by side, they sat uttering low cries, Tyto still with the vole in his beak. Then he stepped away, deposited the carcass on the branch outside and flew off, renewing the hunt.

The next night, Tyto repeated the performance, this time with no offering. Again Brila responded, snapping her bill and uttering a bubbling, chattering sound. Tyto, too, clicked his beak while he stretched his neck up and down as though trying hard to swallow. Both birds ruffled out their feathers as if putting on a display of aggression, and when Tyto began to sway his whole body from side to side, Brila followed suit. Now she was the one to edge closer to Tyto and the clacking sound turned into a churring snore. As on the previous night, they rubbed their heads together, lowering and raising themselves while clicking their bills. Finally, Tyto did something he had not done before: he stretched forward and seized Brila by her neck feathers, shaking her from side to side. A loud squawk from the hen softened quickly to a chatter of acceptance. Well pleased with his reception, Tyto released her and the two birds stayed together. When Tyto stretched out his wings to fly, Brila followed immediately and the two soared over the pines, scattering the midges, their shadows freezing the shrew foraging among the pine needles into petrified immobility.

Five nights later, as the fierce March gale blew itself out, Brila flew back from the river after an unsuccessful foray and settled in the tower roost. Tyto followed minutes later with a field vole in his claws. He flew into the crevice where she was waiting. For the eighth night in succession, Tyto repeated his ritual display. Tonight he added something new. He raised and ruffled his feathers, then compressed them again, repeating this many times. His manner, too, was more aggressive, just as Brila's was more submissive. When he stretched

Tyto rejected Brila's rebuffals and persevered with his immature courtship.

to rub heads, she took the vole from his beak. Pinning it with a claw she began to devour it. Suddenly, after loud bill clapping, Tyto seized her neck feathers and shook her as though savaging a prey. When he released her, Brila raised and lowered herself, uttering soft plaintive calls. She was begging Tyto to mount her, and Tyto did so. For several seconds the confined space echoed with the loud beat of wings as he struggled to keep his balance on top of her. Brila crouched, mewing, in total submission as the two owls attempted to couple. But the coupling, doomed before it started, failed not only because of immaturity. There was a more deadly reason.

When Tyto stumblingly dismounted, he immediately began to preen his ruffled feathers as though nothing had happened. Brila's behaviour was the opposite. She stretched her neck and preened Tyto's head feathers with her bill. Pressed side to side, the two owls mutually groomed each other, uttering soft cries. Tyto departed only because Brila was overtaken by a violent fit of trembling. Tyto always left her when she suffered these attacks, as though he could tell there was nothing he could do. Brila was slowly dying of poison.

Brila had been born in a cow shed, eight miles north of Merford. The shed was on the land of a farmer who had taken every possible precaution to safeguard his crops and his livelihood. He had liberally dressed the seed with dieldrin before the spring sowing, and when the crops were through, he had sprayed them with a solution containing DDT. Insect pests on his farm, the farmer intended, would never stand a chance. Unwittingly, he was meting out destruction to more than insects.

A small proportion of the spring seed was eaten by the usual seed-eaters, birds and rodents alike; the ground-feeders flocked, sparrows, chaffinches, greenfinches, linnets and pigeons; mice and voles scratched their way to some of the grain. Small quantities of poison went into the bodies of all these creatures. But when the young green shoots showed their heads and the crop spray was applied, much more damage was done. This deadlier poison, though it dispersed gradually in the soil, stayed as a protective coat on the plants. Every bud swallowed by the birds and rodents had poison still on it, a poison that stayed a very long time in all living tissue, scarcely dispersing at all. Every meal, every grain, added one more minute dose of poison to the amount already built up in their systems. To some it brought death, but to most of them it simply slowed their reactions so that they were the first to fall prey to the hawks and the owls. Poisoned rodents and birds, by the score night after night, week after week, were fed to Brila and her sister chick. The parent owls themselves were doomed to sterility and death. Now, a year later, the poison absorbed by Brila had spread throughout her body, finally reaching her brain, causing increasing convulsions.

★　　　★　　　★　　　★

Once the attempt at mating had taken place, Brila's earlier suspicion of Tyto vanished on the night wind and mutual affection grew up between them. The ensuing two weeks were spent in nights of easy hunting and days of companionship and trust. Often now, as the soft rains heralded the approach of April, Tyto would return to Brila in the water tower with an offering of food—sometimes a water vole, a shrew, a mouse, a frog, even a young grey squirrel. And Brila accepted everything eagerly, devouring it and mewing for more. She made hunting forays of her own less and less now and stayed huddled and disconsolate in the roost.

During the day, Tyto would sit close to Brila and they would groom each other with much bill-clapping and soft calls. Brila's bouts of shivering occurred more frequently and more severely. Sometimes she seemed to lose her balance and staggered, other times her whole body would shake in a spasm of pain.

There was one dawn, however, when their troubles were forgotten. Tyto returned from devouring a newly hatched coot he had discovered in the reeds to find Brila clucking in the corner of the crevice with unfamiliar excitement. Her first egg was laid. She nodded rapidly, drawing Tyto's attention to it, a small white sphere, sterile in any event, but now smashed beneath her tail where she had dropped it. The poison in Brila's system had caused an abnormality to the calcium formation of the eggshell so that it was paper-thin. With the yellow yolk of the life that was never to be spreading beneath her feet, Brila chittered proudly while Tyto hopped to and fro in excited satisfaction at the greatest feeling of fulfillment he had ever known.

For a night and another day, the two birds cherished the pathetic white object beneath the shivering, dull-eyed Brila. She laid a second egg, but this was even thinner-shelled and broke on emerging. Even Brila took no pride in this, for she clawed the mess away with desultory scratching. In doing so, she utterly crushed the first egg, and now the situation was apparent to both birds.

That night, the two owls left the nest and the broken remains, though neither bird felt any strong inclination to hunt. That part of Tyto which had been so completely fulfilled was now empty and frustrated. As he listlessly scoured the edge of the wood, it was as though he was hunting from habit more than the need to survive. Eventually, a snuffling shrew crossed a bare patch of ground and was snatched, killed and eaten in seconds.

Brila, too, caught a shrew, then a field vole, but this she left on the branch of the tree where she took it. Crying plaintively, she flew to where Tyto was quartering the field and followed him.

For the next week, the two birds went through the motions of their natural routine, roosting by day, hunting by night, in a lacklustre, benumbed fashion. But as spring turned into summer, and the drawn-out evenings proffered plump pickings from the season's crop of new-grown creatures, the two owls responded to Nature's reassuring mood. At least, Tyto responded. Brila, whose shivering bouts had increased in spite of her recent renewal of appetite, began to get worse. In July, the birds tried mating again but Brila, in spite of Tyto's elaborate overtures, this time did not respond. She rejected him savagely, her instinct telling her she would never brood another clutch of eggs, and Tyto quickly dropped his attentions. As the summer wore on, she hunted less, until by August she was eating only the offerings that Tyto brought to her. Day by day Brila grew weaker, barely eating at all.

Towards the end of July, both birds went into the moult which owls and most birds undergo once the breeding season is over. The once-bright feathers, which had become worn and bedraggled from the ardours of raising their broods, needed replacing with new. In Tyto's case, true to his kind, the feathers fell in regular sequence over the next three weeks, his large wing feathers going first, not pushed out by the new growths as with some birds, but dropping like dead hair as fresh plumes grew alongside. At the same time as his wing feathers changed, so did his tail, the outside feathers falling first, the others going in sequence to the centre until all the old had been replaced. Next, from rump to head, his body feathers dropped as new ones appeared. Bedraggled and half-plucked in appearance, Tyto's spirits were low during this time, and he spent the long days hunched unhappily and the nights embarrassed by his imperfect flight.

The moult took even more out of Brila, weakened as she was. For days she had not even eaten the prey that Tyto brought her. On a night in early September, when the first wisps of autumn drifted from the river at dusk, Brila did something she had not done for weeks. When Tyto flew from the tower to hunt, she followed at once, as though she knew that this night would be different. Taking off from the ledge, she spiralled almost to the ground before she could coordinate her muscles. Only at the last split second did she stall above the grass and soar in pursuit of Tyto's white form.

Tyto reached the river and found his favourite reed bed. Brila stopped, exhausted, in the willow. She perched on a branch above the flowing stream, her breath a hoarse croak in her throat. As Tyto swooped at—and missed—a diving water vole, a severe convulsion shook the whole of Brila's body. She died as she sat there, toppling slowly as her talons loosened their grip. Her fluttering form fell into the water. Tyto, thinking it another vole diving for its life, did not even turn his head. He never saw the sodden bundle of feathers swirl past the reeds and out of his life. Instead, his keen eyes stayed riveted on a young rabbit in the middle of the field and he winged silently to it. A scream, a second's frenzied kicking and the white wings rose and beat their way back to the tower.

There was no answering cry as he landed. Leaving the rabbit on the ledge outside, for it had been intended as a gift, Tyto called softly. He rose and circled the pines, then flew back to the river. Up and down, the white shape, now silver in the moon's light, now black against the stars, quartered the riverbanks for a mile each way. Back and forth to the silent tower, only the distant yap of a fox mocked his calls. He returned to the willow where the leaves whispered in secret, and across the black rippling water his screech echoed like a soul in torment.

BOY ON A DOLPHIN

Horace E. Dobbs

Of all the creatures in the sea dolphins have a unique place: for centuries they have been renowned for their friendliness towards man. Telemachos, the legendary son of Ulysses, was saved from drowning by a dolphin and pushed ashore. Many sculptures and ancient coins, such as the didrachma from Tarentum (331–302 BC) have depicted boys riding on dolphins. Were the stories of rescues and rides that have been passed down through the ages simply myths? Before 1974 I had some reservations about the authenticity of these tales. But now I have none, and I will tell you why.

It started, as these things so often happen with me, by events not working out as planned. I had arranged to run a short course on underwater photography at Dale Fort, on the remote tip of south west Wales. It was to incorporate a short family holiday, and we were to be joined by our Italian underwater photographer friend, Luciano. A few days before he arrived I received a message to say the photography course was cancelled due to unrelenting south westerly gales.

It was Luciano's first diving visit to Great Britain and I was resolved that he should not go back to Milan without seeing something of the wealth of underwater life that the British Isles has to offer. The question was, where could we go? A visit to Douglas the previous

83

year had brought me into contact with the Isle of Man Branch of the British Sub-Aqua Club. Two members of the club, Mike and Maura, had met my 'plane on arrival and the few dives I had there were memorable both for the prolific sea life I saw and the clarity of the water. The advantage of a large island is that a lee shore can be found; thus, theoretically, it should be possible to find a diving site even in bad conditions. So I telephoned Maura Mitchell to see if a last-ditch operation could be mounted to save our holiday and get Luciano wet—in the sea. She reported that conditions were far from good; nonetheless, we decided to risk making the Isle of Man the base for our mini-holiday. Maura quietly and efficiently organized accommodation for us. It was then only up to us to get there.

We arrived at Douglas after a hair-raising journey by car ferry in a force eight gale. Luciano, as he struggled to open the door against the pressure of the fierce wind, said he had never encountered such conditions before. Tongue in cheek, I told him the conditions were quite normal and would not deter us from diving. Poor Luciano was not sure whether to take my remark seriously. I told him that we British regard the Mediterranean (the only sea in which he had dived) as no more than a large warm swimming pool. I pressed the point further, telling him that his introduction to *real* diving—diving off the British Coast—would be a baptism by fire, as the conditions would undoubtedly deteriorate even further.

As it turned out the converse was true. It would be more accurate to describe Luciano's introduction to British diving as a baptism by cold for the water temperature on our first dive was 58°F and the sea was flat and calm.

During our stay Maura mentioned that a number of divers on the island had made friends with a wild dolphin which had been given the name Donald. Many stories had been told about him. The consternation at the sudden, unexpected appearance of a fast-moving, twelve-foot-long, shark-like, living torpedo amongst unsuspecting divers who seldom see a fish more than two feet long, can be imagined. But those who remained in the water found that Donald was only trying to be friendly and came very close because he was extremely inquisitive. If a non-diver can imagine going for a walk in the country and suddenly being charged by a rhino, which then stops and gently nuzzles him with its horn, he will have some idea of how they felt.

I had had a similar encounter with a wild dolphin off the Scottish Coast at Eyemouth. It had been one of the most memorable of my diving experiences. I had filmed the dolphin and he had become more and more excited when I found an old oildrum on the seabed and banged it with my snorkel tube. I felt sure from what I had heard about him that Donald would behave in the same way. The problem was to locate him. Sightings had been reported at Douglas, Castletown, Port Erin and Port St Mary, places which were miles apart.

Maura had observed, however, that on a number of mornings Donald had been seen playing amongst the boats in the harbour at Port St Mary, so that seemed as good a place as any to start our hunt. At the attractive, busy little harbour, we met a group of divers from Blackpool who were about to launch their boats for a sea dive. Maura, Luciano, my thirteen-year-old son Ashley and I strolled along the jetty looking at the vessels in the harbour. Suddenly Maura pointed to a blue fishing boat moving rapidly through the water on its mooring line. It stopped moving when it reached the limit permitted by the mooring line, and drifted back to its original position.

'That was Donald pushing that boat,' said Maura excitedly. 'I'm sure he's here!'

'Are you sure it wasn't a stray gust of wind?'

'No. That was Donald all right.'

Luciano and I scanned the other boats.

'Look! There. He's doing it again.'

Sure enough, the fishing boat was again moving forward, followed by a splash in the middle of the harbour as Donald leapt out of the water. The effect on me was electrifying. Every nerve in my body seemed to tingle.

'We haven't a second to lose,' I said to Luciano. At any moment Donald could decide to depart and leave us with an empty sea.

We ripped off our clothes and tossed them in the back of the car. Luciano was ready dressed for the sea, complete with camera, in a matter of moments, and so were Ashley and I.

We started to snorkel out on the surface towards the fishing boat which was moored about two hundred yards off the shore. Halfway there Ashley saw a huge, dark-grey submarine pass underneath him at great speed. Donald had come across to see who we were. Some of the divers from Blackpool were also in the water and they shouted excitedly as they caught glimpses of him.

I have seldom seen an animal so delighted to see people and so overtly overflowing with joy and energy. He inspected all the divers, swimming from one to another with incredible speed, looking at each one quizzically for a few seconds and then bounding away with powerful flicks of his tail fluke. Between inspections he would give the fishing boat a quick shove, pushing his belly against the keel and finning vigorously with his tail. He had the exuberance of a basketful of kittens.

Luciano was very thrilled to have seen and photographed Donald. To celebrate he took us to the Crow's Nest Restaurant overlooking Douglas Harbour. The 6 September 1974 was a special day, for it was both Luciano's birthday, and—we all agreed—'the day of the dolphin'. That same day the gales that had been battering the south coast of England made headlines in the newspapers. We counted ourselves very lucky to have chosen the Isle of Man for our brief holiday.

On the way back to Liverpool Luciano and I discussed the pictures we had taken of Donald.

'Did you manage to get any shots with another diver in the picture?' I asked.

'No,' replied Luciano.

'I didn't either. He was too excited. You couldn't tell where he would be next.'

We agreed that we were extremely lucky to see and photograph a dolphin in the wild. Luciano reminded me of the old-fashioned standard divers who were sometimes called 'copper-nobs' because of their copper helmets. They wore rubberised canvas suits with lead-soled shoes, and had air pumped down to their helmets from the surface through long rubber hoses. During the first half of this century 'copper-nob' divers from Greece used to search for sponges to be dried and used in bathrooms—before synthetic sponges were widely manufactured. The Greek sponge divers led very dangerous lives, since they did not fully understand the bends which would cripple them if they were hauled up to the surface too quickly after a prolonged deep dive.

Even more than the bends, the sponge divers feared sharks. However, on their way to sponge grounds they would sometimes be accompanied by dolphins, which would weave to and fro in the bow wave in front of the boats. When this happened they would be delighted: they knew that with dolphins around they would not be troubled by sharks. Dolphins can easily kill sharks: they rush at them and ram them with their snouts, or beaks as they are called. Although sharks are primitive fish they have the sense to keep well clear of dolphins. Thus even in bygone days there has been a happy association between divers and dolphins.

The Greek sponge fishermen also noted something which is a riddle that has still to be resolved. Although the dolphins would often accompany their boats for many miles, they moved away as soon as the boats stopped. And the divers, who were so close to the dolphins on the surface that they could almost touch them, seldom saw their friends underwater. As they plummeted down to the seabed they could sometimes hear the dolphins whistling to one another, and sometimes, if they were lucky, they got a fleeting glimpse of them swimming excitedly in the distance. But that was all.

Even today, when divers wear scuba equipment (self-contained underwater breathing apparatus), they seldom see dolphins when submerged. So you can understand the excitement that we felt at having been at close quarters with a wild dolphin swimming in the sea.

Four weeks later Ashley and I set sail again for the Isle of Man; our objective was to photograph and film Donald in the open sea. (Unfortunately, Luciano was unable to get away from Milan.)

On the morning following our arrival we lashed Maura's inflatable boat to the roof-rack of the car and headed for Port St Mary, where a gusty north-westerly wind was blowing into the corner of the harbour where we hoped to find Donald. Fortunately for us, Donald had become a dolphin of habit. For there he was, pushing the boats back and forth as he had done on our last visit. The prospect of diving with him again made me feel like a rocket with the touch paper alight.

We changed into our diving suits on the cold windy slipway. Maura took the oars (hurrah for women's lib!) and urged the inflatable reluctantly into the direction of an anchored fishing boat. We tied up alongside and Maura slipped into the water. She had kept up her contact with Donald during the four weeks since my first dive with him, and he recognized her instantly. I joined her a few minutes later.

It is well known that dolphins are extremely intelligent, and Maura feels sure that Donald tries to communicate with her when she is in the water. She can hear him squeaking and is annoyed that she cannot understand dolphinese. First of all she nods her head to Donald and he nods back. He likes being stroked.

After a few minutes Maura climbed back aboard the inflatable to put on her aqualung. As I already had mine on I stayed in the water, and Donald came and inspected me at very close quarters. When Maura was fully kitted up I held on to the side of the inflatable and discussed the tactics we would employ on the dive. All the time I was aware that Donald was hovering a few inches behind me, waiting for the fun to start.

We were all set. I put my hand down to grasp my camera, complete with its new fish-eye lens which I had bought specially for this occasion—and my heart skipped several beats. The camera, which a few minutes before had been hanging around my neck on its strap, was not there any more.

I told the others my alarming news. For a short time I forgot Donald and looked down on to a seabed consisting of sand and silt with outcrops of seaweed. With little hope of finding my camera I descended to the bottom. Then I looked up and saw Donald in the distance with his head down, excitedly looking at something on the seabed. I swam over to him and there under his beak was my lost camera.

'Donald, you are a wonderful dolphin,' I said to my bottlenosed friend.

With the aqualung mouthpiece clenched between my teeth I was not sure how it sounded to Donald. But I felt certain he understood that I was delighted. As his eyes were set on the sides of his head I could see only one of them at a time; nonetheless this single eye could be very expressive. And when he looked at me brightly and nodded his head I got the distinct feeling that he was trying to tell me that he was pleased to be of assistance.

After that our photography session progressed well, with Maura and Donald enjoying one another's company. I used the entire film before we headed back for shore and lunch in Port Erin.

In the afternoon we returned to Port St Mary to find the wind blowing strongly and Donald still frolicking amongst the moored boats. Maura and Ashley were very reluctant to leave the cosy warmth of the car and put on their clammy diving suits in the chilly wind outside. With a mixture of threats and encouragement I persuaded them, and myself, that there was nothing more important in the world than another session with Donald.

Once we were all in the water they were pleased to have made the sacrifice, for Donald was in high spirits. As we approached the end of the dive the sun was very low in the sky. Maura was clinging to the keel of the fishing boat close to the rudder and propeller, Donald a few feet away, admiring her. The sun, reflected by the gently moving waves on the far side of the boat, streamed down through the water in a series of star bursts. I looked through the large external view-finder of the camera, which gave me a fish-eye view of the scene, and watched the delightful play of brilliant white light and black shade among the interesting arrangement of shapes underneath the boat and the human and dolphin forms of Maura and Donald. A word often used by friends who worked in television flitted through my mind. Mind-blowing—that described it. I pressed the shutter and took a picture. I tried to take another, but the film would not wind on. It was the last one on the roll.

A happy group rowed back to the slipway.

The following day dawned full of promise. The sky was as clear as a bowl of light blue ink. Our sponge rubber diving suits had dried out completely. The air was still. It is hard at times like that not to accept that the weather will remain perfect. But experience has taught me not to expect too much from our fickle climate. When I went into the garden before breakfast to examine the diving equipment that had been hung out to dry I had a niggling sense that it was all too good to be true.

My premonition was correct. When we arrived at Port St Mary at lunchtime the wind was blowing very strongly from the north west. It set up waves across the harbour and sent them slapping into the fishing boats moored against the jetty. The underwater visibility was very poor. Diving was out of the question. Donald appeared to be thoroughly enjoying himself, as always, and could be seen jumping out of the waves.

We returned later in the afternoon. As so often happens on blustery days the wind slackened towards evening and by 5 o'clock we decided to go for a dive despite the fact that Donald was no longer jumping. I rowed the inflatable out across the still choppy water and we tied up to the moored fishing boat which had become our regular rendezvous with Donald.

Dolphins are very perceptive to sound. As soon as I was in the water I whistled and called to attract Donald's attention. He did not appear. I sank to the seabed and picked up two stones which I cracked together. I could hear the sound quite clearly. But still there was no sign of Donald. I surfaced and told Ashley and Maura that we appeared to be out of luck. Should Maura come into the water and then have to go through the performance of drying out both herself and her equipment again? If Donald was no longer in the vicinity it would be a wasted effort.

She decided to risk it and joined me on the bottom, where she picked up an old tin can and banged it with a stone. I again began whistling, shouting and banging stones together. I could not help thinking how foolish the pair of us looked—like a couple of eccentrics calling in the cat for the night. I looked towards Maura. Behind her, with his large beak six inches from the back of her head, was Donald, quite still, apparently fascinated by the streams of bubbles issuing from Maura's demand valve. Maura continued to bang her tin, quite unaware that her boyfriend was playing peek-a-boo behind her. Dolphins are not only intelligent—they also have a sense of humour.

I swam to the surface and from the boat Ashley handed me the camera with the fish-eye lens. As I dived again Donald left Maura and came to say hello to me. He was extremely interested in the shiny dome of the fish-eye lens and inspected it carefully, actually touching it with his snout. He then started to investigate all the other parts of me and my equipment. The weights on the back of my weightbelt tended to tilt me backwards when I sat on the bottom, and as I adjusted the lens settings I ended up with my legs stuck up like a victory sign. I looked up from the camera to see that Donald had his huge jaws open with one of my legs inside them. I could see the neat row of triangular teeth that could sever my leg in a moment. However, I remembered reading a book on dolphins which stated that no dolphin had ever attacked or molested a man. As I took a photograph of my leg in the dolphin's mouth I prayed that Donald was as well read on his species as I was.

Immediately afterwards Donald switched his attention to Maura who was sketching him on an underwater notepad. He clearly took exception to this exercise and snatched the white plastic sheets away from her.

We left the water when dusk fell and there was insufficient light to take further photographs. It should have been our last session with Donald for we proposed to leave at 11.55 the following day. However, when I came to check the ferry departure time I found that the Isle of Man Steam Packet Company was not using a twenty-four-hour clock: the departure time was five to midnight. And that gave me an extra day's diving with Donald.

On Sunday 6 October, 1974, I awoke to the sound of wind lashing rain against the window and my diving suit flapping against the wall outside. Over breakfast I told the others that I had a feeling inside that told me not to give up hope, and that we should all go to Port St Mary. To say that Maura and Ashley were less than enthusiastic would be understating their reaction. However, their protests fell on my deaf ear and after breakfast I mustered enough faith in my weather-forecasting to get them to pack up their wetsuits and load the C-Craft on top of the mini for the last time.

By the time we arrived at Port St Mary the sun was shining, it was high water and the sea was only slightly choppy. Fearing that the wind would rise and swing to the north west, as threatened on the weather forecast, I metaphorically whipped Ashley and Maura into putting on their wet, cold wetsuits. I had to pretend, as I stripped off on the slipway, that the goose pimples on my arms were signs of anticipation.

Donald was waiting for us. As soon as we launched the inflatable he appeared underneath us, as if he knew what the routine was going to be. He escorted us to the fishing boat and stayed beside the inflatable watching us get kitted up.

Ashley joined Maura and myself in the water. He was using a snorkel tube, fins and mask and could only stay underwater for as long as he could hold his breath, so he spent most of his time swimming on the surface, with occasional dives down to us. For some reason Ashley's

We enjoyed the morning playing underwater with Donald.

presence in the water sent Donald into a frenzy of excitement. He swam round and round Maura and me before shooting up to the surface and leaping well clear of the water. From underneath I could see Ashley and Donald in silhouette. From the clouds of bubbles that periodically burst into the watery sky over my head I could tell that Donald was making some tremendous splashes.

I was not worried until I next looked up. Ashley was floating on the surface immediately above my head. As I watched him I saw a huge plume of bubbles suddenly appear a few inches away from him and out of the plume of bubbles swam Donald at great speed. The dolphin, whose weight we estimated to be in the region of seven hundred pounds, was jumping out of the water and had landed back in the sea just a few inches away from my son. If he did it again and misjudged his distance, he might hit Ashley—and there was a good chance that my son would be killed. I rushed upwards to tell Ashley to get out of danger and climb into the inflatable.

As my mask broke the surface I saw an unbelievable sight. I saw Ashley rise out of the water and sit on the surface. He raised both of his hands in the air and smiled at me. At the same time he started to move swiftly and smoothly across the harbour, still with his hands in the air and apparently sitting on the surface of the water. Donald was taking him for a trip. My son Ashley was sitting astride the head of a completely wild dolphin going for a ride on the open sea.

Donald carried Ashley around the harbour at Port St Mary and brought the boy back to me. Then he dived, leaving Ashley floating beside me.

'How on earth did you do that?' I enquired.

'I didn't do it,' replied Ashley. 'Donald just came and picked me up.'

'You mean you did nothing' I said incredulously, still unable to believe what I had seen.

'No,' said Ashley. 'I was as surprised as you.'

When I discussed the event with Maura later she said that Donald could sense my anxiety about Ashley's safety. And that the dolphin had given Ashley the ride of a lifetime to put my mind at rest.

Well, that is the end of my story—except to say that next time you see a statue or a picture of a boy riding on a dolphin don't think that such events could have happened only in ancient times.

PEPINO AND VIOLETTA

Paul Gallico

Approaching Assisi via the chalky, dusty road that twists its way up Monte Subasio, now revealing, now concealing the exquisite little town, as it winds its way through olive and cypress groves, you eventually reach a division where your choice lies between an upper and a lower route.

If you select the latter, you soon find yourself entering Assisi through the twelfth-century archway of the denticulated door of St Francis. But if, seduced by the clear air, the wish to mount even closer to the canopy of blue Italian sky and expose still more of the delectable view of the rich Umbrian valley below, you choose the upper way, you and your vehicle eventually become inextricably entangled in the welter of humanity, oxen, goats, bawling calves, mules, fowl, children, pigs, booths and carts gathered at the market place outside the walls.

It is here you would be most likely to encounter Pepino, with his donkey Violetta, hard at work, turning his hand to anything whereby a small boy and a strong, willing beast of burden could win for themselves the crumpled ten and twenty lira notes needed to buy food and pay for lodging in the barn of Niccolo the stableman.

Pepino was ten years old and an orphan, his father, mother and near relatives having been killed in the war. In self-reliance, wisdom and demeanour he was, of course, much older, a circumstance aided by his independence, for Pepino was an unusual orphan in that having a heritage he need rely on no one. Pepino's heritage was Violetta.

She was a good, useful and docile donkey, alike as any other with friendly, gentle eyes, soft taupe-coloured muzzle, and long, pointed brown ears, with one exception that distinguished her. Violetta had a curious expression about the corners of her mouth, as though she were smiling gently over something that amused or pleased her. The combination of Pepino's dark lustrous eyes and Violetta's smile was so harmonious that people favoured them and they were able not only to earn enough for their keep but, aided and advised by Father Damico, the priest of their parish, to save a little as well.

But Violetta was more than just the means of his livelihood. She was mother to him, and father, brother, playmate, companion, and comfort. At night, in the straw of Niccolo's stable, Pepino slept curled up close to her when it was cold, his head pillowed on her neck.

On his part, he fed her, watered her, searched her for ticks and parasites, picked stones from her hoofs, scratched and groomed and curried her, lavished affection on her, particularly when they were alone, while in public he never beat her with the donkey stick more than was necessary. For this treatment Violetta made a god of Pepino, and repaid him with loyalty, obedience and affection.

Thus, when one day in the early spring Violetta fell ill, it was the most serious thing that had ever happened to Pepino.

Drawing upon his carefully hoarded reserves of lira notes and parting with several of the impressive denomination of a hundred, Pepino called in Dr Bartoli, the vet.

The vet examined her in good faith, dosed her, and tried his best; but she did not improve and, instead, continued to lose weight and grow weaker. He recommended resting the beast and feeding her lightly. If the illness passed from her and God willed, she might live. Otherwise, she would surely die and there would be an end to her suffering.

After he had gone away, Pepino put his cropped head on Violetta's heaving flank and wept unrestrainedly. But then, when the storm, induced by the fear of losing his only companion in the world, had subsided, he knew what he must do. If there was no help for Violetta

95

With urgings and caresses Pepino led Violetta through the villages.

on earth, the appeal must be registered above. His plan was nothing less than to take Violetta into the crypt beneath the lower church of the Basilica of St Francis, where rested the remains of the Saint who had so dearly loved God's creations, including all the feathered and the four-footed brothers and sisters who served Him. There he would beg St Francis to heal her. Pepino had no doubt that the Saint would do so when he saw Violetta.

These things Pepino knew from Father Damico, who had a way of talking about St Francis as though he were a living person who might still be encountered in his frayed cowl, bound with a hemp cord at the middle, merely by turning a corner of the Main Square in Assisi or by walking down one of the narrow, cobbled streets.

With considerable difficulty, he persuaded the sick and shaky donkey to rise, and with urgings and caresses and minimum use of the stick drove her through the crooked streets of Assisi and up the hill to the Basilica of St Francis. At the beautiful twin portal of the lower church he respectfully asked Fra Bernard, who was on duty there, for permission to take Violetta down to St Francis, so that she might be made well again.

Fra Bernard was a new monk, and, calling Pepino a young and impious scoundrel, ordered him and his donkey to be off. It was strictly forbidden to bring livestock into the church, and even to think of taking an ass into the crypt of St Francis was a desecration. And besides, how did he imagine she would get down there when the narrow, winding staircase was barely wide enough to accommodate humans in single file, much less four-footed animals? Pepino must be a fool as well as a shiftless rascal.

Despite the tragedy that had struck Pepino's early life and robbed him of his family, he really considered himself a most fortunate boy, compared with many, since he had acquired not only a heritage to aid him in earning a living but also an important precept by which to live.

This maxim, the golden key to success, had been left with Pepino, together with bars of chocolate, chewing gum, peanut brittle, soap, and other delights, by a corporal in the United States Army who had, in the six months he had been stationed in the vicinity of Assisi, been Pepino's demigod and hero. His name was

97

Francis Xavier O'Halloran, and what he told Pepino before he departed out of his life for ever was, 'If you want to get ahead in this world, kid, don't never take no for an answer. Get it?' Pepino never forgot this important advice.

He thought now that his next step was clear; nevertheless, he went first to his friend and adviser, Father Damico, for confirmation.

Father Damico, who had a broad head, lustrous eyes, and shoulders shaped as though they had been especially designed to support the burdens laid upon them by his parishioners, said, 'You are within your rights, my son, in taking your request to the lay Supervisor and it lies within his power to grant or refuse it.'

There was no malice in the encouragement he thus gave Pepino, but it was also true that he was not loathe to see the Supervisor brought face to face with an example of pure and innocent faith. For in his private opinion that worthy man was too much concerned with the twin churches that formed the Basilica and the crypt as a tourist attraction. He was curious about how the Supervisor would react, even though he thought he knew in advance.

However, he did not impart his fears to Pepino and merely called after him as he was leaving, 'And if the little one cannot be got in from above, there is another entrance from below, through the old church, only it has been walled up for a hundred years. But it could be opened. You might remind the Supervisor when you see him. He knows where it is.'

Pepino thanked him and went back alone to the Basilica and the monastery attached to it and asked permission to see the Supervisor.

This personage was an accessible man, and even though he was engaged in a conversation with the Bishop, he sent for Pepino, who walked into the cloister gardens where he waited respectfully for the two great men to finish.

As it happened, they were speaking of St Francis, and the Bishop was just remarking with a sigh, 'He has been gone too long from this earth. The lesson of his life is plain to all who can read. But who in these times will pause to do so?'

The Supervisor said, 'His tomb in the crypt attracts many to Assisi. But in a Holy Year, relics are even better. If we but had the tongue of the Saint, or a lock of his hair, or a fingernail.'

The Bishop had a far-away look in his eyes, and he was shaking his head gently. 'It is a message we are in need of, my dear Supervisor, a message from a great heart that would speak to us across the gap of seven centuries to remind us of The Way.' And here he paused and coughed, for he was a polite man and noticed that Pepino was waiting.

The Supervisor turned also and said, 'Ah yes, my son, what is it that I can do for you?'

Pepino said, 'Please, sir, my donkey Violetta is very sick. Please, I would like permission to take her into the tomb of Saint Francis and ask him to cure her. He loved all animals, and particularly little donkeys. I am sure he will make her well.'

The Supervisor looked shocked. 'A donkey. In the crypt. Of course we can have no such goings on,' he said. 'The next thing you know, everyone would be coming, bringing a sick dog, or an ox, or a goat, or even a pig. And then where should we end up? A veritable sty.'

'But, sir,' Pepino pleaded, 'no one need know. We would come and go very quickly.'

The Supervisor equivocated: 'And besides, even if we were to allow it, you would never be able to get your donkey around the turn at the bottom of the stairs. So, you see, it is quite impossible.'

'But there is another entrance,' Pepino said. 'From the old church. It has not been used for a long time, but it could be opened just this once—couldn't it?'

The Supervisor was indignant. 'What are you saying—destroy church property? The entrance has been walled up for over a century, ever since the new crypt was built.'

The Bishop said gently to the boy, 'Why do you not go home and pray to Saint Francis to assist you? If you open your heart to him and have faith, he will surely hear you.'

'But it wouldn't be the same,' Pepino cried, and his voice was shaking with the sobs that wanted to come. 'I must take her where Saint Francis can see her. She does not smile any more since she has been so ill. But perhaps she would, just once more for Saint Francis. And when he saw it he would not be able to resist her, and he would make her well. I know he would!'

The Supervisor knew his ground now. He said, 'I am sorry, my son, but the answer is no.'

But even through his despair and the bitter tears he shed as he went away, Pepino knew that if Violetta was to live he must not take no for an answer.

'Who is there, then?' Pepino asked of Father Damico later. 'Who is above the Supervisor and my lord the Bishop who might tell them to let me take Violetta into the crypt?'

Father Damico's stomach felt cold as he thought of the dizzying hierarchy between Assisi and Rome. Nevertheless, he explained as best he could, concluding with, 'And at the top is His Holiness, the Pope himself. Surely his heart would be touched by what has happened if you were able to tell him, for he is a great and good man. But he is busy with important weighty affairs, Pepino, and it would be impossible for him to see you.

Pepino went back to Niccolo's stable, where he ministered to Violetta, fed and watered her and rubbed her muzzle a hundred times. Then he withdrew his money from the stone jar buried under the straw and counted it. He had almost three hundred lire. A hundred of.it he set aside and promised to his friend Giani if he would look after Violetta, while Pepino was gone, as if she were his own. Then he patted her once more, brushed away the tears that had started again at the sight of how thin she was, put on his jacket, and went out on the high road, where, using his thumb as he had learned from Corporal Francis Xavier O'Halloran, he got a lift in a lorry going to Foligno and the main road. He was on his way to Rome to see the Holy Father.

★.   ★   ★   ★

Never had any small boy looked quite so infinitesimal and forlorn as Pepino standing in the boundless and almost deserted, since it was early in the morning, St Peter's Square.

For now that he was at last in Rome, the gigantic proportions of the buildings and monuments, their awe and majesty began to sap his courage, and he seemed to have a glimpse into the utter futility and hopelessness of his mission. And then there would arise in his mind a picture of the sad little donkey who did not smile any more, her heaving flanks and clouded eyes, and who would surely die unless he could find help for her. It was thoughts like these that enabled him finally to cross the piazza and timidly approach one of the smaller side entrances to the Vatican.

The Swiss guard, in his slashed red, yellow, and blue uniform, with his long halberd, looked enormous and forbidding. Nevertheless, Pepino edged up to him and said, 'Please, will you take me to see the Pope? I wish to speak to him about my donkey Violetta, who is very ill and may die unless the Pope will help me.'

The guard smiled, not unkindly, for he was used to these ignorant and innocent requests, and the fact that it came from a dirty, ragged little boy made it all the more harmless. But, nevertheless, he was shaking his head as he smiled, and then said that His Holiness was a very busy man and could not be seen.

Pepino backed away. At the side of the piazza he saw an old woman sitting under an umbrella, selling little bouquets and nosegays of spring flowers—daffodils and jonquils, snowdrops and white narcissus, Parma violets and lilies of the valley, vari-coloured carnations, pansies, and tiny sweetheart roses.

Looking at them made Pepino think of home and Father Damico and what he had said of the love St Francis had for flowers. If St Francis, who had been a holy man, had been so fond of flowers, perhaps the Pope, who according to his position was even holier, would love them, too.

For fifty lire he bought a tiny bouquet in which a spray of lilies of the valley rose from a bed of dark violets and small red roses crowded next to yellow pansies all tied about with leaf and feather fern and paper lace.

From a stall where postcards and souvenirs were sold, he begged pencil and paper, and laboriously composed a note:

Dear and most sacred Holy Father: These flowers are for you. Please let me see you and tell you about my donkey Violetta who is dying, and they will not let me take her to see Saint Francis so that he may cure her. I live in the town of Assisi, but I have come all the way here to see you.

Your loving Pepino

Thereupon, he returned to the door, placed the bouquet and the note in the hand of the Swiss guard, and begged, 'Please take these up to the Pope. I am sure he will see me when he receives the flowers and reads what I have written.'

The guard was not without experience in handling such matters. He had only to place a colleague at his post, go to the Guard Room, throw the flowers and the note into the wastepaper basket, and then return to tell the boy that His Holiness thanked him for the gift of the flowers and regretted that press of important business made it impossible for him to grant him an audience.

But he found to his amazement that somehow he could not bring himself to do it. There was the wastepaper basket, yawning to receive the offering, but the little nosegay seemed to be glued to his fingers. How gay, sweet, and cool the flowers were. He saw again the snow-capped mountains of his youth, the little gingerbread houses, the grey, soft-eyed cattle grazing in the blossom-carpeted meadows, and he heard the heart-warming tinkling of their bells.

Dazed by what had happened to him, he left the Guard Room and wandered through the corridors. He was eventually encountered by a busy little Monsignor, one of the vast army of clerks and secretaries employed in the Vatican, who paused, astonished at the sight of the burly guard helplessly contemplating a tiny posy.

And thus occurred the minor miracle whereby Pepino's plea and offering crossed the boundary in the palace that divided the mundane from the spiritual, the lay from the ecclesiastical.

For to the great relief of the guard, the Monsignor took over the burning articles that he had been unable to relinquish; and this priest they touched, too, as it is the peculiar power of flowers that while they are universal and spread their species over the world, they invoke in each beholder the dearest and most cherished memories.

In this manner, the little bouquet passed on and upward from hand to hand, pausing briefly in the possession of the clerk of the Apostolic Chamber, the Privy Almoner, the Papal Sacristan, the Master of the Sacred Palaces, the Papal Chamberlain.

Eventually, they were deposited with the missive that accompanied them on the desk of the man for whom they had been destined. He read the note and then sat there silently contemplating the blossoms. He closed his eyes for a moment.

When he opened his eyes at last, he said to his secretary, 'Let the child be brought here. I will see him.'

Thus it was that Pepino at last came into the presence of the Pope, seated at his desk in his office.

And when, at the end of half an hour, he was ushered from the presence, he was quite sure he was the happiest boy in the world. For he had not only the blessing of the Pope, but also, under his jacket, two letters, one addressed to the lay Supervisor of the Monastery of Assisi and the other to Father Damico.

★　　★　　★　　★

After a visit to Violetta, Pepino proudly went to Father Damico and presented his letters as he had been instructed to do.

The Father fingered the envelope for the Supervisor and then, with a great surge of warmth and happiness, read the one addressed to himself. He said to Pepino, 'Tomorrow we will take the Supervisor's letter to him. He will summon masons and the old door will be broken down and you will be able to take Violetta into the tomb and pray there for her recovery. The Pope himself has approved it.'

The clink of the stonemason's pick rang again and again through the vaulted chamber of the lower church, where the walled-up door of the passage-way leading to the crypt was being removed.

The Supervisor watched humbly and impassively while broken bricks and clods of mortar fell as the breach widened and the freed current of air from the passages swirled the plaster dust in clouds. He was a just man for all his weakness, and had invited the Bishop to witness his rebuke.

A portion of the wall proved obstinate. The mason attacked the arch-way at the side to weaken its support. Then the loosened masonry began to tumble again. A narrow passage-way was effected, and through the opening they could see the distant flicker of the candles placed at the altar wherein rested the remains of St Francis.

Pepino stirred towards the opening. Or was it Violetta who had moved nervously, frightened by the unaccustomed place and noises?

Father Damico said, 'Wait,' and Pepino held her; but the donkey's uncertain feet slipped on the rubble and then lashed out in panic,

striking the side of the archway where it had been weakened. A brick
fell out. A crack appeared.

Father Damico leaped and pulled boy and animal out of the way as,
with a roar, the side of the arch collapsed, laying bare a piece of the
old wall and the hollow behind it before everything vanished in a cloud
of dust.

But when the dust settled, the Bishop, his eyes starting from his
head, was pointing to something that rested in a niche of the hollow
just revealed. It was a small, grey, leaden box. Even from there they
could see the year 1226, when St Francis died, engraved on the side,
and the large initial 'F'.

The Bishop's breath came out like a sigh. 'Ah, could it be? The
legacy of Saint Francis! Fra Leo mentions it. It was hidden away
centuries ago, and no one had ever been able to find it since.'

Father Damico, who was a poet and to whom St Francis was a
living spirit, cried, 'Open it, I beg of you! All who are here are humble.
Surely Heaven's plan has guided us to it.'

The Abbot held the lantern. The mason with his careful, honest
workman's hands deftly loosed the bindings and pried the lid of the
airtight box. It opened with an ancient creaking of its hinge and
revealed what had been placed there more than seven centuries before.

There was a piece of hempen cord, knotted as though, perhaps, once
it had been worn about the waist. Caught in the knot, as fresh as though
it had grown but yesterday, was a single sprig of wheat. Dried and
preserved, there lay, too, the stem and starry flower of a mountain
primrose and, next to it, one downy feather from a tiny meadow bird.

Silently the men stared at these objects from the past to try to read
their meaning, and Father Damico wept, for to him they brought the
vivid figure of the Saint, half-blinded, worn and fragile, the cord
knotted at his waist, singing, riding through a field of wheat.

The Bishop, too, was close to tears as, in his own way, he interpreted
what they had found. 'Ah, what could be clearer than the message of
the Saint? Poverty, love, and faith. This is his bequest to all of us.'

Pepino said, 'Please, lords and sirs, may Violetta and I go into the
crypt now?'

Father Damico cleared the tears from his eyes. The doorway was
freed now, and there was room for boy and donkey to pass. 'Ah, yes,'

he said. 'Yes, Pepino. You may enter now. And may God go with you.'

The hoofs of the donkey went sharply *clip-clop, clip-clop* on the ancient flagging of the passage-way. Pepino did not support her now, but walked beside, hand just resting lightly and lovingly on her neck. His round, cropped head with the outstanding ears was held high, and his shoulders were bravely squared.

And to Father Damico it seemed, as they passed, whether because of the uneven light and the dancing shadows, or because he wished it so, that the ghost, the merest wisp, the barest suspicion of a smile had returned to the mouth of Violetta.

Thus the watchers saw boy and donkey silhouetted against the flickering oil lamps and altar candles of the crypt as they went forward to complete their pilgrimage of faith.

THE PIPER AT THE GATES OF DAWN

Kenneth Grahame

The Willow-Wren was twittering his thin little song, hidden himself in the dark selvedge of the river bank. Though it was past ten o'clock at night, the sky still clung to and retained some lingering skirts of light from the departed day; and the sullen heats of the torrid afternoon broke up and rolled away at the dispersing touch of the cool fingers of the short midsummer night. Mole lay stretched on the bank, still panting from the stress of the fierce day that had been cloudless from dawn to late sunset, and waited for his friend to return. He had been on the river with some companions, leaving the Water Rat free to keep an engagement of long standing with Otter; and he had come back to find the house dark and deserted, and no sign of Rat, who was doubtless keeping it up late with his old comrade. It was still too hot to think of staying indoors, so he lay on some cool dock-leaves, and thought over the past day and its doings, and how very good they all had been.

The Rat's light footfall was presently heard approaching over the parched grass. 'O, the blessed coolness!' he said, and sat down, gazing thoughtfully into the river, silent and preoccupied.

'You stayed to supper, of course?' said the Mole presently.

'Simply had to,' said the Rat. 'They wouldn't hear of my going before. You know how kind they always are. And they made things as jolly for me as ever they could, right up to the moment I left. But I felt a brute all the time, as it was clear to me they were very unhappy, though they tried to hide it. Mole, I'm afraid they're in trouble. Little Portly is missing again; and you know what a lot his father thinks of him, though he never says much about it.'

'What, that child?' said the Mole lightly. 'Well, suppose he is; why worry about it? He's always straying off and getting lost, and turning up again; he's so adventurous. But no harm ever happens to him. Everybody hereabouts knows him and likes him, just as they do old Otter, and you may be sure some animal or other will come across him and bring him back again all right. Why, we've found him ourselves, miles from home and quite self-possessed and cheerful!'

'Yes; but this time it's more serious,' said the Rat gravely. 'He's been missing for some days now, and the Otters have hunted everywhere, high and low, without finding the slightest trace. And they've asked every animal, too, for miles around, and no one knows anything about him. Otter's evidently more anxious than he'll admit. I got out of him that young Portly hasn't learnt to swim very well yet, and I can see he's thinking of the weir. There's a lot of water coming down still, considering the time of year, and the place always had a fascination for the child. And then there are—well, traps and things—*you* know. Otter's not the fellow to be nervous about any son of his before it's time. And now he *is* nervous. When I left, he came out with me— said he wanted some air, and talked about stretching his legs. But I could see it wasn't that, so I drew him out and pumped him, and got it all from him at last. He was going to spend the night watching by the ford. You know the place where the old ford used to be, in bygone days before they built the bridge?'

'I know it well,' said the Mole. 'But why should Otter choose to watch there?'

'Well, it seems that it was there he gave Portly his first swimming lesson,' continued the Rat. 'From that shallow, gravelly spit near the bank. And it was there he used to teach him fishing, and there young Portly caught his first fish, of which he was very proud. The child loved the spot, and Otter thinks that if he came wandering back from wherever he is—if he *is* anywhere by this time, poor little chap—he might make for the ford he was so fond of; or if he came across it he'd remember it well, and stop there and play, perhaps. So Otter goes there every night and watches—on the chance, you know, just on the chance!'

They were silent for a time, both thinking of the same thing—the lonely, heart-sore animal, crouched by the ford, watching and waiting, the long night through—on the chance.

'Well, well,' said the Rat presently, 'I suppose we ought to be thinking about turning in.' But he never offered to move.

'Rat,' said the Mole, 'I simply can't go and turn in, and go to sleep, and *do* nothing, even though there doesn't seem to be anything to be done. We'll get the boat out, and paddle up-stream. The moon will be up in an hour or so, and then we will search as well as we can—anyhow, it will be better than going to bed and doing *nothing*.'

'Just what I was thinking myself,' said the Rat. 'It's not the sort of night for bed anyhow; and daybreak is not so far off, and then we may pick up some news of him from early risers as we go along.'

They got the boat out, and the Rat took the sculls, paddling with caution. Out in mid-stream there was a clear, narrow track that faintly reflected the sky; but wherever shadows fell on the water from bank, bush, or tree, they were as solid to all appearance as the banks themselves, and the Mole had to steer with judgement accordingly. Dark and deserted as it was, the night was full of small noises, song and chatter and rustling, telling of the busy little population who were up and about, plying their trades and vocations through the night till sunshine should fall on them at last and send them off to their well-earned repose. The water's own noises, too, were more apparent than by day, its gurglings and 'cloops' more unexpected and near at hand; and constantly they started at what seemed a sudden clear call from an actual articulate voice.

The line of the horizon was clear and hard against the sky, and in one particular quarter it showed black against a silvery climbing phosphorescence that grew and grew. At last, over the rim of the waiting earth the moon lifted with slow majesty till it swung clear of the horizon and rode off, free of moorings; and once more they began to see surfaces—meadows widespread, and quiet gardens, and the river itself from bank to bank, all softly disclosed, all washed

The Rat and Mole stood worshipping at the Piper's feet.

clean of mystery and terror, all radiant again as by day, but with a difference that was tremendous. Their old haunts greeted them again in other raiment, as if they had slipped away and put on this pure new apparel and come quietly back, smiling as they shyly waited to see if they would be recognized again under it.

Fastening their boat to a willow, the friends landed in this silent, silver kingdom, and patiently explored the hedges, the hollow trees, the tunnels and their little culverts, the ditches and dry water-ways. Embarking again and crossing over, they worked their way up the stream in this manner, while the moon, serene and detached in a cloudless sky, did what she could, though so far off, to help them in their quest; till her hour came and she sank earthwards reluctantly, and left them, and mystery once more held field and river.

Then a change began slowly to declare itself. The horizon became clearer, field and tree came more into sight, and somehow with a different look; the mystery began to drop away from them. A bird piped suddenly, and was still; and a light breeze sprang up and set the reeds and bulrushes rustling. Rat, who was in the stern of the boat, while Mole sculled, sat up suddenly and listened with a passionate intentness. Mole, who with gentle strokes was just keeping the boat moving while he scanned the banks with care, looked at him with curiosity.

'It's gone!' sighed the Rat, sinking back in his seat again. 'So beautiful and strange and new! Since it was to end so soon, I almost wish I had never heard it. For it has roused a longing in me that is pain, and nothing seems worthwhile but just to hear that sound once more and go on listening to it for ever. No! There it is again!' he cried, alert once more. Entranced, he was silent for a long space, spellbound.

'Now it passes on and I begin to lose it,' he said presently. 'O, Mole! the beauty of it! The merry bubble and joy, the thin, clear, happy call of the distant piping! Such music I never dreamed of, and the call in it is stronger even than the music is sweet! Row on, Mole, row! For the music and the call must be for us.'

The Mole, greatly wondering, obeyed. 'I hear nothing myself,' he said, 'but the wind playing in the reeds and rushes and osiers.'

The Rat never answered, if indeed he heard. Rapt, transported, trembling, he was possessed in all his senses by this new divine thing that caught up his helpless soul and swung and dandled it, a powerless but happy infant, in a strong sustaining grasp.

In silence Mole rowed steadily, and soon they came to a point where the river divided, a long backwater branching off to one side. With a slight movement of his head Rat, who had long dropped the rudder-lines, directed the rower to take the backwater. The creeping tide of light gained and gained, and now they could see the colour of the flowers that gemmed the water's edge.

'Clearer and nearer still,' cried the Rat joyously. 'Now you must surely hear it! Ah—at last—I see you do!'

Breathless and transfixed the Mole stopped rowing as the liquid run of that glad piping broke on him like a wave, caught him up, and possessed him utterly. He saw the tears on his comrade's cheeks, and bowed his head and understood. For a space they hung there, brushed by the purple loosestrife that fringed the bank; then the clear imperious summons that marched hand-in-hand with the intoxicating melody imposed its will on Mole, and mechanically he bent to his oars again. And the light grew steadily stronger, but no birds sang as they were wont to do at the approach of dawn; and but for the heavenly music all was marvellously still.

On either side of them, as they glided onwards, the rich meadow-grass seemed that morning of a freshness and a greeness unsurpassable. Never had they noticed the roses so vivid, the willow-herb so riotous, the meadow-sweet so odorous and pervading. Then the murmur of the approaching weir began to hold the air, and they felt a consciousness that they were nearing the end, whatever it might be, that surely awaited their expedition.

A wide half-circle of foam and glinting lights and shining shoulders of green water, the great weir closed the backwater from bank to bank, troubled all the quiet surface with twirling eddies and floating foam-streaks, and deadened all other sounds with its solemn and soothing rumble. In midmost of the stream, embraced in the weir's shimmering arm-spread, a small island lay anchored, fringed close with willow and silver birch and alder. Reserved, shy, but full of significance, it hid whatever it might hold behind a veil, keeping it till the hour should come, and, with the hour, those who were called and chosen.

Slowly, but with no doubt or hesitation whatever, and in something of a solemn expectancy, the two animals passed through the broken, tumultuous water and moored their boat at the flowery margin of the island. In silence they landed, and pushed through the blossom and scented herbage and undergrowth that led up to the level ground, till they stood on a little lawn of a marvellous green, set round with Nature's own orchard-trees—crab-apples, wild cherry, and sloe.

'This is the place the music played to me,' whispered the Rat, as if in a trance. 'Here, in this holy place, here if anywhere, surely we shall find Him!'

Then suddenly the Mole felt a great Awe fall upon him, an awe that turned his muscles to water, bowed his head, and rooted his feet to the ground. It was no panic terror—indeed he felt wonderfully at peace and happy—but it was an awe that smote and held him and, without seeing, he knew it could only mean that some august Presence was very, very near. With difficulty he turned to look for his friend, and saw him at his side cowed, stricken, and trembling violently. And still there was utter silence in the populous bird-haunted branches around them; and still the light grew and grew.

Perhaps he would never have dared to raise his eyes, but that, though the piping was now hushed, the call and the summons seemed still dominant and imperious. He might not refuse, were Death himself waiting to strike him instantly, once he had looked with mortal eye on things rightly kept hidden. Trembling he obeyed, and raised his humble head; and then, in that utter clearness of the imminent dawn, while Nature, flushed with fullness of incredible colour, seemed to hold her breath for the event, he looked in the very eyes of the Friend and Helper; saw the backward sweep of the curved horns, gleaming in the growing daylight; saw the stern, hooked nose between the kindly eyes that were looking down on them humorously, while the bearded mouth broke into a half-smile at the corners; saw the rippling muscles on the arm that lay across the broad chest, the long supple hand still holding the pan-pipes only just fallen away from the parted lips; saw the splendid curves of the shaggy limbs disposed in majestic ease on the sward; saw, last of all, nestling between his very hooves, sleeping soundly in entire peace and contentment, the little, round, podgy, childish form of the baby otter. All this he saw, for one moment breathless and intense, vivid on the morning sky; and still, as he looked, he lived; and still, as he lived, he wondered.

'Rat!' he found breath to whisper, shaking. 'Are you afraid?'

'Afraid?' murmured the Rat, his eyes shining with unutterable love. 'Afraid Of *Him*? O, never, never! And yet—and yet—O, Mole, I am afraid!'

Then the two animals, crouching to the earth, bowed their heads and did worship.

Sudden and magnificent, the sun's broad golden disc showed itself over the horizon facing them; and the first rays, shooting across the level water-meadows, took the animals full in the eyes and dazzled them. When they were able to look once more, the Vision had vanished, and the air was full of the carol of birds that hailed the dawn.

As they stared blankly, in dumb misery deepening as they slowly realized all they had seen and all they had lost, a capricious little breeze, dancing up from the surface of the water, tossed the aspens, shook the dewy roses, and blew lightly and caressingly in their faces, and with its soft touch came instant oblivion. For this is the last best gift that the kindly demigod is careful to bestow on those to whom he has revealed himself in their helping; the gift of forgetfulness. Lest the awful remembrance should remain and grow, and overshadow mirth and pleasure, and the great haunting memory should spoil all the after-lives of little animals helped out of difficulties, in order that they should be happy and light-hearted as before.

Mole rubbed his eyes and stared at Rat, who was looking about him in a puzzled sort of way. 'I beg your pardon; what did you say, Rat?' he asked.

'I think I was only remarking,' said Rat slowly, 'that this was the right sort of place, and that here, if anywhere, we should find him. And look! Why, there he is, the little fellow!' And with a cry of delight he ran towards the slumbering Portly.

But Mole stood still a moment, held in thought. As one wakened suddenly from a beautiful dream, who struggles to recall it, and can recapture nothing but a dim sense of the beauty of it, the beauty! Till that, too, fades away in its turn, and the dreamer bitterly accepts the hard, cold waking and all its penalties; so Mole, after struggling with his memory for a brief space, shook his head sadly and followed the Rat.

Portly woke up with a joyous squeak, and wriggled with pleasure at the sight of his father's friends, who had played with him so often in past days. In a moment, however, his face grew blank, and he fell to hunting round in a circle with pleading whine. As a child that has fallen happily asleep in its nurse's arms, and wakes to find itself alone and laid in a strange place, and searches corners and cupboards, and runs from room to room, despair growing silently in its heart, even so Portly searched the island and searched, dogged and unwearying, till at last the black moment came for giving it up, and sitting down and crying bitterly.

The Mole ran quickly to comfort the little animal; but Rat, lingering, looked long and doubtfully at certain hoof-marks deep in the sward.

'Some—great—animal—has been here,' he murmured slowly and thoughtfully; and stood musing, musing; his mind strangely stirred.

'Come along, Rat!' called the Mole. 'Think of poor Otter, waiting up there by the ford!'

Portly had soon been comforted by the promise of a treat—a jaunt on the river in Mr Rat's real boat; and the two animals conducted him to the water's side, placed him securely between them in the bottom of the boat, and paddled off down the backwater. The sun was fully up by now, and hot on them, birds sang lustily and without restraint, and flowers smiled and nodded from either bank, but somehow—so thought the animals—with less of richness and blaze of colour than they seemed to remember seeing quite recently somewhere—they wondered where.

The main river reached again, they turned the boat's head upstream, towards the point where they knew their friend was keeping his lonely vigil. As they drew near the familiar ford, the Mole took the boat in to the bank, and they lifted Portly out and set him on his legs on the tow-path, gave him his marching orders and a friendly farewell pat on the back, and shoved out into mid-stream. They watched the little animal as he waddled along the path contentedly and with importance; watched him till they saw his muzzle suddenly lift and his waddle break into a clumsy amble as he quickened his pace with shrill whines and wriggles of recognition. Looking up the river, they could see Otter start up, tense and rigid, from out of the shallows where he crouched in dumb patience, and could hear his amazed and joyous bark as he bounded up through the osiers on to the path. Then the Mole, with a strong pull on one oar, swung the boat round and let the full stream bear them down again whither it would, their quest now happily ended.

'I feel strangely tired, Rat,' said the Mole, leaning wearily over his oars as the boat drifted. 'Its being up all night, you'll say, perhaps; but that's nothing. We do as much half the nights of the week, at this time of the year. No; I feel as if I had been through something very exciting and rather terrible, and it was just over; and yet nothing particular has happened.'

'Or something very surprising and splendid and beautiful,' murmured the Rat, leaning back and closing his eyes. 'I feel just as you do, Mole; simply dead tired, though not body-tired. It's lucky we've got the stream with us, to take us home. Isn't it jolly to feel the sun again, soaking into one's bones! And hark to the wind playing in the reeds!'

'It's like music—far-away music,' said the Mole, nodding drowsily.

'So I was thinking,' murmured the Rat, dreamful and languid. 'Dance-music—the lilting sort that runs on without a stop—but with words in it, too—it passes into words and out of them again—I catch them at intervals—then it is dance-music once more, and then nothing but the reeds' soft thin whispering.'

'You hear better than I,' said the Mole sadly. 'I cannot catch the words.'

'Let me try and give you them,' said the Rat softly, his eyes still closed. 'Now it is turning into words again—faint but clear—*Lest the awe should dwell—And turn your frolic to fret—You shall look on my power at the helping hour—But then you shall forget!* Now the reeds take it up—*forget, forget,* they sigh, and it dies away in a rustle and a whisper. Then the voice returns—

'*Lest limbs be reddened and rent—I spring the trap that is set—As I loose the snare you may glimpse me there—For surely you shall forget!* Row nearer, Mole, nearer to the reeds! It is hard to catch, and grows each minute fainter.

'*Helper and healer, I cheer—Small waifs in the woodland wet—Strays*

I find in it, wounds I bind in it—Bidding them all forget! Nearer, Mole, nearer! No, it is no good; the song has died away into reed-talk.'

'But what do the words mean?' asked the wondering Mole.

'That I do not know,' said the Rat simply. 'I passed them on to you as they reached me. Ah! now they return again, and this time full and clear! This time, at last, it is the real, the unmistakable thing, simple—passionate—perfect—'

'Well, let's have it then,' said the Mole, after he had waited patiently for a few minutes, half dozing in the hot sun.

But no answer came. He looked, and understood the silence. With a smile of much happiness on his face, and something of a listening look still lingering there, the weary Rat was fast asleep.

HOW THESEUS SLEW THE MINOTAUR

Charles Kingsley

Theseus, the hero of this Greek myth, was the son of Aegeus, King of Athens but was brought up by his mother, Princess Aithra of Troezene. At sixteen, when he was strong enough to lift a heavy rock under which lay his father's sword and sandals, he was told the secret of his birth and sent to Athens to join his father. On the journey his strength and courage were put to use in destroying monsters and punishing tyrants. And even after his arrival, his adventures were not over. In Crete the Minotaur, half-man, half-bull, awaited the yearly tribute demanded by King Minos.

So Theseus stayed with his father all the winter, and when the spring equinox drew near, all the Athenians grew sad and silent, and Theseus saw it, and asked the reason; but no one would answer him a word.

Then he went to his father, and asked him: but Aegeus turned away his face and wept.

'Do not ask, my son, beforehand, about evils which must happen: it is enough to have to face them when they come.'

And when the spring equinox came a herald came to Athens, and stood in the market, and cried: 'O people and King of Athens, where is your yearly tribute?' Then a great lamentation arose throughout the city. But Theseus stood up to the herald, and cried:

'And who are you, dog-faced, who dare demand tribute here? If I did not reverence your herald's staff, I would brain you with this club.'

And the herald answered proudly, for he was a grave and ancient man:

'Fair youth, I am not dog-faced or shameless; but I do my master's bidding, Minos, the King of hundred-citied Crete, the wisest of all kings on earth. And you must surely be a stranger here, or you would know why I come, and that I come by right.'

'I am a stranger here. Tell me then why you come.'

'To fetch the tribute which King Aegeus promised to Minos, and confirmed his promise with an oath. For Minos conquered all this land, and Megara which lies to the west, when he came hither with a great fleet of ships, enraged about the murder of his son. For his son Androgeos came hither to the Panathenaic games, and overcame all the Greeks in the sports, so that the people honoured him as a hero. But when Aegeus saw his valour, he envied him, and feared lest he should join the sons of Pallas, and take away the sceptre from him. So he plotted against his life, and slew him basely, no man knows how or where. Some say that he waylaid him by Oinoe, on the road which goes to Thebes, and some that he sent him against the bull of Marathon, that the beast might kill him. But Aegeus says that the young men killed him from envy, because he had conquered them in the games. So Minos came hither and avenged him, and would not depart till this land had promised him tribute—seven youths and seven maidens every year, who go with me in a black-sailed ship, till they come to hundred-citied Crete.'

And Theseus ground his teeth together, and said: 'Wert thou not a herald I would kill thee for saying such things of my father; but I will go to him, and know the truth.' So he went to his father, and asked him, but he turned away his head and wept, and said: 'Blood was shed in the land unjustly, and by blood it is avenged. Break not my heart by question; it is enough to endure in silence.'

Then Theseus groaned inwardly, and said: 'I will go myself with these youths and maidens, and kill Minos upon his royal throne.'

And Aegeus shrieked and cried: 'You shall not go, my son, the light of my old age, to whom alone I look to rule this people after I am dead and gone. You shall not go, to die horribly, as those youths and maidens die; for Minos thrusts them into a labyrinth, which Daidalos made for him among the rocks—Daidalos the renegade, the accursed, the pest of this his native land. From that labyrinth no one can escape, entangled in its winding ways, before they meet the Minotaur, the monster who feeds upon the flesh of men. There he devours them horribly, and they never see this land again.'

Then Theseus grew red and his ears tingled and his heart beat loud in his bosom. And he stood awhile like a tall stone pillar on the cliffs above some hero's grave, and at last he spoke:

'Therefore all the more I will go with them, and slay the accursed beast. Have I not slain all evil-doers and monsters, that I might free this land? Where are Periphetes, and Sinis and Kerkyon and Phaia the wild sow? Where are the fifty sons of Pallas? And this Minotaur shall go the road which they have gone, and Minos himself, if he dare stay me.'

'But how will you slay him, my son? For you must leave your club and your armour behind, and be cast to the monster, defenceless and naked like the rest.'

And Theseus said: 'Are there no stones in that labyrinth; and have I not fists and teeth? Did I need my club to kill Kerkyon, the terror of all mortal men?'

Then Aegeus clung to his knees, but he would not hear; and at last he let him go, weeping bitterly, and said only this one word:

'Promise me but this, if you return in peace, though that may hardly be: take down the black sail of the ship (for I shall watch for it all day upon the cliffs) and hoist instead a white sail; that I may know afar off that you are safe.'

And Theseus promised and went out and to the market-place where the herald stood, while they drew lots for the youths and maidens, who were to sail in that doleful crew. And the people stood wailing and weeping, as the lot fell on this one and on that; but Theseus strode into the midst, and cried:

'Here is a youth who needs no lot. I myself will be one of the seven.'

And the herald asked in wonder: 'Fair youth, know you whither you are going?'

And Theseus said: 'I know. Let us go down to the black-sailed ship.'

So they went down to the black-sailed ship, seven maidens and seven youths and Theseus before them all, and the people following them lamenting. But Theseus whispered to his companions: 'Have hope, for the monster is not immortal. Where are Periphetes and Sinis and Sciron and all whom I have slain?' Then their hearts were comforted a little, but they wept as they went on board, and the cliffs of Sunium rang, and all the isles of the Aegean Sea with the voice of their lamentation, as they sailed on towards their deaths in Crete.

★　　　★　　　★　　　★

And at last they came to Crete, and to Cnossus, beneath the peaks of Ida, and to the palace of Minos, the great king, to whom Zeus himself taught laws. So he was the wisest of all mortal kings, and conquered all the Aegean isles, and his ships were as many as the sea-gulls, and his palace like a marble hill. And he sat among the pillars of the hall, upon his throne of beaten gold, and around him stood the speaking statues which Daidalos had made by his skill. For Daidalos was the most cunning of all Athenians, and he invented the plumb-line and the auger and glue, and many a tool with which wood is wrought. And he first set up masts in ships, and yards, and his son made sails for them; but Perdix his nephew excelled him, for he invented the saw and its teeth, copying it from the backbone of a fish, and invented, too, the chisel and the compasses, and the potter's wheel which moulds the clay. Therefore Daidalos envied him, and hurled him headlong from the temple of Athené; but the goddess pitied him (for she loves the wise) and changed him into a partridge, which flits for ever about the hills. And Daidalos fled to Crete, to Minos, and worked for him many a year, till he did a shameful deed, at which the sun hid his face on high.

Then he fled from the anger of Minos, he and Icaros his son having made themselves wings of feathers, and fixed the feathers with wax. So they flew over the sea towards Sicily; but Icaros flew too near the sun; and the wax of his wings was melted, and he fell into the Icarian Sea. But Daidalos came safe to Sicily, and there wrought many a wondrous work, for he made for King Cocalos a reservoir, from which a great river watered all the land, and a castle and a treasury on a mountain, which the giants themselves could not have stormed. And in Selinos he took the steam which comes up from the fires of Aetna, and made of it a warm bath of vapour, to cure the pains of mortal men, and he made a honeycomb of gold, in which the bees came and stored their honey, and in Egypt he made the forecourt of the temple of Hephaistos in Memphis, and a statue of himself within it, and many another wondrous work. And for Minos he made statues which spoke and moved, and the temple of Britomartis, and the dancing-hall of Ariadne, which he carved of fair white stone. And in Sardinia he worked for Iölaos, and in many a land beside, wandering up and down for ever with his cunning, unlovely and accursed by men.

But Theseus stood before Minos, and they looked each other in the face. And Minos bade take them to prison, and cast them to the monster one by one, that the death of Androgeos might be avenged. Then Theseus cried:

'A boon, O Minos! Let me be thrown first to the beast. For I came hither for that very purpose of my own will, and not by lot.'

'Who art thou, then, brave youth?'

'I am the son of him whom of all men thou hatest most—Aegeus the King of Athens; and I am come here to end this matter.'

And Minos pondered awhile, looking steadfastly at him, and he thought: 'The lad means to atone by his own death for his father's sin'; and he answered at last mildly:

'Go back in peace, my son. It is a pity that one so brave should die.'

But Theseus said: 'I have sworn that I will not go back till I have seen the monster face to face.'

And at that Minos frowned, and said: 'Then thou shalt see him; take the madman away.'

And they led Theseus away into the prison, with the other youths and maids.

But Ariadne, Minos' daughter, saw him, as she came out of her white stone hall; and she loved him for his courage and his majesty, and said: 'Shame that such a youth should die!' And by night she went down to the prison, and told him all her heart, and said:

'Flee down to your ship at once, for I have bribed the guards before the door. Flee, you and all your friends, and go back in peace to Greece, and take me, take me with you! For I dare not stay after you are gone, for my father will kill me miserably, if he knows what I have done.'

And Theseus stood silent awhile, for he was astonished and confounded by her beauty; but at last he said: 'I cannot go home in peace, till I have seen and slain this Minotaur, and avenged the deaths of the youths and maidens and put an end to the terrors of my land.'

'And will you kill the Minotaur? How, then?'

'I know not, nor do I care: but he must be strong, if he be too strong for me.'

Then she loved him all the more, and said:

'But when you have killed him, how will you find your way out of the labyrinth?'

'I know not, neither do I care: but it must be a strange road, if I do not find it out before I have eaten up the monster's carcass.'

Then she loved him all the more, and said:

'Fair youth, you are too bold; but I can help you, weak as I am. I will give you a sword, and with that perhaps you may slay the beast; and a clue of thread, and by that, perhaps, you may find your way out again. Only promise me that if you escape safe you will take me home with you to Greece, for my father will surely kill me, if he knows what I have done.'

Then Theseus laughed and said: 'Am I not safe enough now?' And he hid the sword in his bosom, and rolled up the clue in his hand, and then he swore to Ariadne, and fell down before her and kissed her hands and her feet, and she wept over him a long while, and then went away; and Theseus lay down and slept sweetly.

And when the evening came, the guards came in and led him away to the labyrinth.

And he went down into that doleful gulf, through winding paths among the rocks, under caverns and arches and galleries and over heaps of fallen stone. And he turned on the left hand and on the right hand, and went up and down, till his head was dizzy; but all the while he held his clue. For when he went in he had fastened it to a stone, and left it to unroll out of his hand as he went on; and it lasted him till he met the Minotaur, in a narrow chasm between black cliffs.

And when he saw him he stopped awhile, for he had never seen so strange a beast. His body was a man's; but his head was the head of a bull, and his teeth were the teeth of a lion, and with them he tore his prey. And when he saw Theseus he roared, and put his head down, and rushed right at him.

But Theseus stept aside nimbly, and as he passed by, cut him in the

The unnatural beast bellowed and charged at Theseus.

knee; and ere he could turn in the narrow path, he followed him, and stabbed him again and again from behind, till the monster fled bellowing wildly; for never before had he felt a wound. And Theseus followed him at full speed, holding the clue of thread in his left hand.

Then on, through cavern after cavern, under dark ribs of sounding stone, and up rough glens and torrent beds, among the sunless roots of Ida, and to the edge of the eternal snow, went they, the hunter and the hunted, while the hills bellowed to the monster's bellow.

And at last Theseus came up with him, where he lay panting on a slab among the snow, and caught him by the horns, and forced his head back and drove the keen sword through his throat.

Then he turned, and went back limping and weary, feeling his way down by the clue of thread, till he came to the mouth of that doleful place; and saw waiting for him—whom but Ariadne!

And he whispered: 'It is done!' and showed her the sword; and she laid her finger on her lips and led him to the prison, and opened the doors, and set all the prisoners free, while the guards lay sleeping heavily, for she had silenced them with wine.

Then they fled to their ship together and leapt on board and hoisted up the sail; and the night lay dark around them, so that they passed through Minos' ships and escaped all safe to Naxos; and there Ariadne became Theseus' wife.

THE WHITE SEAL

Rudyard Kipling

Oh! hush thee, my baby, the night is behind us,
And black are the waters that sparkled so green.
The moon, o'er the combers, looks downward to find us
At rest in the hollows that rustle between.
Where billow meets billow, there soft be thy pillow;
Ah, weary wee flipperling, curl at thy ease!
The storm shall not wake thee, nor shark overtake thee,
Asleep in the arms of the slow-swinging seas.

Seal Lullaby

All these things happened several years ago at a place called Novastoshnah, or North East Point, on the Island of St Paul, away and away in the Bering Sea. Limmershin, the Winter Wren, told me the tale when he was blown on to the rigging of a steamer going to Japan, and I took him down into my cabin and warmed and fed him for a couple of days till he was fit to fly back to St Paul's again. Limmershin is a very odd little bird, but he knows how to tell the truth.

Nobody comes to Novastoshnah except on business, and the only people who have regular business there are the seals. They come in the summer months by hundreds and hundreds of thousands out of the cold grey sea; for Novastoshnah Beach has the finest accommodation for seals of any place in all the world.

Sea Catch knew that, and every spring would swim from whatever place he happened to be in—would swim like a torpedo-boat straight for Novastoshnah, and spend a month fighting with his companions for a good place on the rocks as close to the sea as possible. Sea Catch was fifteen years old, a huge grey fur-seal with almost a mane on his shoulders, and long, wicked dog-teeth. When he heaved himself up on his front flippers he stood more than four feet clear of the ground, and his weight, if any one had been bold enough to weigh him, was nearly seven hundred pounds. He was scarred all over with the marks of savage fights, but he was always ready for just one fight more. He would put his head on one side, as though he were afraid to look his enemy in the face; then he would shoot it out like lightning, and when the big teeth were firmly fixed on the other seal's neck, the other seal might get away if he could, but Sea Catch would not help him.

Yet Sea Catch never chased a beaten seal, for that was against the Rules of the Beach. He only wanted room by the sea for his nursery; but as there were forty or fifty thousand other seals hunting for the same thing each spring, the whistling, bellowing, roaring, and blowing on the beach were something frightful.

From a little hill called Hutchinson's Hill you could look over three and a half miles of ground covered with fighting seals; and the surf was dotted all over with the heads of seals hurrying to land and begin their share of the fighting. They fought in the breakers, they fought in the sand, and they fought on the smooth-worn basalt rocks of the nurseries; for they were just as stupid and unaccommodating as men. Their wives never came to the island until late in May or early in June, for they did not care to be torn to pieces; and the young two-, three-, and four-year-old seals who had not begun housekeeping went inland about half a mile through the ranks of the fighters and played about on the sand-dunes in droves and legions, and rubbed off every single green thing that grew. They were called the holluschickie,—the bachelors,—and there were perhaps two or three hundred thousand of them at Novastoshnah alone.

Sea Catch had just finished his forty-fifth fight one spring when Matkah, his soft, sleek, gentle-eyed wife, came up out of the sea, and he caught her by the scruff of the neck and dumped her down on his reservation, saying gruffly: 'Late, as usual. Where *have* you been?'

It was not the fashion for Sea Catch to eat anything during the four months he stayed on the beaches, and so his temper was generally bad. Matkah knew better than to answer back. She looked round and cooed: 'How thoughtful of you! You've taken the old place again.'

'I should think I had,' said Sea Catch. 'Look at me!'

He was scratched and bleeding in twenty places; one eye was almost blind, and his sides were torn to ribbons.

'Oh, you men, you men!' Matkah said, fanning herself with her hind flipper. 'Why can't you be sensible and settle your places quietly? You look as though you had been fighting with the Killer Whale.'

'I haven't been doing anything *but* fight since the middle of May. The beach is disgracefully crowded this season. I've met at least a hundred seals from Lukannon Beach, house-hunting. Why can't people stay where they belong?'

'I've often thought we should be much happier if we hauled out at Otter Island instead of this crowded place,' said Matkah.

'Bah! Only the holluschickie go to Otter Island. If we went there they would say we were afraid. We must preserve appearances, my dear.'

Sea Catch sunk his head proudly between his fat shoulders and pretended to go to sleep for a few minutes, but all the time he was keeping a sharp look-out for a fight. Now that all the seals and their wives were on the land, you could hear their clamour miles out to sea above the loudest gales. At the lowest counting there were over a million seals on the beach,—old seals, mother seals, tiny babies, and holluschickie, fighting, scuffling, bleating, crawling, and playing together,—going down to the sea and coming up from it in gangs and regiments, lying over every foot of ground as far as the eye could reach, and skirmishing about in brigades through the fog. It is nearly always foggy at Novastoshnah, except when the sun comes out and makes everything look all pearly and rainbow-coloured for a little while.

Kotick, Matkah's baby, was born in the middle of that confusion, and he was all head and shoulders, with pale, watery-blue eyes, as tiny seals must be; but there was something about his coat that made his mother look at him very closely.

'Sea Catch,' she said at last, 'our baby's going to be white!'

'Empty clam-shells and dry seaweed!' snorted Sea Catch. 'There never has been such a thing in the world as a white seal.'

'I can't help that,' said Matkah; 'there's going to be now'; and she sang the low, crooning seal-song that all the mother seals sing to their babies:

> *You mustn't swim till you're six weeks old,*
> *Or your head will be sunk by your heels;*
> *And summer gales and Killer Whales*
> *Are bad for baby seals.*
>
> *Are bad for baby seals, dear rat,*
> *As bad as bad can be;*
> *But splash and grow strong,*
> *And you can't be wrong,*
> *Child of the Open Sea!*

Of course the little fellow did not understand the words at first. He paddled and scrambled about by his mother's side, and learned to scuffle out of the way when his father was fighting with another seal, and the two rolled and roared up and down the slippery rocks. Matkah used to go to sea to get things to eat, and the baby was fed only once in two days; but then he ate all he could, and throve upon it.

The first thing he did was to crawl inland, and there he met tens of thousands of babies of his own age, and they played together like puppies, went to sleep on the clean sand, and played again. The old people in the nurseries took no notice of them, and the holluschickie kept to their own grounds, so the babies had a beautiful playtime.

When Matkah came back from her deep-sea fishing she would go straight to their playground and call as a sheep calls for a lamb, and wait until she heard Kotick bleat. Then she would take the straightest of straight lines in his direction, striking out with her fore flippers and knocking the youngsters head over heels right and left. There were always a few hundred mothers hunting for their children through the playgrounds, and the babies were kept lively; but, as Matkah told Kotick, 'So long as you don't lie in muddy water and get mange, or rub the hard sand into a cut or scratch, and so long as you never go swimming when there is a heavy sea, nothing will hurt you here.'

Little seals can no more swim than little children, but they are unhappy till they learn. The first time that Kotick went down to the sea a wave carried him out beyond his depth, and his big head sank and his little hind flippers flew up exactly as his mother had told him in the song, and if the next wave had not thrown him back again he would have drowned.

After that he learned to lie in a beach-pool and let the wash of the waves just cover him and lift him up while he paddled, but he always kept his eye open for big waves that might hurt. He was two weeks learning to use his flippers; and all that while he floundered in and out of the water, and coughed and grunted and crawled up the beach and took cat-naps on the sand, and went back again, until at last he found that he truly belonged to the water.

Then you can imagine the times that he had with his companions, ducking under the rollers; or coming in on top of a comber and landing with a swash and a splutter as the big wave went whirling far up the beach; or standing up on his tail and scratching his head as the old people did; or playing 'I'm the King of the Castle' on slippery, weedy rocks that just stuck out of the wash. Now and then he would see a thin fin, like a big shark's fin, drifting along close to the shore, and he knew that that was the Killer Whale, the Grampus, who eats young seals when he can get them; and Kotick would head for the beach like an arrow, and the fin would jig off slowly, as if it were looking for nothing at all.

Late in October the seals began to leave St Paul's for the deep sea, by families and tribes, and there was no more fighting over the nurseries, and the holluschickie played anywhere they liked. 'Next year,' said Matkah to Kotick, 'you will be a holluschickie; but this year you must learn how to catch fish.'

They set out together across the Pacific, and Matkah showed Kotick how to sleep on his back with his flippers tucked down by his side and his little nose just out of the water. No cradle is so comfortable as the long, rocking swell of the Pacific. When Kotick felt his skin tingle all over, Matkah told him he was learning the 'feel of the water', and that tingly, prickly feelings meant bad weather coming, and he must swim hard and get away.

'In a little time,' she said, 'you'll know where to swim to, but just now we'll follow Sea Pig, the Porpoise, for he is very wise.' A school of porpoises were ducking and tearing through the water, and little Kotick followed them as fast as he could. 'How do you know where to go to?' he panted. The leader of the school rolled his white eyes, and ducked under. 'My tail tingles, youngster,' he said. 'That means there's a gale behind me. Come along! When you're south of the Sticky Water [he meant the Equator], and your tail tingles, that means there's a gale in front of you and you must head north. Come along! The water feels bad here.'

This was one of the very many things that Kotick learned, and he was always learning. Matkah taught him to follow the cod and the halibut along the undersea banks, and wrench the rockling out of his hole among the weeds; how to skirt the wrecks lying a hundred fathoms below water, and dart like a rifle-bullet in at one port-hole and out at another as the fishes ran; how to dance on the top of the waves when the lightning was racing all over the sky, and wave his flipper politely to the stumpy-tailed Albatross and the Man-of-War Hawk as they went down the wind; how to jump three or four feet clear of the water, like a dolphin, flippers close to the side and tail curved; to leave the flying-fish alone because they are all bony; to take the shoulder-piece out of a cod at full speed ten fathoms deep; and never to stop and look at a boat or a ship, but particularly a row-boat. At the end of six months, what Kotick did not know about deep-sea fishing was not worth knowing, and all that time he never set flipper on dry ground.

One day, however, as he was lying half asleep in the warm water somewhere off the Island of Juan Fernandez, he felt faint and lazy all over, just as human people do when the spring is in their legs, and he remembered the good firm beaches of Novastoshnah seven thousand miles away, the games his companions played, the smell of the sea-weed, the seal roar, and the fighting. That very minute he turned north, swimming steadily, and as he went on he met scores of his mates, all bound for the same place, and they said: 'Greeting, Kotick! This year we are all holluschickie, and we can dance the Fire-dance in the breakers off Lukannon and play on the new grass. But where did you get that coat?'

Kotick's fur was almost pure white now, and though he felt very proud of it, he only said: 'Swim quickly! My bones are aching for the land.' And so they all came to the beaches where they had been born, and heard the old seals, their fathers, fighting in the rolling mist.

That night Kotick danced the Fire-dance with the yearling seals. The sea is full of fire on summer nights all the way down from Novastoshnah to Lukannon, and each seal leaves a wake like burning oil behind him, and a flaming flash when he jumps, and the waves break in great phosphorescent streaks and swirls. Then they went inland to the holluschickie grounds, and rolled up and down in the new wild wheat, and told stories of what they had done while they had been at sea. They talked about the Pacific as boys would talk about a wood that they had been nutting in, and if any one had understood them, he could have gone away and made such a chart of that ocean as never was. The three- and four-year-old holluschickie romped down from Hutchinson's Hill, crying: 'Out of the way, youngsters! The sea is deep, and you don't know all that's in it yet. Wait till you've rounded the Horn. Hi, you yearling, where did you get that white coat?'

'I didn't get it,' said Kotick; 'it grew.' And just as he was going to roll the speaker over, a couple of black-haired men with flat red faces came from behind a sand-dune, and Kotick, who had never seen a man before, coughed and lowered his head. The holluschickie just bundled off a few yards and sat staring stupidly. The men were no less than Kerick Booterin, the chief of the seal-hunters on the island, and Patalamon, his son. They came from the little village not half a mile from the seal-nurseries, and they were deciding what seals they would drive up to the killing-pens (for the seals were driven just like sheep), to be turned into sealskin jackets later on.

'Ho!' said Patalamon. 'Look! There's a white seal!'

Kerick Booterin turned nearly white under his oil and smoke, for he was an Aleut, and Aleuts are not clean people. Then he began to mutter a prayer. 'Don't touch him, Patalamon. There has never been a white seal since—since I was born. Perhaps it is old Zaharrof's ghost. He was lost last year in the big gale.'

'I'm not going near him,' said Patalamon. 'He's unlucky. Do you really think he is old Zaharrof come back? I owe him for some gulls' eggs.'

Kotick returned triumphantly to tell them of his miraculous find.

'Don't look at him,' said Kerick. 'Head off that drove of four-year-olds. The men ought to skin two hundred today, but it's the beginning of the season, and they are new to the work. A hundred will do. Quick!'

Patalamon rattled a pair of seal's shoulder-bones in front of a herd of holluschickie, and they stopped dead, puffing and blowing. Then he stepped near, and the seals began to move, and Kerick headed them inland, and they never tried to get back to their companions. Hundreds and hundreds of thousands of seals watched them being driven, but they went on playing just the same. Kotick was the only one who asked questions, and none of his companions could tell him anything, except that the men always drove seals in that way for six weeks or two months of every year.

'I am going to follow,' he said, and his eyes nearly popped out of his head as he shuffled along in the wake of the herd.

'The white seal is coming after us,' cried Patalamon. 'That's the first time a seal has ever come to the killing-grounds alone.'

'Hsh! Don't look behind you,' said Kerick. 'It *is* Zaharrof's ghost! I must speak to the priest about this.'

The distance to the killing-grounds was only half a mile, but it took an hour to cover, because if the seals went too fast Kerick knew that they would get heated and then their fur would come off in patches when they were skinned. So they went on very slowly, past Sea-Lion's Neck, past Webster House, till they came to the Salt House just beyond the sight of the seals on the beach. Kotick followed, panting and wondering. He thought that he was at the world's end, but the roar of the seal-nurseries behind him sounded as loud as the roar of a train in a tunnel. Then Kerick sat down on the moss and pulled out a heavy pewter watch and let the drove cool off for thirty minutes, and Kotick could hear the fog-dew dripping from the brim of his cap. Then ten or twelve men, each with an iron-bound club three or four feet long, came up, and Kerick pointed out one or two of the drove that were bitten by their companions or were too hot, and the men kicked those aside with their heavy boots made of the skin of a walrus's throat, and then Kerick said: 'Let's go!' and then the men clubbed the seals on the head as fast as they could.

Ten minutes later little Kotick did not recognize his friends any more, for their skins were ripped off from the nose to the hind flippers—whipped off and thrown down on the ground in a pile.

That was enough for Kotick. He turned and galloped (a seal can gallop very swiftly for a short time) back to the sea, his little new moustache bristling with horror. At Sea-Lion's Neck, where the great sea-lions sit on the edge of the surf, he flung himself flipper over head into the cool water, and rocked there, gasping miserably. 'What's here?' said a sea-lion gruffly; for as a rule the sea-lions keep themselves to themselves.

'*Scoochnie! Ochen scoochnie!*' ('I'm lonesome, very lonesome!') said Kotick. 'They're killing *all* the holluschickie on *all* the beaches!'

The sea-lion turned his head inshore. 'Nonsense!' he said; 'your friends are making as much noise as ever. You must have seen old Kerick polishing off a drove. He's done that for thirty years.'

'It's horrible,' said Kotick, backing water as a wave went over him, and steadying himself with a screw-stroke of his flippers that brought him up all standing within three inches of a jagged edge of rock.

'Well done for a yearling!' said the sea-lion, who could appreciate good swimming. 'I suppose it *is* rather awful from your way of looking at it; but if you seals will come here year after year, of course the men get to know of it, and unless you can find an island where no men ever come, you will always be driven.'

'Isn't there any such island?' began Kotick.

'I've followed the *poltoos* [the halibut] for twenty years, and I can't say I've found it yet. But look here—you seem to have a fondness for talking to your betters; suppose you go to Walrus Islet and talk to Sea Vitch. He may know something. Don't flounce off like that. It's a six-mile swim, and if I were you I should haul out and take a nap first, little one.'

Kotick thought that that was good advice, so he swam round to his own beach, hauled out, and slept for half an hour, twitching all over, as seals will. Then he headed straight for Walrus Islet, a little low sheet of rocky island almost due north-east from Novastoshnah, all ledges of rock and gulls' nests, where the walrus herded by themselves.

He landed close to old Sea Vitch—the big, ugly, bloated, pimpled, fat-necked, long-tusked walrus of the North Pacific, who has no manners except when he is asleep—as he was then, with his hind flippers half in and half out of the surf.

'Wake up!' barked Kotick, for the gulls were making a great noise.

'Hah! Ho! Hmph! What's that?' said Sea Vitch, and he struck the next walrus a blow with his tusks and waked him up, and the next struck the next, and so on till they were all awake and staring in every direction but the right one.

'Hi! It's me,' said Kotick, bobbing in the surf and looking like a little white slug.

'Well! May I be—skinned!' said Sea Vitch, and they all looked at Kotick as you can fancy a club full of drowsy old gentlemen would look at a little boy. Kotick did not care to hear any more about skinning just then; he had seen enough of it; so he called out: 'Isn't there any place for seals to go where men don't ever come?'

'Go and find out,' said Sea Vitch, shutting his eyes. 'Run away. We're busy here.'

Kotick made his dolphin-jump in the air and shouted as loud as he could: 'Clam-eater! Clam-eater!' He knew that Sea Vitch never caught a fish in his life, but always rooted for clams and seaweeds, though he pretended to be a very terrible person. Naturally the Chickies and the Gooverooskies and the Epatkas, the Burgomaster Gulls and the Kittiwakes and the Puffins, who are always looking for a chance to be rude, took up the cry, and—so Limmershin told me—for nearly five minutes you could not have heard a gun fired on Walrus Islet. All the population was yelling and screaming: 'Clam-eater! *Stareek* [old man]!' while Sea Vitch rolled from side to side grunting and coughing.

'*Now* will you tell?' said Kotick, all out of breath.

'Go and ask Sea Cow,' said Sea Vitch. 'If he is living still, he'll be able to tell you.'

'How shall I know Sea Cow when I meet him?' said Kotick, sheering off.

'He's the only thing in the sea uglier than Sea Vitch,' screamed a Burgomaster Gull, wheeling under Sea Vitch's nose. 'Uglier, and with worse manners! *Stareek!*'

Kotick swam back to Novastoshnah, leaving the gulls to scream. There he found that no one sympathized with him in his little attempts to discover a quiet place for the seals. They told him that men had always driven the holluschickie—it was part of the day's work—and that if he did not like to see ugly things he should not have gone to the killing-grounds. But none of the other seals had seen the killing, and that made the difference between him and his friends. Besides, Kotick was a white seal.

'What you must do,' said old Sea Catch, after he had heard his son's adventures, 'is to grow up and be a big seal like your father, and have a nursery on the beach, and then they will leave you alone. In another five years you ought to be able to fight for yourself.' Even gentle Matkah, his mother, said: 'You will never be able to stop the killing. Go and play in the sea, Kotick.' And Kotick went off and danced the Fire-dance with a very heavy little heart.

That autumn he left the beach as soon as he could, and set off alone because of a notion in his bullet-head. He was going to find Sea Cow, if there was such a person in the sea, and he was going to find a quiet island with good firm beaches for seals to live on, where men could not get at them. So he explored and explored by himself from the North to the South Pacific, swimming as much as three hundred miles in a day and night. He met with more adventures than can be told, and narrowly escaped being caught by the Basking Shark, and the Spotted Shark, and the Hammerhead, and he met all the untrustworthy ruffians that loaf up and down the seas, and the heavy polite fish, and the scarlet-spotted scallops that are moored in one place for hundreds of years, and grow very proud of it; but he never met Sea Cow, and he never found an island that he could fancy.

If the beach was good and hard, with a slope behind it for seals to play on, there was always the smoke of a whaler on the horizon, boiling down blubber, and Kotick knew what *that* meant. Or else he could see that seals had once visited the island and been killed off, and Kotick knew that where men had come once they would come again.

He picked up with an old stumpy-tailed albatross, who told him that Kerguelen Island was the very place for peace and quiet, and when Kotick went down there he was all but smashed to pieces against some wicked black cliffs in a heavy sleet-storm with lightning and thunder. Yet as he pulled out against the gale he could see that even there had once been a seal-nursery. And so it was in all the other islands that he visited.

Limmershin gave a long list of them, for he said that Kotick spent five seasons exploring, with a four months' rest each year at Novastoshnah, when the holluschickie used to make fun of him and his imaginary islands. He went to the Galapagos, a horrid dry place on the Equator, where he was nearly baked to death; he went to the Georgia Islands, the South Orkneys, Emerald Island, Little Nightingale Island, Gough's Island, Bouvet's Island, the Crossets, and even to a little speck of an island south of the Cape of Good Hope. But everywhere the People of the Sea told him the same things. Seals had come to those islands once upon a time, but men had killed them all off. Even when he swam thousands of miles out of the Pacific, and got to a place called Cape Corrientes (that was when he was coming back from Gough's Island), he found a few hundred mangy seals on a rock, and they told him that men came there too.

That nearly broke his heart, and he headed round the Horn back to his own beaches; and on his way north he hauled out on an island full of green trees, where he found an old, old seal who was dying, and Kotick caught fish for him, and told him all his sorrows. 'Now,' said Kotick, 'I am going back to Novastoshnah, and if I am driven to the killing-pens with the holluschickie I shall not care.'

The old seal said: 'Try once more. I am the last of the Lost Rookery of Masafuera, and in the days when men killed us by the hundred thousand there was a story on the beaches that some day a white seal would come out of the north and lead the seal people to a quiet place. I am old and I shall never live to see that day, but others will. Try once more.'

And Kotick curled up his moustache (it was a beauty), and said: 'I am the only white seal that has ever been born on the beaches, and I am the only seal, black or white, who ever thought of looking for new islands.'

That cheered him immensely; and when he came back to Novastoshnah that summer, Matkah, his mother, begged him to marry and settle down, for he was no longer a holluschick, but a full-grown sea-catch, with a curly white mane on his shoulders as heavy, as big, and as fierce as his father. 'Give me another season,' he said.

'Remember, Mother, it is always the seventh wave that goes farthest up the beach.'

Curiously enough, there was another seal who thought that she would put off marrying till the next year, and Kotick danced the Fire-dance with her all down Lukannon Beach the night before he set off on his last exploration.

This time he went westward, because he had fallen on the trail of a great shoal of halibut, and he needed at least one hundred pounds of fish a day to keep him in good condition. He chased them till he was tired, and then he curled himself up and went to sleep on the hollows of the ground-swell that sets in to Copper Island. He knew the coast perfectly well, so about midnight, when he felt himself gently bumped on a weed-bed, he said, 'H'm, tide's running strong tonight,' and turning over under water opened his eyes slowly and stretched. Then he jumped like a cat, for he saw huge things nosing about in the shoal water and browsing on the heavy fringes of the weeds.

'By the Great Combers of Magellan!' he said, beneath his moustache. 'Who in the Deep Sea are these people?'

They were like no walrus, sea-lion, seal, bear, whale, shark, fish, squid, or scallop that Kotick had ever seen before. They were between twenty and thirty feet long, and they had no hind flippers, but a shovel-like tail that looked as if it had been whittled out of wet leather. Their heads were the most foolish-looking things you ever saw, and they balanced on the ends of their tails in deep water when they weren't grazing, bowing solemnly to one another and waving their front flippers as a fat man waves his arm.

'Ahem!' said Kotick. 'Good sport, gentlemen?' The big things answered by bowing and waving their flippers like the Frog-Footman. When they began feeding again Kotick saw that their upper lip was split into two pieces that they could twitch apart about a foot and bring together again with a whole bushel of seaweed between the splits. They tucked the stuff into their mouths and chumped solemnly.

'Messy style of feeding, that,' said Kotick. They bowed again, and Kotick began to lose his temper. 'Very good,' he said. 'If you do happen to have an extra joint in your front flipper you needn't show off so. I see you bow gracefully, but I should like to know your names.'

The split lips moved and twitched, and the glassy green eyes stared; but they did not speak.

'Well!' said Kotick, 'you're the only people I've ever met uglier than Sea Vitch—and with worse manners.'

Then he remembered in a flash what the Burgomaster Gull had screamed to him when he was a little yearling at Walrus Islet, and he tumbled backward in the water, for he knew that he had found Sea Cow at last.

The sea cows went on schlooping and grazing and chumping in the weed, and Kotick asked them questions in every language that he had picked up in his travels: and the Sea People talk nearly as many languages as human beings. But the Sea Cow did not answer, because Sea Cow cannot talk. He has only six bones in his neck where he ought to have seven, and they say under the sea that that prevents him from speaking even to his companions; but, as you know, he has an extra joint in his fore flipper, and by waving it up and down and about he makes a sort of clumsy telegraphic code.

By daylight Kotick's mane was standing on end and his temper was gone where the dead crabs go. Then the Sea Cow began to travel northward very slowly, stopping to hold absurd bowing councils from time to time, and Kotick followed them, saying to himself: 'People who are such idiots as these are would have been killed long ago if they hadn't found out some safe island; and what is good enough for the Sea Cow is good enough for the Sea Catch. All the same, I wish they'd hurry.'

It was weary work for Kotick. The herd never went more than forty or fifty miles a day, and stopped to feed at night, and kept close to the shore all the time; while Kotick swam round them, and over them, and under them, but he could not hurry them on one half-mile. As they went farther north they held a bowing council every few hours, and Kotick nearly bit off his moustache with impatience till he saw that they were following up a warm current of water, and then he respected them more.

One night they sank through the shiny water—sank like stones— and, for the first time since he had known them, began to swim quickly. Kotick followed, and the pace astonished him, for he never dreamed that Sea Cow was anything of a swimmer. They headed for a cliff by the shore—a cliff that ran down into deep water, and plunged into a dark hole at the foot of it, twenty fathoms under the sea. It was a long, long swim, and Kotick badly wanted fresh air before he was out of the dark tunnel that they led him through.

'My wig!' he said, when he rose, gasping and puffing, into open water at the farther end. 'It was a long dive, but it was worth it.'

The sea cows had separated, and were browsing lazily along the edges of the finest beaches that Kotick had ever seen. There were long stretches of smooth-worn rock running for miles, exactly fitted to make seal-nurseries, and there were playgrounds of hard sand sloping inland behind them, and there were rollers for seals to dance in, and long grass to roll in, and sand-dunes to climb up and down; and, best of all, Kotick knew by the feel of the water, which never deceives a true Sea Catch, that no men had ever come there.

The first thing he did was to assure himself that the fishing was good, and then he swam along the beaches and counted up the delightful low sandy islands half hidden in the beautiful rolling fog. Away to the northward out to sea ran a line of bars and shoals and rocks that would never let a ship come within six miles of the beach; and between the islands and the mainland was a stretch of deep water that ran up to the perpendicular cliffs, and somewhere below the cliffs was the mouth of the tunnel.

'It's Novastoshnah over again, but ten times better,' said Kotick. 'Sea Cow must be wiser than I thought. Men can't come down the cliffs, even if there were any men; and the shoals to seaward would knock a ship to splinters. If any place in the sea is safe, this is it.'

He began to think of the seal he had left behind him, but though he was in a hurry to go back to Novastoshnah, he thoroughly explored the new country, so that he would be able to answer all questions.

Then he dived and made sure of the mouth of the tunnel, and raced through to the southward. No one but a sea cow or a seal would have dreamed of there being such a place, and when he looked back at the cliffs even Kotick could hardly believe that he had been under them.

He was six days going home, though he was not swimming slowly; and when he hauled out just above Sea-Lion's Neck the first person he met was the seal who had been waiting for him, and she saw by the look in his eyes that he had found his island at last.

But the holluschickie and Sea Catch, his father, and all the other seals, laughed at him when he told them what he had discovered, and a young seal about his own age said: 'This is all very well, Kotick, but you can't come from no one knows where and order us off like this. Remember we've been fighting for our nurseries, and that's a thing you never did. You preferred prowling about in the sea.'

The other seals laughed at this, and the young seal began twisting his head from side to side. He had just married that year, and was making a great fuss about it.

'I've no nursery to fight for,' said Kotick. 'I want only to show you all a place where you will be safe. What's the use of fighting?'

'Oh, if you're trying to back out, of course I've no more to say,' said the young seal, with an ugly chuckle.

'Will you come with me if I win?' said Kotick; and a green light came into his eyes, for he was very angry at having to fight at all.

'Very good,' said the young seal carelessly. '*If* you win, I'll come.'

He had no time to change his mind, for Kotick's head darted out and his teeth sank in the blubber of the young seal's neck. Then he threw himself back on his haunches and hauled his enemy down the beach, shook him, and knocked him over. Then Kotick roared to the seals: 'I've done my best for you these five seasons past. I've found you the island where you'll be safe, but unless your heads are dragged off your silly necks you won't believe. I'm going to teach you now. Look out for yourselves!'

Limmershin told me that never in his life—and Limmershin sees ten thousand big seals fighting every year—never in all his little life did he see anything like Kotick's charge into the nurseries. He flung himself at the biggest sea-catch he could find, caught him by the throat, choked him and bumped him and banged him till he grunted for mercy, and then threw him aside and attacked the next. You see, Kotick had never fasted for four months as the big seals did every year, and his deep-sea swimming-trips kept him in perfect condition, and, best of all, he had never fought before. His curly white mane stood up with rage, and his eyes flamed, and his big dog-teeth glistened, and he was splendid to look at.

Old Sea Catch, his father, saw him tearing past, hauling the grizzled old seals about as though they had been halibut, and upsetting the young bachelors in all directions; and Sea Catch gave one roar and shouted: 'He may be a fool, but he is the best fighter on the Beaches. Don't tackle your father, my son! He's with you!'

Kotick roared in answer, and old Sea Catch waddled in, his moustache on end, blowing like a locomotive, while Matkah and the seal that was going to marry Kotick cowered down and admired their men-folk. It was a gorgeous fight, for the two fought as long as there was a seal that dared lift up his head, and then they paraded grandly up and down the beach side by side, bellowing.

At night, just as the Northern Lights were winking and flashing through the fog, Kotick climbed a bare rock and looked down on the scattered nurseries and the torn and bleeding seals. 'Now,' he said, 'I've taught you your lesson.'

'My wig!' said old Sea Catch, boosting himself up stiffly, for he was fearfully mauled. 'The Killer Whale himself could not have cut them up worse. Son, I'm proud of you, and what's more, *I'll* come with you to your island—if there is such a place.'

'Here you, fat pigs of the sea! Who comes with me to the Sea Cow's tunnel? Answer, or I shall teach you again,' roared Kotick.

There was a murmur like the ripple of the tide all up and down the beaches. 'We will come,' said thousands of tired voices. 'We will follow Kotick, the White Seal.'

Then Kotick dropped his head between his shoulders and shut his eyes proudly. He was not a white seal any more, but red from head to tail. All the same, he would have scorned to look at or touch one of his wounds.

A week later he and his army (nearly ten thousand holluschickie and old seals) went away north to the Sea Cow's tunnel, Kotick leading them, and the seals that stayed at Novastoshnah called them idiots. But next spring, when they all met off the fishing-banks of the Pacific, Kotick's seals told such tales of the new beaches beyond Sea Cow's tunnel that more and more seals left Novastoshnah.

Of course it was not all done at once, for the seals need a long time to turn things over in their minds, but year by year more seals went away from Novastoshnah, and Lukannon, and the other nurseries, to the quiet, sheltered beaches where Kotick sits all the summer through, getting bigger and fatter and stronger each year, while the holluschickie play round him, in that sea where no man comes.

WILLIAM AND THE PRIZE CAT

Richmal Crompton

William and Ginger ambled slowly down the lane. Henry and Douglas had succumbed to a local epidemic of mumps and so William and Ginger were the only two representatives of the Outlaws at large. Each carried sticks and slashed at the grass by the roadside as he went along. The action was purely mechanical. Neither felt properly dressed out of doors unless he had a stick to slash at things with.

'Couldn't we get underneath the flap?' Ginger was saying.

'No,' said William, 'I thought of that. They've got someone there to stop you. Jimmy Barlow says he tried that yesterday, and it wasn't any good.'

'You asked your father for money, din't you?' said Ginger.

'Yes,' replied William bitterly, 'and he said that he'd give me some if ever he noticed me being clean and tidy and quiet for three days together. That's a jolly mean way of sayin' "no". 'Sides, if ever I was like that there prob'ly wouldn't be any circus here so it would all be wasted and if there was I bet I wouldn't feel like goin' to it if I'd been clean and tidy and quiet for three days. I bet you wouldn't feel much like doin' anythin' if you'd been clean and tidy and quiet for three days. You asked your father, too, din't you?'

'Yes,' said Ginger gloomily, 'an' he went on and on and on about every window or anythin' that had got broke in our house for—for all my life I should think. He even remembered that time that I fell through the roof and broke the skylight. Well, that's so long ago I'd almost quite forgot that till he said about it. Anyway I hurt myself jolly badly over it an' you'd have thought he'd've been sorry instead of makin' it an excuse not to give me money to go an' see a circus.'

'We haven't even anythin' we can sell,' said William taking up the antiphonic lament. 'I tried to sell my whistle to Frankie Dakers, but it hasn't any whistle in and he wouldn't buy it. He'd been to the circus.'

'Jolly fine one, isn't it?' said Ginger wistfully.

'He said it was a rippin' one,' said William. They walked on for a moment in silence, frowning and slashing absently at the roadside with their sticks.

Then suddenly round a bend in the roadway, all unprepared and unexpecting, they ran into the Hubert Laneites, their rivals and enemies from time immemorial. Hubert Lane, standing in the centre of his little band, smiled fatly at them. It happened to be a period of armed neutrality between the two bands. Had it been a period of open warfare the Hubert Laneites would have fled on sight of even two of the Outlaws, for the Hubert Laneites, though possessed of deep cunning, lacked courage and strength in open warfare. But as it was, Hubert Lane smiled at them fatly.

'Hello,' he said, 'been to the circus?'

Hubert Lane had a knack of finding out most things about his enemies, and he was well aware that the Outlaws had not been to the circus, because they had not enough money for their entrance fee.

'Circus?' said William carelessly. 'What circus?'

'Why the one over at Little Marleigh?' said Hubert, slightly deflated.

'Oh *that* one,' said William smiling, 'you mean *that* one. It's not much of a circus, is it?'

Hubert Lane had recourse to heavy sarcasm.

'Oh no,' he said. 'It takes a much grander circus than *that* to satisfy *you*, I s'pose?'

'Well,' said William mysteriously, 'I know a jolly sight more about circuses than *most* people.'

The Hubert Laneites laughed mockingly.

'*How* do you know more about circuses than most people?' challenged Hubert.

William considered this in silence for a moment, wondering whether to have been in a circus and worked in it till he was rescued and adopted by his present parents, or to have an uncle who owned all the circuses in England and took him to see one every week. He rejected both claims as being too easy for Hubert to disprove, and contented himself with saying still more mysteriously:

'*Wouldn't* you like to know?'

Hubert eyed him uncertainly. He suspected that William's assurance of manner and deep mysteriousness of tone was bluff, and yet he was half impressed by it.

'All right,' retorted William. 'You jolly well wait and see.'

Hubert snorted contemptuously, deciding that this unfounded claim of William's would make a good weapon of offence against him for some time to come, and already framing in his mind simple unvarnished allusions to it as, 'Who said he knew all about circuses an' couldn't afford to go to the one at Little Marleigh?' Such challenges, however, needed to be issued from a safe distance, so for the present he turned to another subject.

'I'm gettin' up a cat show tomorrow,' he said innocently. 'There's a big box of chocolates for the prize. Would you like to bring your cat along?'

The brazen shamelessness of this for a minute took away William's breath. It was well known that Hubert's mother possessed a cat of gigantic proportions, who had won many prizes at shows. That the Hubert Laneites should thus try to win public prestige for themselves, and secure their own box of chocolates by organizing a cat show at which their own exhibit was bound to win the prize was a piece of assurance worthy of them.

'Like to enter your cat?' repeated Hubert carelessly.

William thought of the mangy and undersized creature who represented the sole feline staff of his household. Hubert thought of it too.

'I suppose it wouldn't have much chance,' said Hubert at last, with nauseating pity in his voice.

'It would. It's a jolly fine cat,' said William indignantly.

'Want to enter it then?' said Hubert, satisfied with the cunning that had made William thus court public humiliation. The Brown cat was the worst-looking cat of the village.

'All right,' he said, 'I'll put you down. Bring it along this afternnon.'

William and Ginger walked dejectedly away.

★   ★   ★   ★

Early that afternoon they set off, William carefully carrying the Brown cat, brushed till it was in a state bordering on madness, and adorned with a blue bow (taken off a boudoir cap of Ethel's) at which it tore furiously in the intervals of scratching William.

'It's got spirit, anyway,' said William proudly, 'and that ought to count. It's got more spirit than that fat ole thing of Hubert's mother's. I think spirit ought to count.'

But Ginger refused to be roused from his dejection.

'It doesn't count,' he said. 'I mean it doesn't count *for* them—scratchin' the judges an' such like.' He inspected their entry more closely and his dejection increased. 'Why are there so many places where it hasn't got any fur?'

'It's always like that,' said William. 'It's quite healthy. It eats a lot. But it never has fur on those places. It's all right. It doesn't mean that there's anything wrong with it. It just means that—that it hasn't got fur on those places.'

'And look at its ear. It's gone funny.'

'That's where it had a fight,' explained William, 'it goes out fighting every night. It's a jolly brave cat. I bet there's not many cats that fight as much as this one does.'

As if to corroborate his statement, the cat shot out a paw and gave him a scratch from forehead to chin, then, taking advantage of his suddenly relaxed hold, leapt from his arms and fled down the road still tearing madly at its blue bow.

'There!' said Ginger. 'Now you've gone and done it. Now we've got to go without a cat or not go at all, and they'll laugh at us if we go without a cat, and they'll call us funks if we don't go at all.'

William considered these alternatives gloomily.

147

'An' they'll go on and on 'cause they know we can't go to the circus,' he added.

'Go after it and try and catch it again,' suggested Ginger.

'No, I'm jolly well not going to,' said William. 'I'm sick of it. I'd rather fight someone.'

'Well, what shall we do?' said Ginger. 'Go without a cat or just not go?'

'Let's sit down and wait a bit,' said William, 'an' try'n think of a plan. We might find a stray cat bigger'n theirs. Let's jus' sit down an' think.'

Ginger shook his head at William's optimism.

'I bet there aren't any stray cats nowadays. I never see any. And if there were they wouldn't just come when you wanted them. And if they did they wouldn't be the big fat sort of cat what like the Lane cat is.'

They were sitting down on the roadside, their backs to the wood that bordered the road. William turned to look into the wood.

'There's wild cats anyway,' he said, 'I bet there's still a few wild cats left in England. I bet *they're* bigger than his mother's old cat. I bet that if we could find a wild cat and tame it and take it along it'd get the prize all right. I shun't be a bit surprised if there was some wild cats left in this wood. I'm goin' to have a look anyway.'

And he was just going to make his way through the hedge that bordered the wood when the most amazing thing happened. Out of the wood gambolling playfully came a gigantic—was it a cat? It was certainly near enough to a cat to be called a cat. But it was far from wild. It greeted Ginger and William affectionately, rolling over on to its back and offering itself to be stroked and rubbed.

They stared at it in amazement.

'It's a wild cat,' said William, 'a tame, wild cat. P'raps hunger made it tame, or perhaps now that there aren't any other wild animals to fight wild cats have got tame. P'raps it's the last wild cat left in England. Puss! Puss! Puss!'

It leapt upon him affectionately.

'It's a *jolly* fine wild cat,' he said, stroking it, 'and we're jolly lucky to have found a cat like this. Look at it. It *knows* it belongs to us now. Let's find something for it to eat.'

'We'd better take it to the show first,' said Ginger, 'it's nearly time.'

So they made a collar for it by tying Ginger's tie loosely round its neck, and a lead by taking a boot-lace out of William's boot and attaching it to the tie and set off towards the Lanes' house.

The wild cat ambled along the road with them in friendly fashion. William walked slowly and ungracefully in the laceless boot, but his heart was overflowing with pride and affection for his new pet.

'I bet it's the finest wild cat anyone's ever found,' he said.

The show was to be held in the shed at the back of the Lane's house. The other competitors were all there, holding more or less unwilling exhibits, and in the place of honour was Hubert Lane holding his mother's enormous tabby. But the Lane tabby was a kitten compared with William's wild cat. The assembled competitors stared at it speechlessly as William, with a nonchalant air, took his seat with it amongst them.

'That—that's not a cat,' gasped Hubert Lane.

William had with difficulty gathered his exhibit upon his knee. He challenged them round its head.

'What is it, then?' he said.

They had no answer. It was certainly more like a cat than anything.

''Course it's a cat,' said William, pursuing his advantage.

'Well, whose is it then?' said Hubert indignantly. 'I bet it's not yours.'

'It *is* mine,' said William.

'Well, why've we never seen it before then?' said Hubert.

'D'you think,' said William, 'that we'd let a valu'ble cat like this run about all over the place? Why, this is one of the most famous cats in all the world. We'd have it stole in no time if we let it run about all over the place like an ordin'ry cat. This isn't an ordin'ry cat, this isn't. Let *me* tell you this is one of the most famous cats in all the world, a speshully famous cat that never comes out except to go to shows, and that's won prizes all over the world. An' we don't tell people about it either for fear of it being stole. Well, I've not got much time and I've got to get it back home, so if our cat's bigger'n yours you'd better give me the prize now, 'cause this cat's not used to be kept hangin' about before being give its prize.'

The Hubert Laneites stared at William and his burden limply. It was no good. They had not the resilience to withstand this shock. They sagged visibly, eyes and mouth open to their fullest extent, gazing at the monster who sat calmly on William's knee rubbing its face against his neck affectionately.

Hubert Lane at last roused himself with an effort from his paralysis of amazement. He knew when he had met defeat. He took the large box of chocolates on which the Hubert Laneites had meant to feast that afternoon and handed it to William, still gaping at the prize winner. The other exhibitors cheered. They were not at all sorry to see the Hubert Laneites worsted. William put the box of chocolates under his arm and set off, leading his exhibit and shuffling awkwardly in his laceless boot. It was not till they reached the gate leading to the road that the Hubert Laneites recovered from their stupefaction. They recovered all at the same time and yelled as with one accord.

'Who can't afford to go to the circus? *Yah.*'

William was still drunk with the pride of possession.

'It's a *jolly* fine wild cat,' he said again.

'Where'll we keep it?' said Ginger practically.

'In the old barn,' said William, 'an' we'll not tell anyone about it. They'll only manage to spoil it somehow if they find out. We'll keep it there an' take it out walks in the woods an' bring it food from home to eat. Then I vote we send it in for some real cat shows. I bet it'll win a lot of money. I bet it'll make us millionaires. An' when I'm a millionaire I'm goin' to buy a circus with every sort of animal in the world in it, an' I bet I'll have a jolly fine time.'

The mention of the circus rather depressed them and Ginger, to cheer them up, suggested eating the chocolates. They descended into the ditch (fortunately dry), and sat there with the prize cat between them. It seemed that the prize cat, too, liked chocolates and the three shared them equally, eating one each in turn till the box was finished.

'Well, it's had its tea now,' said Ginger, 'so let's take it straight to the old barn for the night.'

'You don't know that it's had enough,' said William, 'it might want a bit of something else. I bet we get it up to my bedroom without anyone seeing us and give it a bit of something else to eat there. I bet we can easily get it up without anyone seein'.'

They had reached William's house now.

He picked the animal up in both arms and concealing it inadequately in his coat entered the side door in a conspiratorial fashion followed by Ginger. As soon as he had reached the foot of the stairs, however, there came the sound of the opening of his mother's bedroom door and her footsteps on the landing. William turned and fled into the drawing-room still followed by the faithful Ginger.

'We'll just wait here till she's gone,' he whispered.

Her footsteps descended the stairs and unmistakably began to approach the drawing-room.

'Here! Quick!' gasped William plunging behind a Chesterfield that was placed across a corner of the room. The triangular space thus formed was rather inadequate for the accommodation of William, Ginger and the prize cat, but by squeezing themselves together they just managed to get themselves into it.

The door opened almost as soon as they had reached their hiding place and Mrs Brown entered.

'I don't expect she'll stay here,' whispered William breathlessly, holding his pet in both arms to keep it still.

But Mrs Brown closed the door and sat down. From her bedroom window she had caught sight of a visitor coming up the drive and she had come down to the drawing-room in order to receive and dispose of her as quickly as possible.

Almost as soon as she had entered the maid announced 'Miss Messiter,' and a tall lady wearing horn-rimmed spectacles entered and, after greeting her effusively, took her seat on the Chesterfield behind which were William, Ginger and the prize cat.

William was so much occupied in restraining his prize cat as soundlessly as possible that he did not hear what the visitor and his mother were saying till they had been talking for several minutes. Then as his pet seemed to have settled down to sleep on the top of Ginger he turned his attention to what the visitor was saying.

'I *do* hope you'll come,' she was saying. 'I'm trying to get everyone in the village to promise to come. He's a *marvellous* speaker. In the forefront of the movement.'

'Yes?' said Mrs Brown vaguely. 'The movement?'

'I told you, you know,' said the visitor earnestly, 'the Thought Mastery Movement. It's closely allied to Christian Science, of course, but it's wider. It embraces more spheres, so to speak. It begins with that of pain, of course, teaching that there's no such thing. No such thing at all. I never feel pain. Never. Why? Because my thoughts know that there's no such thing as pain so naturally they don't feel it. Never.'

At this moment the prize cat who had made its way under the Chesterfield and discovered one of Miss Messiter's ankles on the other side put out an exploratory paw and touched it with extended claws. Miss Messiter uttered a scream.

'Whatever's the matter? said Mrs Brown.

The visitor was clutching her ankle.

'A sudden excruciating pain,' she said.

'Neuritis perhaps, or arthritis,' suggested Mrs Brown soothingly. 'They do come on suddenly.'

'Where had I got to?' said the visitor, still rubbing her ankle.

'About your never feeling pain,' said Mrs Brown.

'Oh yes . . . well the *reason* I don't feel pain is simply that I've trained my thoughts to ignore it. My thoughts mechanically reject the notion of pain. It's all so simple.'

At this minute the prize cat put out his paw again in order to experience a second time the delicious sensation of sinking his claws through Miss Messiter's woollen stockings into her skin beneath.

'*Whatever's* the matter?' said Mrs Brown when Miss Messiter's scream had died away.

'Another of those excruciating pains,' said Miss Messiter. 'I can't explain it. I've never known anything of the sort before. Excruciating.'

'Neuritis probably,' said Mrs Brown, showing more interest than she had shown in the Thought Mastery Movement. 'I had a cousin who used to have it. It came on just like that.'

But Miss Messiter was looking behind her.

'There's a boy behind the sofa,' she said excitedly, 'and he must have been running pins into my foot.'

'I didn't,' said William rising, partly to refute this accusation and partly in order to prevent the visitor's discoveries extending to Ginger and the prize cat. 'I *never* stuck pins into her foot.'

'But whatever are you doing there at all, William?' said his mother in a bewildered fashion.

'I jus'—jus' happened to be there,' explained William coming out

The assembled competitors stared speechlessly as William took his seat.

into the room, 'when you came in an' I thought I'd jus'—jus' stay there till you'd gone but I never stuck pins in her foot. I couldn't have even if I'd wanted to 'cause I haven't any pins. And what's more,' he continued bitterly, 'I haven't any money to buy any pins even if I wanted some. If I'd got money to buy pins to stick into her foot I'd be going to the circus.'

'How do you account for the excruciating pain that I felt then?' demanded Miss Messiter of him sternly.

'It must be neuritis,' said William's mother. 'I'm sure he didn't stick pins into your foot. He's very troublesome and untidy and I can't think *why* he was behind the sofa but I'm *sure* he wouldn't stick pins into your foot. He's never done anything like that.'

'Then I must go at once and consult a specialist,' said Miss Messiter firmly. 'It was an *excruciating* pain. It came on quite suddenly, then went quite suddenly.'

'I think that's the best plan,' said Mrs Brown deeply sympathetic. 'I know that neuritis can often be cured if you catch it in the early stages.'

'And I shall give up the organisation of the Thought Mastery Campaign. I think that it has been too much for me. I'm highly strung.'

They drifted out into the hall. William cautiously returned to the corner of the room. Ginger was engaged in a fierce struggle with the prize cat who wanted to return to his investigations under the Chesterfield. He wanted to find the thing into which it was so pleasant to sink one's claws. He was uttering soft little growls as he fought with Ginger.

'Let's get him out quick,' said William, 'while they're talkin' at the front door.'

Ginger, who was suffering agonies from cramp and was pinned helplessly beneath the prize cat, said in a muffled voice:

'A'right. You take him off me an' I'll try to get up.'

William bundled his pet under his arm, and followed by the bowed and limping Ginger, went to the open window, scrambled through with a skill born of long practice and made his unobtrusive way through the shrubbery to the hole in the hedge that was the Outlaws' unofficial entrance to William's garden. Ginger was still limping.

'I've got that pain like what she said she'd got,' he said. 'Cruciating like what she said it was. I bet I've caught it off her. It mus' be something infectious. I shun't be surprised if I die of it.'

'I think hers was the cat scratchin' her,' said William.

'Was it?' said Ginger with interest. 'I couldn't see what it was doin'. It'd got one of its hind feet in my mouth an' I couldn't get it out. It's a wonder I'm not choked.'

But his pins and needles were wearing off and the prize cat, gambolling by their side, was so engaging that it gradually ousted every other thought from their minds.

'We'll take it to the old barn,' said William, 'then you go home an' get some food for it. I'd better not go home jus' now 'cause of that woman sayin' I stuck pins into her foot. My mother'll prob'ly want to go on talkin' about it.'

'All right,' said Ginger, 'what'll I get it?'

'Milk an' a bit of bread an' butter an' a bit of cake,' said William.

'Oh yes,' said Ginger sarcastically. 'Why don't you say a bit of roast turkey as well?'

'A'right,' said William, 'if you can find a bit of roast turkey, bring it along. I bet it'd eat it.'

'I'll bring it what I can find with no one catchin' me,' said Ginger. 'It'll depend whether the larder window's open. I can't do more'n that, can I?'

'Get it as much as you can anyway,' said William.

Ginger departed and William amused himself by playing with his prize cat. It was an excellent play-fellow. It made little feints and darts at William. It rolled over on the ground. It ran away and challenged him to catch it. It growled and pretended to fight him. The time passed on wings till Ginger returned. Ginger's arms were full. Evidently the larder window had been open. He was carrying two buns, half an apple pie, and a piece of cheese. And yet, despite this rich haul, his expression was one of deepest melancholy. He placed the things down absently upon a packing-case, and said:

'I met a boy in the road and he'd just met a man and he said that they were looking for a lion cub that had got away from the circus.'

William's face dropped. They both gazed thoughtfully at the prize cat.

'I—I sort of thought it was a lion cub all the time,' said William.

'So did I,' said Ginger hastily.

After a long and pregnant silence, William said in a faraway voice:

'Well—I suppose we've gotter take it back.' He spoke as one whose world has crashed about him. In his mind had been roseate dreams of a future in which every day the lion cub gambolled round his feet, played hide and seek with him and attacked him with growls of mock ferocity. Life without the lion cub stretched grey and dark before him, hardly worth living.

'I s'pose we've gotter,' said Ginger. 'I s'pose it's stealin' if we don't, now that we know.'

They placed the food before the cub and watched it with melancholy tenderness.

It ate the buns, sat on the apple pie and played football with the piece of cheese.

Then they took up the end of William's boot-lace again and set off sorrowfully with it to Little Marleigh.

★ ★ ★ ★

The proprietor of the circus received the truant with relief, and complimented the rescuers on its prompt return. They gazed at it sadly, Ginger replacing his tie and William his boot-lace.

'He's a cute little piece, isn't he?' said the proprietor. 'Don't appear yet. Too young. But goin' to lap up tricks like milk soon . . . Well, I'd better be gettin' a move on. Early show's jus' goin' to begin. Thank you, young sirs.'

'I s'pose,' said William wistfully, 'I s'pose we couldn't *do* anythin' in the show?'

The proprietor scratched his head.

'What c'n you do?' he said.

'I c'n stand on my hands,' said William, 'an' Ginger can pull funny faces. Jolly funny ones.'

The proprietor shook his head.

'Not in our line,' he said. 'But—tell you what. I *am* short-handed, as it happens. A man jus' come over queer an' gone home. We could do with another hand. Jus' movin' things off an' on between turns. Care to help with that?'

So deep was their emotion that William broke his boot-lace and Ginger nearly throttled himself with his tie.

'I should—jolly well—think—we would,' said William hoarsely.

*　　　*　　　*　　　*

The Hubert Laneites sat together in the front row. They'd all been to the circus earlier in the week but they'd come again for this last performance, partly in order to be able to tell the Outlaws that they'd been twice and partly to comfort themselves for the fiasco of their cat show.

'I say,' said Hubert Lane to Bertie Franks, 'I say, won't ole William be mad when we tell him we've been again?'

'Yah,' said Bertie Franks, 'an' I say, fancy him havin' the cheek to say he knew more about circuses than us an' not even been once. We won't half rag him about it. We—'

His voice died away. He stared down into the ring. For there unmistakably was William setting out the little tubs on which the performing ponies performed. He rubbed his eyes and looked again. He hadn't been mistaken. It was William.

'Golly!' he said faintly.

All the Hubert Laneites were staring at William, paralysed with amazement.

'Golly!' they echoed and drew another deep breath as Ginger appeared carrying the chairs on which the clown pretended to do acrobatic feats. Then the circus began. The Hubert Laneites did not see the circus at all. They were staring fascinated at the opening of the tent into which William and Ginger had vanished. After the first turn they emerged and moved away the little tubs and brought out a lot of letters which they laid on the ground for the talking horse to spell from. After that turn William came out alone and held a hoop for Nellie, the Wonder Dog to jump through.

Not once did the expression of stupefied amazement fade from the faces of the Hubert Laneites.

After the circus they walked home dazedly as if in a dream.

*　　　*　　　*　　　*

The next day they approached William cautiously, and with something of reverence in their expressions.

'I say, William,' Hubert said humbly, 'tell us about it, will you?'

'About what?' said William.

'About you helpin' at the circus.'

'Oh *that*,' said William carelessly. 'Oh, I gen'rally help at circuses round about here. I don't always go into the ring like what I did yesterday, but I'm gen'rally in the tent behind helpin' with the animals. Trainin' them for their tricks. Gettin' 'em ready an' such-like. I suppose that one circus tells another about me and that's why they're always askin' me to help. I *said* I knew a jolly sight more about circuses than what you did, you remember.'

'Yes,' said Hubert Lane still more humbly, 'it must be jolly fun, isn't it, William?'

'Oh, it's all right,' said William, 'it's hard work an' of course it's jolly dangerous. Trainin' the animals an' lockin' 'em up for the night an' such-like.' He walked a few yards with an ostentatious limp, and then said, 'the elephant trod on my foot yesterday when I was puttin' it in its cage'—and he touched the scratch that his mother's cat had made. It was certainly quite a showy affair—'the bear gave me this the other night when I was combin' it out ready to go on and do its tricks. It's work not everyone would like to do.'

They gazed at him as at a being from another and a higher sphere.

'I say, William,' said Bertie Franks, 'if—if they want anyone else to help you—you'll give us a chance won't you?'

'I don't s'pose they will,' said William. ''Sides this circus has gone now and I don't know when another's comin'. It's dangerous work, you know, but I'm used to it.'

And, followed by their admiring eyes, he limped elaborately away.

He was limping with the other foot this time, but, of course, no one noticed that.

THE GREY CUB

Jack London

He was different from his brothers and sisters. Their hair already betrayed the reddish hue inherited from their mother, the she-wolf; while he alone, in this particular, took after his father. He was the one little grey cub of the litter. He had bred true to the straight wolf-stock—in fact, he had bred true to old One Eye himself, physically with but a single exception, and that was he had two eyes to his father's one.

The grey cub's eyes had not been opened long, yet already he could see with steady clearness. And while his eyes were still closed, he had felt, tasted, and smelled. He knew his two brothers and his two sisters very well. He had begun to romp with them in a feeble, awkward way, and even to squabble, his little throat vibrating with a queer rasping noise (the forerunner of the growl), as he worked himself into a passion. And long before his eyes had opened, he had learned by touch, taste, and smell to know his mother—a fount of warmth and liquid food and tenderness. She possessed a gentle, caressing tongue that soothed him when it passed over his soft little body, and that impelled him to snuggle close against her and to doze off to sleep.

Most of the first month of his life had been passed thus in sleeping; but now he could see quite well, and he stayed awake for longer periods of time, and he was coming to learn his world quite well. His world was gloomy; but he did not know that, for he knew no other world. It was dim-lighted; but his eyes had never had to adjust themselves to any other light. His world was very small. Its limits were the walls of the lair; but as he had no knowledge of the wide world outside, he was never oppressed by the narrow confines of his existence.

But he had early discovered that one wall of his world was different from the rest. This was the mouth of the cave and the source of light. He had discovered that it was different from the other walls long before he had thoughts of his own, any conscious volitions. It had been an irresistible attraction before ever his eyes opened and looked upon it. The light from it had beat upon his sealed lids, and the eyes and the optic nerves had pulsated to little, sparklike flashes, warm coloured and strangely pleasing. The life of his body, and of every fibre of his body, the life that was the very substance of his body and that was apart from his own personal life, had yearned toward this light and urged his body toward it in the same way that the cunning chemistry of a plant urges it toward the sun.

Always, in the beginning, before his conscious life dawned he had crawled toward the mouth of the cave. And in this his brothers and sisters were one with him. Never, in that period, did any of them crawl toward the dark corners of the back-wall. The light drew them as if they were plants; the chemistry of the life that composed them demanded the light as a necessity of being; and their little puppet-bodies crawled blindly and chemically, like the tendrils of a vine. Later on, when each developed individuality and became personally conscious of impulsions and desires, the attraction of the light increased. They were always crawling and sprawling toward it, and being driven back from it by their mother.

It was in this way that the grey cub learned other attributes of his mother than the soft, soothing tongue. In his insistent crawling toward the light, he discovered in her a nose that with a sharp nudge administered rebuke, and later, a paw, that crushed him down and rolled him over and over with swift, calculating stroke. Thus he learned hurt; and on top of it he learned to avoid hurt, first, by not incurring the risk of it; and second, when he had incurred the risk, by dodging and by retreating. These were conscious actions, and were the results of his first generalisations upon the world. Before that he recoiled automatically from hurt, as he had crawled automatically toward the light. After that he recoiled from hurt because he *knew* that it was hurt.

He was a fierce little cub. So were his brothers and sisters. It was to be expected. He was a carnivorous animal. He came of a breed of meat-killers and meat-eaters. His father and mother lived wholly upon meat. The milk he had sucked with his first flickering life, was milk transformed directly from meat, and now, at a month old, when his eyes had been open for but a week, he was beginning himself to eat meat—meat half-digested by the she-wolf and disgorged for the five growing cubs that already made too great a demand upon her breast.

But he was, further, the fiercest of the litter. He could make a louder rasping growl than any of them. His tiny rages were much more terrible than theirs. It was he that first learned the trick of rolling a fellow-cub over with a cunning paw-stroke. And it was he that first gripped another cub by the ear and pulled and tugged and growled through jaws tight-clenched. And certainly it was he that caused the mother the most trouble in keeping her litter from the mouth of the cave.

The fascination of the light for the grey cub increased from day to day. He was perpetually departing on yard-long adventures toward the cave's entrance, and as perpetually being driven back. Only he did not know it for an entrance. He did not know anything about entrances—passages whereby one goes from one place to another place. He did not know any other place, much less of a way to get there. So to him the entrance of the cave was a wall—a wall of light. As the sun was to the outside dweller, this wall was to him the sun of his world. It attracted him as a candle attracts a moth. He was always striving to attain it. The life that was swiftly expanding within him, urged him continually towards the wall of light. The life that was within him knew that it was the one way out, the way he was predestined to tread. But he himself did not know anything about it. He did not know there was any outside at all.

There was one strange thing about this wall of light. His father (he had already come to recognize his father as the one other dweller in the world, a creature like his mother, who slept near the light and was a bringer of meat)—his father had a way of walking right into the white far wall and disappearing. The grey cub could not understand this. Though never permitted by his mother to approach that wall, he had approached the other walls, and encountered hard obstruction on the end of his tender nose. This hurt. And after several such adventures, he left the walls alone. Without thinking about it, he accepted this disappearing into the wall as a peculiarity of his father, as milk and half-digested meat were peculiarities of his mother.

In fact, the grey cub was not given to thinking—at least, to the kind of thinking customary of men. His brain worked in dim ways. Yet his conclusions were as sharp and distinct as those achieved by men. He had a method of accepting things, without questioning the why and wherefore. In reality, this was the act of classification. He was never disturbed over *why* a thing happened. *How* it happened was sufficient for him. Thus, when he had bumped his nose on the back-wall a few times, he accepted that he would not disappear into walls. In the same way he accepted that his father could disappear into walls. But he was not in the least disturbed by desire to find out the reason for the difference between his father and himself. Logic and physics were no part of his mental make-up.

Like most creatures of the Wild, he early experienced famine. There came a time when not only did the meat supply cease, but the milk no longer came from his mother's breast. At first, the cubs whimpered and cried, but for the most part they slept. It was not long before they were reduced to a coma of hunger. There were no more spats and squabbles, no more tiny rages nor attempts at growling; while the adventures toward the far white wall ceased altogether. The cubs slept, while the life that was in them flickered and died down.

One Eye was desperate. He ranged far and wide, and slept but little in the lair that had now become cheerless and miserable. The she-wolf, too, left her litter and went out in search of meat. In the first days after the birth of the cubs, One Eye had journeyed several times back to the Indian camp, and robbed the rabbit snares; but, with the melting of the snow and the opening of the streams, the Indian camp had moved away, and that source of supply was closed to him.

When the grey cub came back to life and again took interest in the far white wall, he found that the population of his world had been reduced. Only one sister remained to him. The rest were gone. As he grew stronger, he found himself compelled to play alone, for the sister no longer lifted her head nor moved about. His little body rounded out with the meat he now ate; but the food had come too late for her. She slept continuously, a tiny skeleton flung round with skin in which the flame flickered lower and lower and at last went out.

Then there came a time when the grey cub no longer saw his father appearing and disappearing in the wall nor lying down asleep in the entrance. This had happened at the end of a second and less severe famine. The she-wolf knew why One Eye never came back, but there was no way by which she could tell what she had seen to the grey cub. Hunting herself for meat, up the left fork of the stream where lived the lynx, she had followed a day-old trail of One Eye. And she had found him, or what remained of him, at the end of the trail. There were many signs of the battle that had been fought, and of the lynx's withdrawal to her lair after having won the victory. Before she went away, the she-wolf had found this lair, but the signs told her that the lynx was inside, and she had not dared to venture in.

After that, the she-wolf in her hunting avoided the left fork. For she knew that in the lynx's lair was a litter of kittens, and she knew the lynx for a fierce, bad-tempered creature and a terrible fighter. It was all very well for half a dozen wolves to drive a lynx, spitting and bristling, up a tree; but it was quite a different matter for a lone wolf to encounter a lynx—especially when the lynx was known to have a litter of hungry kittens at her back.

But the Wild is the Wild, and motherhood is motherhood, at all times fiercely protective whether in the Wild or out of it; and the time was to come when the she-wolf, for her grey cub's sake, would venture the left fork, and the lair in the rocks, and the lynx's wrath.

★　　★　　★　　★

By the time his mother began leaving the cave on hunting expeditions, the cub had learned well the law that forbade his approaching the entrance. Not only had this law been forcibly and many times impressed on him by his mother's nose and paw, but in him the instinct of fear was developing. Never, in his brief cave-life, had he encountered anything of which to be afraid. Yet fear was in him. It had come down to him from a remote ancestry through a thousand lives. It was a heritage he had received directly from One Eye and the she-wolf; but to them, in turn, it had been passed down through all the generations of wolves that had gone before. Fear!—that legacy of the Wild which no animal may escape nor exchange for pottage.

So the grey cub knew fear, though he knew not the stuff of which fear was made. Possibly he accepted it as one of the restrictions of life. For he had already learned that there were such restrictions. Hunger he had known; and when he could not appease his hunger he had felt restriction. The hard obstruction of the cave-wall, the sharp nudge of his mother's nose, the smashing stroke of her paw, the hunger unappeased of several famines, had borne in upon him that all was not freedom in the world, that to life there were limitations and restraints. These limitations and restraints were laws. To be obedient to them was to escape hurt and make for happiness.

He did not reason the question out in this man fashion. He merely classified the things that hurt and the things that did not hurt. And after such classification he avoided the things that hurt, the restrictions and restraints, in order to enjoy the satisfactions and the remunerations of life.

Thus it was that in obedience to the law laid down by his mother, and in obedience to the law of that unknown and nameless thing, fear, he kept away from the mouth of the cave. It remained to him a white wall of light. When his mother was absent, he slept most of the time, while during the intervals that he was awake he kept very quiet, suppressing the whimpering cries that tickled in his throat and strove for noise.

Once, lying awake, he heard a strange sound in the white wall. He did not know that it was a wolverine, standing outside, all a-trembling with its own daring, and cautiously scenting out the contents of the cave. The cub knew only that the sniff was strange, a something unclassified, therefore unknown and terrible—for the unknown was one of the chief elements that went into the making of fear.

The hair bristled up on the grey cub's back, but it bristled silently. How was he to know that this thing that sniffed was a thing at which to bristle? It was not born of any knowledge of his, yet it was the visible expression of the fear that was in him, and for which, in his own life, there was no accounting. But fear was accompanied by another instinct—that of concealment. The cub was in a frenzy of terror, yet he lay without movement or sound, frozen, petrified into immobility, to all appearances dead. His mother, coming home, growled as she smelt the wolverine's track, and bounded into the cave and licked and nozzled him with undue vehemence of affection. And the cub felt that somehow he had escaped a great hurt.

But there were other forces at work in the cub, the greatest of which was growth. Instinct and law demanded of him obedience. But growth demanded disobedience. His mother and fear impelled him to keep away from the white wall. Growth is life, and life is for ever destined to make for light. So there was no damming up the tide of life that was rising within him—rising with every mouthful of meat he swallowed, with every breath he drew. In the end, one day, fear and obedience were swept away by the rush of life, and the cub straddled and sprawled toward the entrance.

Unlike any other wall with which he had had experience, this wall seemed to recede from him as he approached. No hard surface collided with the tender little nose he thrust out tentatively before him. The substance of the wall seemed as permeable and yielding as light. And as condition, in his eyes, had the seeming of form, so he entered into what had been wall to him and bathed in the substance that composed it.

It was bewildering. He was sprawling through solidity. And ever the light grew brighter. Fear urged him to go back, but growth drove him on. Suddenly he found himself at the mouth of the cave. The wall, inside which he had thought himself, as suddenly leaped back before him to an immeasurable distance. The light had become painfully bright. He was dazzled by it. Likewise he was made dizzy by this abrupt and tremendous extension of space. Automatically, his eyes were adjusting themselves to the brightness, focusing themselves to meet the increased distance of objects. At first, the wall had leaped beyond his vision. He now saw it again; but it had taken upon itself a remarkable remoteness. Also, its appearance had changed. It was now a variegated wall, composed of the trees that fringed the stream, the opposing mountain that towered above the trees, and the sky that out-towered the mountain.

A great fear came upon him. This was more of the terrible unknown. He crouched down on the lip of the cave and gazed out on the world. He was very much afraid. Because it was unknown, it was hostile to him. Therefore the hair stood up on end along his back and his lips wrinkled weakly in an attempt at a ferocious and intimidating snarl. Out of his puniness and fright he challenged and menaced the whole wide world.

Nothing happened. He continued to gaze, and in his interest he forgot to snarl. Also, he forgot to be afraid. For the time, fear had been routed by growth, while growth had assumed the guise of curiosity. He began to notice near objects—an open portion of the stream that flashed in the sun, the blasted pine-tree that stood at the base of the slope, and the slope itself, that ran right up to him and ceased two feet beneath the lip of the cave on which he crouched.

Now the grey cub had lived all his days on a level floor. He had never experienced the hurt of a fall. He did not know what a fall was. So he stepped boldly out upon the air. His hind-legs still rested on the cave-lip, so he fell forward head downward. The earth struck him a harsh blow on the nose that made him yelp. Then he began rolling down the slope, over and over. He was in a panic of terror. The unknown had caught him at last. It had gripped savagely hold of him and was about to wreak upon him a terrific hurt. Growth was now routed by fear, and he ki-ki'd like any frightened puppy.

The unknown bore him on he knew not to what frightful hurt, and he yelped and ki-ki'd unceasingly. This was a different proposition from crouching in frozen fear while the unknown lurked just alongside. Now the unknown had caught tight hold of him. Silence would do no good. Besides, it was not fear, but terror, that convulsed him.

But the slope grew more gradual, and its base was grass-covered. Here the cub lost momentum. When at last he came to a stop, he gave one last agonized yelp and then a long, whimpering wail. Also, and quite as a matter of course, as though in his life he had already made a thousand toilets, he proceeded to lick away the dry clay that soiled him.

After that he sat up and gazed about him, as might the first man of the earth who landed upon Mars. The cub had broken through the wall of the world, the unknown had let go its hold of him, and here he was without hurt. But the first man on Mars would have experienced less unfamiliarity than did he. Without any antecedent knowledge, without any warning whatever that such existed, he found himself an explorer in a totally new world.

Now that the terrible unknown had let go of him he forgot that the unknown had any terrors. He was aware only of curiosity in all the things about him. He inspected the grass beneath him, the moss-berry plant just beyond, and the dead trunk of the blasted pine that stood on the edge of an open space among the trees. A squirrel, running around the base of the trunk, came full upon him, and gave him a fright. He cowered down and snarled. But the squirrel was as badly scared. It ran up the tree, and from a point of safety chattered back savagely.

This helped the cub's courage, and though the woodpecker he next encountered gave him a start, he proceeded confidently on his way. Such was his confidence, that when a moose-bird impudently hopped up to him, he reached out at it with a playful paw. The result was a sharp peck on the end of his nose that made him cower down and ki-ki. The noise he made was too much for the moose-bird, who sought safety in flight.

But the cub was learning. His misty little mind had already made an unconscious classification. There were live things and things not alive. Also, he must watch out for the live things. The things not alive remained always in one place; but the live things moved about, and there was no telling what they might do. The thing to expect of them was the unexpected, and for this he must be prepared.

He travelled very clumsily. He ran into sticks and things. A twig that he thought a long way off, would the next instant hit him on the nose or rake along his ribs. There were inequalities of surface. Sometimes he overstepped and stubbed his nose. Quite as often he understepped and stubbed his feet. Then there were the pebbles and stones that turned under him when he trod upon them; and from them he came to know that the things not alive were not all in the same state of stable equilibrium as was his cave; also, that small things not alive were more liable than large things to fall down or turn over. But with every mishap he was learning. The longer he walked the better he walked. He was adjusting himself. He was learning to calculate his own muscular movements, to know his physical limitations, to measure distances between objects, and between objects and himself.

His was the luck of the beginner. Born to be a hunter of meat (though he did not know it), he blundered upon meat just outside his own cave-door on his first foray into the world. It was by sheer blundering that he chanced upon the shrewdly hidden ptarmigan nest. He fell into it. He had essayed to walk upon the trunk of a fallen pine. The rotten bark gave way under his feet, and with a despairing yelp he pitched down the rounded descent, smashed through the leafage and stalks of a small bush, and in the heart of the bush, on the ground, fetched up in the midst of the seven ptarmigan chicks.

They made noises, and at first he was frightened at them. Then he perceived that they were very little, and he became bolder. They moved. He placed his paw on one, and its movements were accelerated. This was a source of enjoyment to him. He smelled it. He picked it up in his mouth. It struggled and tickled his tongue. At the same time he was made aware of a sensation of hunger. His jaws closed together. There was a crunching of fragile bones, and warm blood ran in his mouth. The taste of it was good. This was meat, the same as his mother gave him, only it was alive between his teeth and therefore better. So he ate the ptarmigan. Nor did he stop till he had devoured the whole brood. Then he licked his chops in quite the same way his mother did, and began to crawl out of the bush.

He encountered a feathered whirlwind. He was confused and blinded by the rush of it and the beat of angry wings. He hid his head between his paws and yelped. The blows increased. The mother-ptarmigan was in a fury. Then he became angry. He rose up, snarling, striking out with his paws. He sank his tiny teeth into one of the wings and pulled and tugged sturdily. The ptarmigan struggled against him, showering blows upon him with her free wing. It was his first battle. He was elated. He forgot all about the unknown. He no longer was afraid of anything. He was fighting, tearing at a live thing that was striking at him. Also, this live thing was meat. The lust to kill was on him. He had just destroyed little live things. He would now destroy a big live thing. He was too busy and happy to know that he was happy. He was thrilling and exulting in ways new to him and greater to him than any he had known before.

With a despairing yelp he rolled down into a nest of chicks.

He held on to the wing and growled between his tight-clenched teeth. The ptarmigan dragged him out of the bush. When she turned and tried to drag him back into the bush's shelter, he pulled her away from it and on into the open. And all the time she was making outcry and striking with her free wing, while feathers were flying like a snow-fall. The pitch to which he was aroused was tremendous. All the fighting blood of his breed was up in him and surging through him. This was living, though he did not know it. He was realising his own meaning in the world; he was doing that for which he was made —killing meat and battling to kill it. He was justifying his existence, than which life can do no greater; for life achieves its summit when it does to the uttermost that which it was equipped to do.

After a time the ptarmigan ceased her struggling. He still held her by the wing, and they lay on the ground and looked at each other. He tried to growl threateningly, ferociously. She pecked on his nose, which by now, what of previous adventures, was sore. He winced but held on. She pecked him again and again. From wincing he went to whimpering. He tried to back away from her, oblivious to the fact that by his hold on her he dragged her after him. A rain of pecks fell on his ill-used nose. The flood of fight ebbed down in him, and releasing his prey, he turned tail and scampered off across the open in inglorious retreat.

He lay down to rest on the other side of the open, near the edge of the bushes, his tongue lolling out, his chest heaving and panting, his nose still hurting him and causing him to continue to whimper. But as he lay there, suddenly there came to him a feeling as of something terrible impending. The unknown with all its terrors rushed upon him, and he shrank back instinctively into the shelter of the bush. As he did so, a draught of air fanned him, and a large, winged body swept ominously and silently past. A hawk, driving down out of the blue, had barely missed him.

While he lay in the bush recovering from this fright and peering fearfully out, the mother-ptarmigan on the other side of the open space fluttered out of the ravaged nest. It was because of her loss that she paid no attention to the winged bolt of the sky. But the cub saw, and it was a warning and a lesson to him—the swift downward swoop of the hawk, the short skim of its body just above the ground, the strike of its talons in the body of the ptarmigan, the ptarmigan's squawk of agony and fright, and the hawk's rush upward into the blue, carrying the ptarmigan away with it.

It was a long time before the cub left his shelter. He had learned much. Live things were meat. They were good to eat. Also, live things when they were large enough, could give hurt. It was better to eat small live things like ptarmigan chicks, and to let alone large live things like ptarmigan hens. Nevertheless he felt a little prick of ambition, a sneaking desire to have another battle with that ptarmigan hen—only the hawk had carried her away. Maybe there were other ptarmigan hens. He would go and see.

He came down a shelving bank to the stream. He had never seen water before. The footing looked good. There were no inequalities of surface. He stepped boldly out on it; and went down, crying with fear, into the embraces of the unknown. It was cold, and he gasped, breathing quickly. The water rushed into his lungs instead of the air that had always accompanied his act of breathing. The suffocation he experienced was like the pang of death. To him it signified death. He had no conscious knowledge of death, but like every animal of the Wild, he possessed the instinct of death. To him it stood as the greatest of hurts. It was the very essence of the unknown; it was the sum of the terrors of the unknown, the one culminating and unthinkable catastrophe that could happen to him, about which he knew nothing and about which he feared everything.

He came to the surface, and the sweet air rushed into his open mouth. He did not go down again. Quite as though it had been a long-established custom of his he struck out with all his legs and began to swim. The near bank was a yard away; but he had come up with his back to it, and the first thing his eyes rested upon was the opposite bank, toward which he immediately began to swim. The stream was a small one, but in the pool it widened out to a score of feet.

Midway in the passage, the current picked up the cub and swept him down stream. He was caught in the miniature rapid at the bottom of the pool. Here was little chance for swimming. The quiet water had become suddenly angry. Sometimes he was under, sometimes on top. At all times he was in violent motion, now being turned over or around, and again, being smashed against a rock. And with every rock he struck, he yelped. His progress was a series of yelps, from which might have been adduced the number of rocks he encouraged.

Below the rapid was a second pool, and here, captured by the eddy, he was gently borne to the bank and as gently deposited on a bed of gravel. He crawled frantically clear of the water and lay down. He had learned some more about the world. Water was not any solidity at all. His conclusion was that things were not always what they appeared to be. The cub's fear of the unknown was an inherited distrust, and it had now been strengthened by experience. Thenceforth, in the nature of things, he would possess an abiding distrust of appearances. He would have to learn the reality of a thing before he could put his faith into it.

One other adventure was destined for him that day. He had recollected that there was such a thing in the world as his mother. And then there came to him a feeling that he wanted her more than all the rest of the things in the world. Not only was his body tired with the adventures it had undergone, but his little brain was equally tired. In all the days he had lived it had not worked so hard as on this one day. Furthermore, he was sleepy. So he started out to look for the cave and his mother, feeling at the same time an overwhelming rush of loneliness and helplessness.

He was sprawling along between some bushes, when he heard a sharp intimidating cry. There was a flash of yellow before his eyes. He saw a weasel leaping swiftly away from him. It was a small live thing, and he had no fear. Then, before him, at his feet, he saw an extremely small live thing, only several inches long, a young weasel, that, like himself, had disobediently gone out adventuring. It tried to retreat before him. He turned it over with his paw. It made a queer, grating noise. The next moment the flash of yellow reappeared before his eyes. He heard again the intimidating cry, and at the same instant received a severe blow on the side of the neck and felt the sharp teeth of the mother-weasel cut into his flesh.

Whilst he yelped and ki-yi'd and scrambled backward, he saw the mother-weasel leap upon her young one and disappear with it into the neighbouring thicket. The cut of her teeth in his neck still hurt, but his feelings were hurt more grievously, and he sat down and weakly whimpered. This mother-weasel was so small and so savage! He was yet to learn that for size and weight the weasel was the most ferocious, vindictive, and terrible of all the killers of the Wild. But a portion of this knowledge was quickly to be his.

He was still whimpering when the mother-weasel reappeared. She did not rush him, now that her young one was safe. She approached more cautiously, and the cub had full opportunity to observe her lean, snakelike body, and her head, erect, eager, and snakelike itself. Her sharp, menacing cry sent the hair bristling along his back, and he snarled warningly at her. She came closer and closer. There was a leap, swifter than his unpractised sight, and the lean, yellow body disappeared for a moment out of the field of vision. The next moment she was at his throat, her teeth buried in his hair and flesh.

At first he snarled and tried to fight; but he was very young, and this was only his first day in the world, and his snarl became a whimper, his fight a struggle to escape. The weasel never relaxed her hold. She hung on, striving to press down with her teeth to the great vein where his life-blood bubbled. The weasel was a drinker of blood, and it was ever her preference to drink from the throat of life itself.

The grey cub would have died, and there would have been no story to write about him, had not the she-wolf come bounding through the bushes. The weasel let go the cub and flashed at the she-wolf's throat, missing, but getting a hold on the jaw instead. The she-wolf flirted her head like the snap of a whip, breaking the weasel's hold and flinging it high in the air. And, still in the air, the she-wolf's jaws closed on the lean, yellow body, and the weasel knew death between the crunching teeth.

The cub experienced another excess of affection on the part of his mother. Her joy at finding him seemed greater even than his joy at being found. She nozzled him and caressed him and licked the cuts made in him by the weasel's teeth. Then, between them, mother and cub, they ate the blood-drinker, and after that went back to the cave and slept.

ADOLF

D.H. Lawrence

When we were children our father often worked on the night-shift. Once it was spring-time, and he used to arrive home, black and tired, just as we were downstairs in our nightdresses. Then night met morning face to face, and the contact was not always happy. Perhaps it was painful to my father to see us gaily entering upon the day into which he dragged himself soiled and weary. He didn't like going to bed in the spring morning sunshine.

But sometimes he was happy, because of his long walk through the dewy fields in the first daybreak. He loved the open morning, the crystal and the space, after a night down pit. He watched every bird, every stir in the trembling grass, answered the whinnying of the peewits and tweeted to the wrens. If he could, he also would have whinnied and tweeted and whistled in a native language that was not human. He liked non-human things best.

One sunny morning we were all sitting at table when we heard his heavy slurring walk up the entry. We became uneasy. His was always a disturbing presence, trammelling. He passed the window darkly, and we heard him go into the scullery and put down his tin bottle. But directly he came into the kitchen. We felt at once that he had something to communicate. No one spoke. We watched his black face for a second.

'Give me a drink,' he said.

My mother hastily poured out his tea. He went to pour it out into his saucer. But instead of drinking he suddenly put something on the table among the teacups. A tiny brown rabbit! A small rabbit, a mere morsel, sitting against the bread as still as if it were a made thing.

'A rabbit! A young one! Who gave it you, Father?'

But he laughed enigmatically, with a sliding motion of his yellow-grey eyes, and went to take off his coat. We pounced on the rabbit.

'Is it alive? Can you feel its heart beat?'

My father came back and sat down heavily in his armchair. He dragged his saucer to him, and blew his tea, pushing out his red lips under his black moustache.

'Where did you get it, Father?'

'I picked it up,' he said, wiping his naked forearm over his mouth and beard.

'Where?'

'It is a wild one!' came my mother's quick voice.

'Yes it is.'

'Then why did you bring it?' cried my mother.

'Oh, we wanted it', came our cry.

'Yes, I've no doubt you did—' retorted my mother. But she was drowned in our clamour of questions.

On the field path my father had found a dead mother rabbit and three dead little ones—this one alive, but unmoving.

'But what had killed them, Daddy?'

'I couldn't say, my child. I s'd think she'd aten something.'

'Why did you bring it!' again my mother's voice of condemnation. 'You know what it will be.'

My father made no answer, but we were loud in protest.

'He must bring it. It's not big enough to live by itself. It would die,' we shouted.

'Yes, and it will die now. And then there'll be *another* outcry.'

My mother set her face against the tragedy of dead pets. Our hearts sank.

'It won't die, Father, will it? Why will it? It won't.'

'I s'd think not,' said my father.

'You know well enough it will. Haven't we had it all before!' said my mother.

'They dunna always pine,' replied my father testily.

But my mother reminded him of other little wild animals he had brought, which had sulked and refused to live, and brought storms of tears and trouble in our house of lunatics.

Trouble fell on us. The little rabbit sat on our lap, unmoving, its eye wide and dark. We brought it milk, warm milk, and held it to its nose. It sat still as if it was far away, retreated down some deep burrow, hidden, oblivious. We wetted its mouth and whiskers with drops of milk. It gave no sign, did not even shake off the wet white drops. Somebody began to shed a few secret tears.

'What did I say?' cried my mother. 'Take it and put it down in the field.'

Her command was in vain. We were driven to get dressed for school. There sat the rabbit. It was like a tiny obscure cloud. Watching it, the emotions died out of our breast. Useless to love it, to yearn over it. Its little feelings were all ambushed. They must be circumvented. Love and affection were a trespass upon it. A little wild thing, it became more mute and asphyxiated still in its own arrest, when we approached with love. We must not love it. We must circumvent it, for its own existence.

So I passed the order to my sister and my mother. The rabbit was not to be spoken to, nor even looked at. Wrapping it in a piece of flannel I put it in an obscure corner of the cold parlour, and put a saucer of milk before its nose. My mother was forbidden to enter the parlour while we were at school.

'As if I should take any notice of your nonsense,' she cried affronted. Yet I doubt if she ventured into the parlour.

At midday, after school, creeping into the front room, there we saw the rabbit still and unmoving in the piece of flannel. Strange grey-brown neutralization of life, still living! It was a sore problem to us.

'Why won't it drink its milk, Mother?' we whispered. Our father was asleep.

'It prefers to sulk its life away, silly little thing.' A profound problem. Prefers to sulk its life away! We put young dandelion leaves to its nose. The sphinx was not more oblivious. Yet its eye was bright.

At tea-time, however, it had hopped a few inches, out of its flannel, and there it sat again, uncovered, a little solid cloud of muteness, brown, with unmoving whiskers. Only its side palpitated slightly with life.

Darkness came; my father set off to work. The rabbit was still unmoving. Dumb despair was coming over the sisters, a threat of tears before bed-time. Clouds of my mother's anger gathered as she muttered against my father's wantonness.

Once more the rabbit was wrapped in the old pit-singlet. But now it was carried into the scullery and put under the copper fire-place, that it might imagine itself inside a burrow. The saucers were placed about, four or five, here and there on the floor, so that if the little creature *should* chance to hop abroad, it could not fail to come upon some food. After this my mother was allowed to take from the scullery what she wanted and then she was forbidden to open the door.

When morning came and it was light, I went downstairs. Opening the scullery door, I heard a slight scuffle. Then I saw dabbles of milk all over the floor and tiny rabbit droppings in the saucers. And there the miscreant, the tips of his ears showing behind a pair of boots. I peeped at him. He sat bright-eyed and askance, twitching his nose and looking at me while not looking at me.

He was alive—very much alive. But still we were afraid to trespass much on his confidence.

'Father!' My father was arrested at the door. 'Father, the rabbit's alive.'

'Back your life it is,' said my father.

'Mind how you go in.'

By evening, however, the little creature was tame, quite tame. He was christened Adolf. We were enchanted by him. We couldn't really love him, because he was wild and loveless to the end. But he was an unmixed delight.

We decided he was too small to live in a hutch—he must live at large in the house. My mother protested, but in vain. He was so tiny. So we had him upstairs, and he dropped his tiny pills on the bed and we were enchanted.

Adolf made himself instantly at home. He had the run of the house, and was perfectly happy, with his tunnels and his holes behind the furniture.

We loved him to take meals with us. He would sit on the table humping his back, sipping his milk, shaking his whiskers and his tender ears, hopping off and hobbling back to his saucer, with an air of supreme unconcern. Suddenly he was alert. He hobbled a few tiny paces, and reared himself up inquisitively at the sugar basin. He fluttered his tiny fore-paws, and then reached and laid them on the edge of the basin, while he craned his thin neck and peeped in. He trembled his whiskers at the sugar, then he did his best to lift down a lump.

'*Do* you think I will have it! Animals in the sugar pot!' cried my mother, with a rap of her hand on the table.

Which so delighted the electric Adolf that he flung his hind-quarters and knocked over a cup.

'It's your own fault, Mother. If you left him alone—'

He continued to take tea with us. He rather liked warm tea. And he loved sugar. Having nibbled a lump, he would turn to the butter. There he was shooed off by our parent. He soon learned to treat her shooing with indifference. Still, she hated him to put his nose in the food. And he loved to do it. And one day between them they over-turned the cream-jug. Adolf deluged his little chest, bounced back in terror, was seized by his little ears by my mother and bounced down on the hearth-rug. There he shivered in momentary discomfort, and suddenly set off in a wild flight to the parlour.

This was his happy hunting ground. He had cultivated the bad habit of pensively nibbling certain bits of cloth in the hearth-rug. When chased from this pasture he would retreat under the sofa. There he would twinkle in Buddhist meditation until suddenly, no one knew why, he would go off like an alarm clock. With a sudden bumping scuffle he would whirl out of the room, going through the doorway with his little ears flying. Then we would hear his thunderbolt hurtling in the parlour, but before we could follow, the wild streak of Adolf would flash past us, on an electric wind that swept him round the scullery and carried him back, a little mad thing, flying possessed like a ball round the parlour. After which ebullition he would sit in a corner composed and distant, twitching his whiskers in abstract meditation.

Suddenly he put a tiny, brown rabbit amidst the teacups

And it was in vain we questioned him about his outburst. He just went off like a gun, and was as calm after it as a gun that smokes placidly.

Alas, he grew up rapidly. It was almost impossible to keep him from the outer door.

One day, as we were playing by the stile, I saw his brown shadow loiter across the road and pass into the field that faced the houses. Instantly a cry of 'Adolf!'—a cry he knew full well. And instantly a wind swept him away down the sloping meadow, his tail twinkling and zigzagging through the grass. After him we pelted. It was a strange sight to see him, ears back, his little loins so powerful, flinging the world behind him. We ran ourselves out of breath, but could not catch him. Then somebody headed him off, and he sat with sudden unconcern, twitching his nose under a bunch of nettles.

His wanderings cost him a shock. One Sunday morning my father had just been quarrelling with a pedlar, and we were hearing the aftermath indoors, when there came a sudden unearthly scream from the yard. We flew out. There sat Adolf cowering under a bench, while a great black and white cat glowered intently at him, a few yards away. Sight not to be forgotten. Adolf rolling back his eyes and parting his strange muzzle in another scream, the cat stretching forward in a slow elongation.

Ha, how we hated that cat! How we pursued him over the chapel wall and across the neighbours' gardens.

Adolf was still only half grown.

'Cats!' said my mother. 'Hideous detestable animals, why do people harbour them?'

But Adolf was becoming too much for her. He dropped too many pills. And suddenly to hear him clumping downstairs when she was alone in the house was startling. And to keep him from the door was impossible. Cats prowled outside. It was worse than having a child to look after.

Yet we would not have him shut up. He became more lusty, more callous than ever. He was a strong kicker, and many a scratch on face and arms did we owe to him. But he brought his own doom on himself. The lace curtains in the parlour—my mother was rather proud of them—fell on the floor very full. One of Adolf's joys was to scuffle wildly through them as though through some foamy undergrowth. He had already torn rents in them.

One day he entangled himself altogether. He kicked, he whirled round in a mad nebulous inferno. He screamed—and brought down the curtain-rod with a smash, right on the best beloved pelargonium, just as my mother rushed in. She extricated him, but she never forgave him. And he never forgave either. A heartless wildness had come over him.

Even we understood that he must go. It was decided, after a long deliberation, that my father should carry him back to the wild-woods. Once again he was stowed into the great pocket of the pit-jacket.

'Best pop him i' th' pot,' said my father, who enjoyed raising the wind of indignation.

And so, next day, our father said that Adolf, set down on the edge of the coppice, had hopped away with utmost indifference, neither elated nor moved. We heard it and believed. But many, many were the heartsearchings. How would the other rabbits receive him? Would they smell his tameness, his humanized degradation, and rend him? My mother pooh-poohed the extravagant idea.

However, he was gone, and we were rather relieved. My father kept an eye open for him. He declared that several times passing the coppice in the early morning, he had seen Adolf peeping through the nettle-stalks. He had called him, in an odd-voiced, cajoling fashion. But Adolf had not responded. Wildness gains so soon upon its creatures. And they become so contemptuous then of our tame presence. So it seemed to me. I myself would go to the edge of the coppice, and call softly. I myself would imagine bright eyes between the nettle-stalks, flash of a white, scornful tail past the bracken. That insolent white tail, as Adolf turned his flank on us!

THE ELEPHANT HUNT

Stuart Cloete

In a hunt there are two sides, as in a war, two points of view—that of the hunter and that of the hunted. That of the victor and that of the victim. But sometimes these two sides can merge as the battle joins, the hunter being hunted, and the hunted becoming the hunter. This can only happen under certain circumstances with great beasts. The elephant, the buffalo, the whale; or if the beast is a carnivore, a lion or a leopard. Normally, the odds are weighted in the favour of the hunter and they only change when he has struck—till then he moves in safety.

But when a beast has been hunted as the great elephant they called the lame one, and his brother, had been hunted, and when they have reached an age that is incomprehensible to man, and when they find, on their trail, and following it, on several occasions over a period of years, the same smell, that of a white man, the scent finally gets registered in the convolutions of their ancient brains, and produces a peculiar effect—an effect of show-down, of furious resentment against the monotony of a peaceful old age being broken into, pierced by the irritation of interference. So, when the elephants found the man there, on their spoor again, remorselessly attached to them by his will, the intermediate bond between them being his traces in the bush and their footmarks, their dung, the fallen branches they had torn down, the twigs they had chewed, they planned to make an end. The elephants as much as the man. All now were planning, not as they had been before on other occasions, one to follow and the other to escape, but all to kill.

The elephants stood in a vast, dead island of quazine. Waterless, lifeless except for themselves, who though still alive were without the qualities of full life. Who were like rocks endowed with wisdom, and subject to habit. It is impossible to believe that, as the trackers said, they were waiting for an end, that their minds functioned as men's minds might, as a criminal's might. Yet they had laid ambushes before, had tempted hunters to their deaths before.

They were still uneasy. The fire had not quite died out of their old eyes. They stood swaying on their forelegs, swinging the vast bulk of their bodies from side to side. They were uneasy still with the smell of blood. Its memory had not yet faded from their minds, and, despite their washings and tramplings and mud-wallows, they still had vestigial traces of it in the interstices of the crinkled hides of their legs, in the crevices that surrounded the horn of their toe-nails. They had eaten. They had filled their tanks with water. They had left an unmistakable trail. They had come not too far, but just far enough from the avengers whom they knew would follow them. Not so far that the hunters would think they had got clear and give up, but far enough for the hunt to be stretched to its limit. Everything about them was taut, tightened to the snapping point. The nerves of both the elephants and the hunters. The bow of action was bent, the arrow fitted to the string. The scene of the drama, its next act, all set, latent behind the curtain of silence. The forest seemed to await the final scene. The silence and the heat were unbearable, palpable. Each instant of it poised, each waiting to be shattered by the explosion of a heavy shell, or the screaming trumpet of a charging elephant. But nothing broke it. The elephants waited and the men progressed.

Maniero led with the trackers. Carew followed in a litter. Behind his litter came others—those of his old hunters, carried by their grandsons. It could have been a funeral cortege proceeding through the forest, but the old men who were carried were not dead, only near to death. Behind them again, like mourners, came the carriers, their burdens consisting almost entirely of water in cans and bottles. The food they had with them was simple; biltong, the dried, jerked beef of Africa, boer tusks, which are dehydrated chunks of bread, and mealie meal, divided into small sacks for easy porterage. Maniero had said they need not carry water as they would find pans for the first day at least, and fill up there since there had been rain. He knew this forest, he knew it at least up to the quazine. There he had never hunted. Nothing lived there. But Carew said, 'We will carry water.' And Carew was right because when they reached the pans with the usual fever trees, they found them fouled by the elephants beyond use. They had tramped all over them, leaving their enormous football sign both in the water and on the banks. They had wallowed in it, they had rubbed their backs against the larger trees. Higher than a man could reach with a rifle in his outstretched arm, there was still mud on the bark, dry on the outside, but moist underneath, baked like dough.

'Well you were right,' Maniero said.

'I was right,' Carew said, 'because I know elephants. Because I am older than you. If you had lived to my age, you would have known too. They are aware of us, Maniero. They did not have to do this. They drank their fill and then spoilt the water.'

The native hunters knew it too. This was the way these elephants trapped men. It was one of their tricks, a strategy of war, and were they not inhabited by the spirits of the great ones, the Zulu kings long dead, but masters of the arts of war and massacre?

Carew calmed them. 'My children,' he said, 'this was, as you say, a stratagem. But we have water. My wisdom was greater than theirs.'

The next day they came to the edge of the quazine.

'They are here,' the trackers said. 'They are near.'

They found fresh sign, still cool on the outside, but warm within and moist from the heat of the elephants' bowels. There was the stink of elephants disturbed. It was as if fear and anger liberated foul juices into their excrement. Then they heard the elephants. There was a crash of a tree breaking.

'They've gone,' Maniero said.

'Yes,' Carew said, 'but such elephants do not make a noise when they go. Why would they make a noise except to lead us on?'

'I must follow,' Maniero said. 'What else is there to do?'

'We can wait,' Carew said. 'This is a trick. These elephants'—that there were two was now beyond all doubt since they had been at no pains to disguise their spoor—'are angry. They are at war and will come back.'

'I have never heard of such a thing,' Maniero said.

'Nor have I,' Carew answered, 'but this is no place to think of what we know, or have heard. These are not ordinary elephants.'

'I will follow,' Maniero said.

'Then follow. I shall remain here till the water is nearly done. Make camp,' he said to the boys, 'and good luck, Maniero. But be careful and do not go too far!'

'I will be careful,' Maniero said, laughing. Careful, in this situation, was a word that could not apply. All he could count on was his experience, his senses, and the extra sense that all great hunters have. The ability to feel danger before the danger is critical.

The elephants, when they had heard the hunters coming, had moved on, carelessly crashing their way through the small trees, moving through them as a boy would move through a field of wheat. They moved upwind, so did not know whether they were being followed. They marched all day, hardly pausing to eat, only snatching at branches as they passed.

Time pressed upon both hunter and hunted with an urgency that neither understood. The man forced himself forward. The elephants drove themselves on into the dry lands, digging in, as it is called, moving so fast that a little heap of dust was left in the spoor of their forefeet by the swift running pressure of the hind, as it kicked up the sand. They ran, but not in fear. They were not running to escape. They were not even going into the country where their spoor would be lost on the hard outcrops of flat rock, where there was no water, and where on other occasions, they had suffered the tortures of thirst when pressed, but had waited till the hunt died down before leaving the sanctuary of the desert.

On the contrary, this time, they led their pursuers from water hole to water hole. But they were bad, nearly dried up. And since the man followed them, he took their leavings of water. Water mixed with the mud squeezed up by their great feet, and their urine and defecations. They were forcing the man on, making him follow, but poisoning him and exhausting him. Perhaps they did not know this. It is hard to believe that elephants, as Carew had said, would knowingly foul the water for their pursuers, as men have done in wars, by throwing bodies into the wells. It is more probable that they drank what they could, and then stood cooling themselves, spraying the muddy water over their backs with their trunks. Perhaps lying in the pan for a bath, cooling their tired feet in the ooze, and since they stood there, the natural functions of their body took place in the water which the white hunter, who pursued them, must perforce use. This is what seems more likely, but to Maniero, the elephants had become the devil, were all evil, were deliberately soiling everything and passing on. All that he had heard of these elephants came back to him exaggerated by his explanation. One elephant, two elephants, two in one. Elephants inhabited by spirits. A man could not live as he had done in the forest among natives and have his unconscious mind remain completely immune to their superstitions.

Each drove the other, for the faster the man pursued, the faster the elephants had to go to evade them. On they went, the beasts and the man from pan to pan, from water hole to water hole. But this time Maniero was prepared. He carried only biltong and water. They, he and Joaquim, his tracker, could live on that for days. Biltong and a reserve of water in four canteens, that they had not touched yet, a blanket each and the 10.75 and ammunition. That was all.

★   ★   ★   ★

At last the elephants marched into an area of bush and sandveld, where, no matter how much rain fell, none stayed, every drop being drunk in by the ever thirsty ground. That night they fed, there was some succulent growth here, though there was no water, and then, as if they had consulted each other, they swung north, and then east towards the sea, and then south again, moving fast till they came on to their own spoor once more, and that of the hunter superimposed upon it. Spoor that stank to them, that brought the heat of their ancient blood back, pumping through their great arteries and veins, reddening their eyes with anger. The stink of the white man, the enemy, the aphrodisiac of war.

When the elephants reached the sandveld, Maniero turned back. What a fool he'd been to come so far. It was hopeless to follow elephants when they knew they were pursued and started digging in. Once they began moving in a straight line, only a fool would follow them. Yet he had gone on like a man possessed. Possessed, that was the word, some madness had got into him which cancelled out all previous experience and forced him on. He was tired, but not exhausted—and he still had water. For, despite what the elephants had done to the water, he had drunk it, filtering it through his handkerchief. The taste of elephant and buffalo urine was in his mouth, but his precious water was safe, it would get him back. It would get him back to Carew. Carew would know what to do. There was something here he could not fathom. Perhaps it was the age of his adversaries which only the age of Carew could parallel. Magic was out of the question. His sanity was returning.

★　　★　　★　　★

While Maniero was away, Carew waited. It was not unpleasant to wait, here in the bush and the silence. This was what he had wanted. The last hunt, he thought. Well, Maniero was doing the hunting. He had boasted in vain about leading. He was too old. He sent boys back for more water. They returned with it and food as well—sour, curdled milk, cassavas, monkey nuts, and other things. Some of the porters made traps and set snares and got fresh meat. He would not allow a shot to be fired.

The old men sat with him and they gossiped about the great days of the past. At night a hyena walked round their camp for several hours. He enjoyed hearing its moaning cry that was something between the low of a cow and the scream of a woman. There was more life at night. Once he heard a lion in the distance, an owl hooted from a nearby tree. There were doves, so there must be a little water left somewhere nearby. The time passed very pleasantly for him. It was much nicer here than in town. He was in his element among the people he understood, the old-fashioned Kaffirs who had not been spoilt by learning the worst of the white man's ways, and forgetting the best of their own. They told tales, remembered old legends, smoked and spat as old men do, and the sun that was so hot for the young only served to warm their blood.

And all the time as he waited, he watched and listened. In this stillness, the sound of a shot from a 10.75 would carry a long way. In his heart, he was sure the shot would come from nearby. Sure that the elephants would return. He did not know why, only that if he had been an old elephant, it was what he would have done. It was what he himself had done. Come back to the beginning to make an end. It seemed nearer to him that way, somehow. Those elephants must be about ready to die, he thought. Perhaps they, like himself, wanted one more hunt, wanted to kill one more white man before they went off to die. There was no great elephant graveyard. That was just a story. But elephants did tend to return to the privacy of the swamps where they were born, and die there. Men did that too. It was not sentiment alone that took men back to the scenes of their youth when they felt the end was near. A thousand things called to them. Diet, food, the food that they had been weaned on, and memory, for as the present faded, the past grew stronger, grew irresistible, so that sixty years ago was nearer than yesterday. So that Esther was nearer than Maniero. And all the time he listened and watched, for the hunter in him was never at rest.

★   ★   ★   ★

When the elephants came to their spoor and Maniero's, they did not cross it. They stood back from the track and fingered it with their trunk tips, savouring their anger, building it up. Then moving parallel to the spoor, they went into a thick patch of bush that overhung the trail. Here the tuskless elephant waited at right angles to the track while the lame one stepped into it, leaving a clear spoor. Fifty yards farther down, he too, went into the forest and stood beside the path. They were now in position.

Maniero was tired, but he still hunted. His eyes were everywhere. On the spoor, and in the forest on each side of it. Every few minutes he halted to watch and listen. He might see a tickbird, he might hear the rumble of a giant stomach. He might hear the flap of an ear, or the gentle crack of a branch. He did not miss the spoor of the lame one when he came on to it. So he had come back and was ahead of him again. Carew had been right. He had said they would come back. Maniero stopped. Unseen by him, the trunk of the tuskless elephant was directly over his head. The elephant waited. Perhaps he wanted to take Maniero from behind, to chase him. At any rate, he waited, and Maniero went on with his tracker behind him. The wind was in his favour. He tested it, picking up a little dry dust in the path and letting it run from between his fingers. How near was the lame one? He was not travelling fast now.

Then he saw him. At least he saw a dark patch in the bush that might be an elephant, if it was not an anthill. He moved nearer; at thirty yards he was certain. He saw the elephant's head. He saw the brown tusks, like great, curved limbs of a tree. The head became clearer. Clear enough for a brain shot above the eye. He raised his rifle. In his mind he was thinking how dark the tusks of some of these bulls were, and then, just as he squeezed the trigger, the elephant moved his lower jaw. The bullet crashed into the skull where the brain was protected by vast honeycombs of protective bone. His failure surprised him so much that he was slow in reloading. He was tired too. He was ready, but the wounded elephant was on him, charging. There was still time for a frontal-brain shot. Through the roof of the mouth. He got it. The elephant staggered and fell, landing on his knees, his body supported by the great prong of his tusks. As he reloaded again, the tuskless elephant, who had come up from behind him, struck. For an instant, as he died, he wondered how he had forgotten that there were two elephants. How had a lifetime of experience, a lifetime of hunting, slipped from him?

The tuskless elephant struck only once with the great hawser of his trunk, then he stepped on Maniero's body, popping it like a grape. Then he seized Joaquim by the waist and threw him against the trunk of a tree. The body bounced away from it as a rag doll might, and lay sprawling at its roots. He went back to Maniero. Setting a foot upon his belly, he put his trunk about his waist and pulled him in two. Pulled him as a child pulls a Christmas cracker.

The elephant then went to his fallen brother. He pushed at him with raised trunk, trying with tuskless gums, to raise him. He caressed him and blew on him. Then he gave vent to his fury in wild blasts of

He raised his rifle and aimed at the menacing bull.

his trumpet. He went back to Maniero and mashed him, trampling him, kneeling on him, throwing the empty sacks of his remains this way and that. Holding them with his hind legs while he stretched them with his trunk. He went to the gun bearer and did the same. Then he went back to his brother as if to tell him that he was avenged, as if to apologize for his own mistake in not killing Maniero sooner. He trumpeted again and went off to water, to the muddy pan the hunters had left behind them when they made their forward camp.

*   *   *   *

When Carew heard the shots—they were not more than three miles away—he got up. So Maniero had made contact with the enemy. Two shots—he might have got them both! He picked up his six hundred, slipped some spare shells into his pocket, and walked up the path. Matissa, Lunda, and Siloko, assegais in hand, followed him. Like frail leaves, three brown and one white, they drifted down on the wind of destiny.

But none had lost his skill. Old as they were, they moved fast and silently, almost invisible in their old khaki, and their nakedness. Of the forest, a part of it, as much as the elephants themselves. Then, suddenly, Carew stopped, raised his rifle and fired. The two shots rang out, like shots from a cannon, shattering the shimmering stillness of the afternoon. There was an elephant's scream and a crash as the tuskless one fell, breaking off the small trees like twigs beneath him.

'Maniero!' Carew shouted, 'Maniero!' as he reloaded. There was no answer, there was only a silence that seemed more profound since he had shattered it. 'Wait there,' he said. 'I am going on.'

'Where the Lord goes, we go,' they said, 'for a shadow cannot be separated from its principal.'

They went on till their path was blocked by the great bulk of the fallen, tuskless elephant. They went round him and to make certain, Carew gave him a shot into the root of the tail. It was like shooting into an ant-hill. 'He's dead,' he said. Then he shouted, 'Maniero! Maniero!' There was no answer. Carew went on followed by the trackers. They moved cautiously. Nothing stirred and then they came on to the tusked elephant broadside on. He had fallen on his knees

and was propped up in a position of prayer. He was dead all right—
no doubt about that! Carew shouted. The only answer was a vulture
that flew with heavy wings from a tree. How quickly they came.
'Maniero!' Carew shouted again, 'Maniero!' Maniero was dead. He
must be. They spread out and went round the elephant. There they
found part of Maniero. The rest they found farther away among
the smashed and uprooted trees. A battle ground. At the foot of a big
marula, they found most of the remains of Joaquim.

'I will remain here,' Carew said. 'Bring the men and the gear,
Matissa. Send back for more men. Your spooks are dead and the
great hunter, on whom my mantle was to have fallen, has preceded
me into the land of death. Moselekatse and T'Chaka are no more.
Maniero is no more.'

'Aai,' Lunda said, 'he is dead. Very dead.'

Carew took off his sweaty hat. 'While you go,' he said, 'we will
collect what is left and make a fire. Go fast, old one. There is much
to do.' He sat on the ground and stared at the vast bulk before him, at
the great tusks that were like the bowsprits of a schooner. So the
elephants were dead. Both of them. . . . Their long marches were over.
They were at rest. And Maniero's little farm remained a dead man's
dream.

The body had been torn in two. The head, arms, and torso in one
part, and the legs still joined together on the crushed pelvis in the
other. Carew covered them with branches. The boys would bring
blankets and gear. He would camp beside the body.

When the boys came, he put Maniero's remains in a blanket, salted
them, and folded the blanket over the body, making it into a kind of
parcel which he lashed with riems. That was the best he could do now.
As night fell, the boys chopped out the tusks by the light of an immense
fire.

In the roof of the tusked elephant's mouth, they found the blade of
an assegai. It had not been there long. It must have been flung by the
dead boy, Mashupa. In the left thigh, they cut out the great four-ounce
bullet that Pretorius had fired into him all those years ago.

But even before the tusks were out, crowds of natives had drifted in,
like ghosts, from every track in the wilderness. The news of meat
had been told. The news that the giants that had haunted the forest

were dead had gone with it. Here was sacred meat, mouti, on an unprecedented scale. To eat this meat was to drink the very blood of T'Chaka.

They came marching through the night with flaming torches. They surrounded the recumbent giants. They built great fires. They disappeared into the vast caverns from which the viscera had been withdrawn, and reappeared, plastered with blood and mucus, into the firelight. They climbed the bodies. Their assegais and knives carved great strips of meat from it. Platters of hide were flayed and piled with meat so that the skin, which had once covered the meat of the elephants, was now covered by the meat.

The smell of roasting meat, mixed with the stink of offal, of sweating Negro bodies, of wood smoke and the excrement of the despoilers, filled the air. Like ants, men and women poured into the arena, paused to stare, to butcher, to feast, and finally to leave in a long string, chanting as they marched. The women, laden with their spoils, the blood dripping from the meat on their heads, dripping on to their shoulders, running down between their naked breasts. The men, bloodied from their butchery, assegais in hand, marched with them. At their heels followed the prick-eared dogs still thin, but for once bloated. The devil-god elephants were dead. The old hunter, Carew, whom they had called 'the killer', was back among them. A story that they had heard since childhood come to life—materialized in their midst. There would be songs made of this!

MAXWELL'S OTTER

Gavin Maxwell

After the death of his dog, Johnnie, Gavin Maxwell decided that he would never own a dog again. However, the lonely autumn and winter days at Camusféarna, his West Highland sea-board home, made him crave for some animal life about the house. On a journey to Southern Iraq in 1956 he was given an unusual breed of otter, which he called Mijbil—Mij for short. He brought Mij back to London with him. . . .

I lived at that time in a studio flat near to Olympia, one large room with a sleeping gallery that opened on to the garage roof, and penthouse premises at the back containing kitchen, bathroom and box-room, each of diminutive size and resembling a divided corridor. Despite the absence of a garden, these unconventional premises held certain advantages for an otter, for the garage roof eliminated the normal difficulties of keeping a house-trained animal in a London flat, and the box-room opening from the bathroom provided quarters in which at any time he might be left for short periods with all his essential requirements. But just how short those periods would be—a maximum of four or five hours—had never struck me until Mij had already become the centre point round which, eccentrically, revolved my life. Otters that have been reared by human beings demand human company, much affection, and constant co-operative play; without these things they quickly become unhappy, and for the most part they are tiresome in direct ratio to their discontent. They can be trying, too, out of sheer inquisitiveness and exuberance of spirits, but not in the seemingly calculated way that is born of deprivation.

The spacious tile-floored bedroom of the Consulate-General at Basra, with its minimum of inessential furniture or bric-à-brac, had done little to prepare me for the problems that my crowded and vulnerable studio would present in relation to Mijbil. Exhausted as he was that first night, he had not been out of his box for five minutes before he set out with terrifying enthusiasm to explore his new quarters. I had gone to the kitchen to find fish for him, expected by prearrangement with my charlady, but I had hardly got there before I heard the first crash of breaking china in the room behind me. The fish and the bath solved the problem temporarily, for when he had eaten he went wild with joy in the water and romped ecstatically for a full half hour, but it was clear that the flat would require considerable alteration if it was to remain a home for both of us. Meanwhile sleep seemed long overdue, and I saw only one solution; I laid a sleeping bag on the sofa, and anchored Mij to the sofa-leg by his lead.

I have never been able fully to make up my mind whether certain aspects of otter behaviour merely chance to resemble that of human beings, or whether, in the case of animals as young as Mij was, there is actual mimicry of the human foster parent. Mij, anyway, seemed to regard me closely as I composed myself on my back with a cushion under my head; then, with a confiding air of knowing exactly what to do, he clambered up beside me and worked his body down into the sleeping-bag until he lay flat on his back inside it with his head on the cushion beside mine and his fore-paws in the air. In this position, such an attitude as a child devises for its teddy-bear in bed, Mij heaved an enormous sigh and was instantly asleep.

There is, in fact, much about otters that encourages humans to a facile anthropomorphizing. A dry otter at play is an animal that might have been specifically designed to please a child; they look like 'invented' animals, and are really much more like Giovannetti's 'Max' than anything else, a comparison that has instantly struck many people upon seeing my otters for the the first time—the same short legs, the same tubby, furry torso, vast whiskers, and clownish good humour. In the water they take on quite a different aspect and personality, supple as an eel, fast as lightning, and graceful as a ballet dancer, but very few people have watched them for long below the surface, and I have yet to see a zoo that gives its otters a glass-sided tank—a spectacle that I believe would steal the show from the whole aquarium.

★　　　★　　　★　　　★

Mij and I remained in London for nearly a month, while, as my landlord put it, the studio came to look like a cross between a monkey-house and a furniture repository. The garage roof was fenced in, and a wire gate fitted to the gallery stairs, so that he could occasionally be excluded from the studio itself; the upstairs telephone was enclosed in a box (whose fastening he early learned to undo); my dressing-table was cut off from him by a wire flap hinging from the ceiling, and the electric light wires were enclosed in tunnels of hardboard that gave the place the appearance of a power-house.

All these precautions were entirely necessary, for if Mij thought that he had been excluded for too long, more especially from visitors whose acquaintance he wished to make, he would set about laying waste with extraordinary invention. No amount of fore-thought that I could muster was ever able to forestall his genius; there was always something that I had overlooked, something that could be made to speak with a crash for his mood of frustration, and it did not take me long to learn that prophylaxis was more convenient than treatment.

There was nothing haphazard about the demonstrations he planned; into them went all the patience and ingenuity of his remarkable brain and all the agility of his muscular little body. One evening, for example, after the contractors had departed for the third of fourth time, leaving, as I thought, an otter-proof situation at last, I had confined Mij to the gallery for an hour in deference to the wishes of a female visitor who feared for her nylons. He appeared, after a few moments, balancing adroitly on the top of the gallery railing, paying no attention either to us or to the formidable drop below him, for his plan was evidently already mature. At various points along the length of this railing were suspended certain decorative objects, a

Cretan shepherd's bag, a dagger, and other things whose identity now eludes me. Purposefully, and with an air of enormous self-satisfaction, Mij began to chew through the cords from which these *objets d'art* or *de voyage* hung. After each severance he would pause to watch his victim crash to the parquet floor below, then he would carefully renew his precarious, straddling progress along the rail until he reached the next. We stood, my visitor and I, waiting to catch the more fragile items as they fell, and I remember that when the last fruit, as it were, had fallen from the bough she turned to me with a sigh and said, 'Don't you ever feel that this just simply can't go on?'

More usually, however, when he was loose in the studio, he would play for hours at a time with what soon became an established selection of toys, ping-pong balls, marbles, india-rubber fruit, and a terrapin shell that I brought back from his native marshes. The smaller among these objects he became adept at throwing right across the room with a flick of his head, and with a ping-pong ball he invented a game of his own which would keep him engrossed for up to half an hour at a time. An expanding suitcase that I had taken to Iraq had become damaged on the journey home, so that the lid, when closed, remained at a slope from one end to the other. Mij discovered that if he placed the ball on the high end it would run down the length of the suitcase unaided. He would dash round to the other end to ambush its arrival, hide from it, crouching, to spring up and take it by surprise as it reached the drop to the floor, grab it and trot off with it to the high end once more.

These games were adequate for perhaps half of all the time he spent indoors and awake, but several times a day he needed, as much psychologically as physically, I think, a prolonged romp with a human playmate. Tunnelling under the carpet and affecting to believe himself thus rendered invisible, he would shoot out with a squeak of triumph if a foot passed within range; or he would dive inside the loose cover of the sofa and play tigers from behind it; or he would simply lay seige to one's person as a puppy does, bouncing around one in a frenzy of excited chirps and squeaks and launching a series of tip-and-run raids. It was the 'tip' that was the trouble, for his teeth were like needles, and however gently he might try to use them, such games used, I am bound to say, to end with a certain amount of visible proof of his success in tactics left on the human hand. It did not hurt, but it made a bad impression upon visitors, many of whom were ready in any case to accord him the distrust appropriate to an alien upstart.

But I soon found an infallible way to distract his attention if he became too excitable, a way whose success was, I think, due to the refusal to be baffled by obstacles that is an otter characteristic. I would take the terrapin shell, wrap it in a towel, and knot the loose ends tightly across. He came to know these preparations, and would wait absolutely motionless until I handed him the bundle; then he would straddle it with his forearms, sink his teeth in the knots, and begin to hump and shuffle round the room in a deceptively aimless-seeming manner. Deceptive, because no matter how complex the knots he would have them all undone in five or ten minutes. At the end of this performance he liked, and seemed to expect, applause, and he would then bring the towel and the terrapin shell to be tied up again. He brought the towel first, dragging it, and then made a second trip for the terrapin, shuffling it in front of him down the room like a football.

At night he slept in my bed, still, at this time, on his back with his head on the pillow, and in the morning he shared my bath. With utter indifference to temperature he would plunge ahead of me into water still too hot for me to enter, and while I shaved he would swim round me playing with the soapsuds or with various celluloid and rubber ducks and ships that had begun to accumulate in my bathroom as they do in a child's.

Outside the house I exercised him on a lead, precisely as if he had been a dog, and, like a dog, he soon showed preference for certain streets and certain corners at which dogs of all sorts and sizes had left stimulating messages; messages that were, perhaps the more fascinating for being, as it were, in a foreign language. Whether or not he could decipher their purport, whether or not they conjured up for him the various erotic, impudent or pugnacious images intended, he would spend minutes at a time sniffing these clearing-houses of local canine information, and would occasionally add to them some liquid comment of his own, tantalisingly cryptic, no doubt, to the next comer.

I was too timid of the result to allow him to meet any dog so to speak nose to nose, and I would pick him up if we met unattended dogs in the street, but for his part he seemed largely indifferent to them. The only time that I was conscious of some mutual recognition taking place, some awareness of similarity between canine and lutrine values, was one morning when, setting out for his walk, he refused to be parted from a new toy, a large rubber ball painted in gaudy segments. This ball was too big for his mouth, so that he could only carry it sticking out from one side of his jaws like a gigantic gum boil, and thus encumbered he set off briskly up the street, tugging at his lead. Rounding the first corner we came face to face with a very fat spaniel, unattended and sedately carrying in its mouth a bundle of newspapers. The respective loads of otter and dog made it difficult for either of them to turn its head far as they came abreast, but their eyes rolled sideways with what appeared to me a wild surmise, and when they were a few paces past each other both suddenly stopped dead for a moment, as though arrested by some momentary mental revelation.

Mij quickly developed certain compulsive habits on these walks in the London streets, akin, clearly, to the rituals of children who on their way to and from school must place their feet squarely on the centre of each paving block; must touch every seventh upright of the iron railings, or pass to the outside of every second lamp post. Opposite to my flat was a single-storied primary school, along whose frontage ran a low wall some two feet high separating a corridor-width strip of garden from the road. On his way home, but never on his way out, Mij would tug me in the direction of this wall, jump up on it, and gallop the full length of its thirty yards, to the hopeless distraction both of pupils and of staff within. There was more than one street of which he would use one pavement only, refusing with dug-in toes to be led to the other side, and there were certain drain grilles through which he would peer motionless for long seconds before he could be led away from them. On return to the flat he would scrabble frantically to be let in, and the moment his lead was unhitched he would roll on his back and squirm with eye-bewildering speed and vigour before returning to his toys.

Many of his actions, indeed, appeared ritual, and I think that

Mij shared my bath, playing with the rubber toys while I shaved.

comparatively few people who keep wild creatures realize the enormous security-value of routine in the maintenance of an animal's contentment. As soon as routine is broken a new element enters, in however minute and unrecognizable a trace—the fear of the unknown which is basic to the behaviour of all animals, including man. Every living creature exists by a routine of some kind; the small rituals of that routine are the landmarks, the boundaries of security, the reassuring walls that exclude a *horror vacui*; thus, in our own species, after some tempest of the spirit in which the landmarks seem to have been swept away, a man will reach out tentatively in mental darkness to feel the walls, to assure himself that they still stand where they tood—a necessary gesture, for the walls are of his own building, without universal reality, and what man makes he may destroy. To an animal these landmarks are of even greater importance, for once removed from its natural surroundings, its ecological norm, comparatively little of what the senses perceive can be comprehended in function or potentiality, and the true conditions for insecurity are already established. As among human beings, animal insecurity may manifest itself as aggression or timidity, ill-temper or ill-health, or as excessive affection for a parental figure; unfortunately this last aspect encourages many to cultivate insecurity in their charges, child or animal, as a means to an end.

★ ★ ★ ★

It was about this time that Mij delivered his first serious, intentional bite. He was fed now upon live eels—which I had learned to be the staple food of many races of otter—supplemented by a mixture of raw egg and unpolished rice, a sticky concoction for which he evinced a gusto no doubt influenced by his early life among the Arabs. The eels I kept in a perforated bucket under the kitchen tap, and fed them to him in the bath; it had become an established way of quieting him when he was obstreperous, to shut him in with a full bath of water and three or four eels. On this occasion I had closed the bathroom door imperfectly, and Mij elected to bring his second eel through and eat it in the studio. To this, though he was sodden with water and the eel very slimy, there seemed no alternative, for it is folly to try to take away from a wild animal its natural prey; but when after a few mouthfuls he decided to carry it upstairs to the gallery I determined to call a halt, visualizing a soaking and eel-slimed bed. I put on three pairs of gloves, the outermost being a pair of heavily-padded flying gauntlets. I caught up with him half-way up the stairway; he laid down the eel, put a paw on it, and hummed at me, a high continuous hum that could break out into a wail. Full of euphoric selfconfidence I talked away quietly to him, telling him that he couldn't possibly hurt me and that I was going to take the eel back to the bathroom. The humming became much louder. I bent down and put my heavily-gloved hand upon the eel. He screamed at me, but still he took no action. Then, as I began to lift it, he bit. He bit just once and let go; the canines of his upper and lower jaws passed through the three layers of glove, through the skin, through muscle and bone, and met in the middle of my hand with an audible crunch. He let go almost in the same instant, and rolled on his back squirming with apology. I still held the eel; I carried it back to the bath, where he refused to pay any further attention to it, fussing round me and over me and muzzling me with little squeals of affection and apparent solicitude.

There were two small bones broken in my hand, and for a week it was the size of a boxing glove, very painful, and an acute embarrassment to me in the presence of those who from the first had been sceptical of Mij's domesticity. I had been given a sharp and necessary reminder that though he might carry painted rubber balls through the London streets he was not a spaniel.

It was not lack of curiosity, so much as lack of time and opportunity, that made me delay for nearly three weeks before making any real effort to establish Mij's identity. It would, I thought, require a day's research in the library of the Zoological Society, and at that early stage Mij could not be left alone for more than an hour or so without fretting. But as may be imagined, he caused no small stir in his walks through the streets of West Kensington, and it was increasingly borne in upon me that I could answer only in the most perfunctory and unsatisfactory terms the fire of questions with which our strolls were punctuated.

It is not, I suppose, in any way strange that the average Londoner should not recognize an otter, but the variety of guesses as to what kind of animal this might be came as no less of a surprise to me than the consistent accuracy with which a minority bracketed the bull's-eye without once touching it. Otters belong to a comparatively small group of animals called Mustellines, shared by the badger, mongoose, weasel, stoat, polecat, marten, mink and others; the official at Cairo airport had set an early precedent of outer scoring when he asked whether Mij was an ermine—which is, of course, a stoat in winter coat. Now, in the London streets, I faced a continual barrage of conjectural questions that sprayed all the Mustellines but the otter; wilder, more random fire hit on practically everything from 'a baby seal' to a squirrel. The seal heresy had deep root, and was perhaps the commonest of them all, though far from being the most bizarre; 'Is that a walrus, mister?' reduced me to giggles outside Harrods, and 'a hippo' made my day outside Cruft's Dog Show. A beaver, a bear cub, a newt, a leopard—one, apparently, that had changed his spots— even, with heaven knows what dim recollections of schoolroom science and a bewildering latinized world of sub-human creatures— a 'brontosaur'; Mij was anything but an otter.

But the question for which I awarded the highest score—a question evading with contemptuous dexterity any possible inaccuracy on the part of the speaker; putting the blame, as it were, for the creature's unfamiliarity squarely on my own shoulders; hinting, or doing more than hint, that someone had blundered, that the hand of the potter had shaken; containing, too, an accusation of unfinished work unfit for exhibition—came from a Herculean labourer engaged, mightily and alone, upon digging a hole in the street. I was still far from him when he laid down his pick, put his hands on his hips, and began to stare. As I drew nearer I saw that this state held an outraged quality, one of surprise, certainly, but also of affront, as though he would have me know that he was not one upon whom to play jokes. I came abreast of him; he spat, glared, and then growled out, ''Ere, mister —*what is that supposed to be?*'

It was, I think, his question more than any other that reminded me of my own ignorance; I did not, in fact, know what Mij was supposed to be. I knew, certainly, that he was an otter, but I also knew that he must be one of a species which, if known to the scientific world, was at least not known to live in the delta marshes of the Tigris and Euphrates, for the scant zoological literature that had accompanied me to Iraq made it plain that the only known otter of the Mesopotamian marshes was the Persian sub-species of the common European otter, *Lutra lutra*. Chahala, the cub that had died, had clearly belonged to that race; she had longer fur with 'guard hairs' in place of Mij's sleek, darker velvet; she was lighter on her throat and belly than upon her back, whereas Mij's body seemed to have been slipped into an evenly dyed plush bag; the under side of her tail was not, as was Mij's, flat like a ruler.

In a village of the marshes between the Tigris and the Persian frontier I had bought two otter skins from the householder with whom we had been staying; both were, apart from any possible scientific interest, objects of fascination, for they had been 'case' skinned, the whole carcase having been removed, without a single incision, through the mouth. One of these skins belonged to Chahala's race; the other, contrast heightened by juxtaposition, was plainly of Mij's, a much larger and darker creature, whose fur was short and shiny and the colour of milkless chocolate. These two skins now reposed in my flat, pregnant with possibility and as yet unexamined by competent authority.

I telephoned to the Natural History department of the British Museum, in Cromwell Road, and the same afternoon Mr Robert Hayman arrived at my flat to examine the two skins and the living specimen. There is in the serious zoological world a dead-pan-ness, an unwillingness for committal, that must rival the most cautious of consulting physicians. Hayman was far too competent a zoologist, far too encyclopedic in his knowledge, to have been unaware in those first moments that he was looking at a skin and a living animal from a habitat that made the race quite unfamiliar to him, but he did not betray it. He took such measurements as Mij would permit, examined him closely, peered at his formidable array of teeth, and left bearing the two skins for comparison with museum series.

But in due course, after the slow, precise, painstaking processes of the taxonomic world, Mij's new race was proclaimed. Hayman summoned me to the museum to see the cabinets of otter skins from all over the Asia, where the larger of mine lay, unlabelled and conspicuously differing from any other, in a drawer by itself, but in apposition to its nearest relatives. These, various sub-species of *Lutrogale*, a short-coated otter with a flat under side to the tail, ranged over most of Eastern Asia; according to their geographical race they were of a variety of hues from pale sandy to medium brown, but none had been recorded west of Sind, in India, and none resembled my specimens in colour.

There are very few people, and even fewer amateur zoologists, who stumble upon a sizeable mammal previously unknown to science; in the nursery world of picture-books of birds and beasts the few who had given their own names to species—Steller's Eider and Sea Eagle, Sharpe's Crow, Humboldt's Woolly Monkey, Meinerzthagen's Forest Hog, Ross's Snow Goose, Grant's Gazelle, Père David's Deer —had been surrounded for me with an aura of romance; they were the creators, partaking a little of the deity, who had contributed to the great panorama of bright living creatures in which, unshadowed and uncomplicated by knowledge, my childish fancy wandered. Now, when Hayman suggested that the new otter should bear my name, I experienced a sharp, brief conflict; I felt that it should bear his, for he, not I, had done the work; but something small and shrill from the nursery days was shouting inside me that I could be translated into the hierarchy of my early gods and wear, however perilously, the halo of a creator. ('Can I have it for my own?') we used to ask when we were small. 'For my *very* own?' Here, surely, was an animal of my very own, to bear my name; every animal that looked like it would always bear my name for ever and ever, unless some odious taxonomist of the future, some leveller, some jealous, dusty scribe of the backroom and the skeletons, were to plot against me and plan the destruction of my tiny, living memorial.)

So Mij and all his race became *Lutrogale perspicillata maxwelli,* and though he is now no more, and there is no ostensible proof that there is another living specimen in the world, I had realized a far-off childish fantasy, and there was a Maxwell's otter.

THE LITTLE MILITARY LEARNED HORSE

Joan Selby-Lowndes

On a bright June day in the year 1765, Mr Philip Astley came riding into London on a white horse to start the new adventure of civilian life. The blue regimentals of the sergeant major were packed away in the bundle strapped to the back of his saddle; in his pocket he carried the certificate of six years loyal service with the dragoons, and the record of his gallantry in battle; hidden inside his coat was a small leather bag that held all his savings; and the horse he was riding was a personal gift from his officer, Sir William Erskine. These were all his worldly goods, and they did not amount to much, but he had youth, ambition and determination. As he trotted past the last milestone at Hyde Park Corner his courage was high.

His plan was to hire a field just outside London, give displays of horsemanship, and start collecting his fortune at once. With this in mind, he made straight for Islington. It was several years since he had last been there, and he found changes at the Three Hats, the former tea garden where Mr Johnson had entertained the public with displays of trick-riding. Johnson had retired with a fortune, and in his place Mr Price now galloped round the arena.

'Things aren't so easy nowadays,' Mr Price told him in the stable yard afterwards as he rubbed down his sweating horses. 'There's too many people in the game.'

Astley found out what he meant when he came across Price's rival, a man called Sampson, who gave displays in a nearby field. Sampson was an old soldier from Lord Ancram's Light Dragoons, and the two men were soon on friendly terms.

'What the public want is novelty,' he told Astley as he stood on his head on the saddle and galloped his horse round a training track. Sampson was a man of ideas. His tricks were new and he was planning to startle the world by introducing his wife as the first female equestrian.

Nearby at Pentonville, Astley discovered yet another competitor in the field. At the Belvedere Tea Gardens Zucker's Little Learned Horse was a great attraction. This was a different style of show, for Zucker's horse had been trained to perform on its own. It lay down and got up to a word of command; carried a handkerchief in its mouth; answered questions by nodding and shaking its head, and even counted by striking the ground with a foreleg.

Astley realized that if he wanted to draw the public he would have to do better than his rivals. With typical energy and thoroughness he set to work, cultivating the friendship of Price and Sampson. He spent many hours in their company, discussing methods of training, watching them at work, and studying their tricks.

With all these important matters filling his mind he was astonished when he suddenly found himself falling in love. Perhaps it was the sight of Mrs Sampson leaping on and off her husband's horses that first gave his thoughts a romantic push in the direction of a young woman he had recently met who was also a skilled horsewoman. For Astley, though, her chief attraction was her hair; a thick pale gold mass piled on her head.

Before the year was out they were married, and on his wedding night Astley discovered that his young bride's hair was even more dramatic than he had dreamed. Unbound it swept the floor. Never had anything so remarkable been seen before. Proudly he boasted of it to everyone he met.

The young couple found rooms and settled near Islington. Astley took work breaking and training horses for a dealer; at the same time he steadily pursued his plan to prepare a display of horsemanship that would combine the best tricks of Sampson and Price with those of

Zucker's Learned Horse. Astley went to the hiding place where he kept his small store of savings, and, telling his wife he was going to buy a horse, set off for Smithfield.

The big horsemarket was thronged with animals of all shapes and sizes. Astley pushed his way through the crowds keeping a tight hand on the money in his pocket and a sharp eye on the livestock offered for sale. He knew exactly what he was looking for.

He found it when he came across a small brown horse called Billy. There was nothing remarkable about him; he was neither handsome nor showy, but he had an engaging air of liveliness that caught Astley's attention. He stared thoughtfully at the sturdy, cheeky young animal, and Billy stared back with bold bright eyes. That decided the matter. Astley approached the owner and the bargaining began.

'That's a genuine horse you've got there,' the dealer told Astley as he finally pocketed his money, wondering whether he ought to have held out for a higher price.

'I shall find that out for myself, soon enough.' Astley walked away leading his new purchase on the end of a rope; he was wondering how much he had been cheated. Neither of them could know that for £5 he had just bought the horse that was to lay the foundation of his fortune and make the name of Astley famous in circus history.

Mrs Astley was not at all impressed when she saw the new arrival in the stable yard. She thought £5 was a lot of money to give for such a small uninteresting-looking animal, and said so. Her husband informed her loftily that outward appearance was of no importance. The only things he looked for were courage and good temper.

'This 'ere animal,' he pointed out to her, 'has eyes bright and resolute, and impudent, that will look at a hobject with a kind of disdain.'

His estimate of Billy's character was perfectly correct. The bold, good-tempered young horse was quick to learn what was wanted of him. Astley soon had him obedient to voice, whip and rein, and started him on dressage and high school work. At the same time he began teaching him some of the tricks he had seen Zucker's horse perform. To his delight he found that Billy was a born actor. He soon learned to lie down and stay on the ground until commanded to rise; and it was not long before he would pick things up in his mouth and carry them about. Astley taught him also to undo his own girths and take off his saddle.

Billy became a great favourite; and whenever Astley went into the stables there would always be an apple or some titbit in his pocket for his bright young pupil.

★　　★　　★　　★

The brassy notes of a trumpet shrilled through the air.

'Walk up! Walk up ladies and gentlemen, and see the amazing exhibition of activity on horseback!'

Passers-by, startled by the stentorian voice, stopped to stare at the splendid figure stationed at the foot of Westminster Bridge. Astley, dressed in full regimentals, sat on his showy white charger distributing handbills.

'That there is the riding school,' he announced, waving his drawn sword at the entire south bank of the river. The people moved on clutching his handbills, and those who could read learned that Mr Astley, late Sergeant Major in His Majesty's Royal Regiment of Light Dragoons, would perform: 'near twenty different attitudes on one, two and three horses, every evening during the summer, Sundays excepted, at his Riding School on Halfpenny Hatch. Doors to be opened at 4, he will mount at 5.'

The grandly styled Riding School was, in fact, a derelict field in the Lambeth Marshes which Astley had hired for the summer. He had chosen this unfashionable corner of the London scene, across the river, because here he was free of rivals. On the other hand, there were no pleasure grounds or tea gardens to bring in the public! Astley himself was to be the sole attraction. He certainly aroused a great deal of curiosity as he paraded each morning at the foot of Westminster Bridge to announce his how. At the end of the week even his powerful voice was feeling the strain, and he was quite hoarse by the time he returned to the field, where his wife was hard at work dragging out the long wooden benches, assisted by a boy who had been engaged to do odd jobs and beat the drum.

'This way, ladies and gentlemen,' Astley bawled, 'one shilling for a seat, sixpence to stand.'

The shillings and sixpences grew heavy in his pocket, and the buzz of voices swelled as the benches filled and the standing people crowded onto the grass behind the roped-off riding arena.

While the crowd waited, they were entertained by the sight of a small boy carrying a large drum, scrambling up to the roof of an old pigeon house in the centre that was to do duty as a bandstand. The rest of the spectators were preparing to see the show free. Astley caught sight of a bunch of grimy inquisitive faces pressed against the cracks in the palings, and directed a blistering fire of sergeant major abuse at them. The faces promptly vanished, only to reappear further along, the moment his back was turned; but Astley had no more time for sentry duty, the show must begin. In the stables, his wife was leading out the first horse.

The boy on the pigeon house began a frenzied beating on his drum as Astley mounted, rode into the ring, and bowed. His powerful voice echoed round the field as he announced his first tricks. There was another roll on the drum, and Astley put his horse at a gallop and stood up on the saddle. The simplest feats came first: he balanced on one leg, then jumped round to face the horse's tail. Working up to a more spectacular display he stood on his head on the saddle. The crowd were silent now, awed by this extraordinary sight, and when they saw him, still upside down, draw a pistol, women covered their ears while the men leaned forward, open-mouthed, waiting for him to break his neck. Astley pressed the trigger. There was a roar and a spurt of flame, but the horse did not falter, and Astley was up on his feet again on the saddle, the smoking pistol still in his hand, acknowledging the applause.

He collected a second horse, and there was a murmur of wonder as the crowd watched him ride them at a gallop round the arena with a foot on each saddle. When he finally put them at a bar, and they sailed over it, jumping neck and neck with their rider standing upright on their backs, enthusiastic applause rang out.

The sweat was running down Astley's face as he slid to the ground, and handed his wife the reins of the two lathered horses. It was now the turn of Little Billy, and he had high hopes of this part of the show.

'Ladies and Gentlemen,' he boomed. 'I now beg leave to introduce for your entertainment the Little Military Learned Horse.' He paused while the crowd gaped at Billy, who stood quietly at his master's side. 'This horse will, in a manner most extraordinary, appear dead.'

At a signal from his master, Billy obligingly lay down, and Astley embarked on a poem that he himself had composed for the occasion. It had needed much head-scratching and pen-chewing to produce these rhymes, for he found it easier to teach Billy to lie down than to write about it.

'My horse lies dead, apparent at your sight.

But I'm the man can set the thing to right,' Astley the poet bawled at the top of his voice, while Billy, obeying the prod of a boot, rolled over on his side and went quite limp.

'Speak when you please, I'm ready to obey,

My faithful horse knows what I want to say.

But first, pray give me leave to move his foot.'

Astley picked up a relaxed foreleg and let it drop in a most realistic manner.

The crowd were deeply impressed.

'That he is dead is quite beyond dispute.

This shows how brutes by heaven were designed

To be in full subjection to mankind.'

Billy lay without moving, and by this time the crowd were almost convinced that he *was* dead. Handkerchiefs began to appear. Astley stood letting the effect sink in until they could bear the suspense no longer and called out to have him brought back to life. He bowed.

'Rise young Bill, and be a little handy

To serve that warlike hero General Granby.'

He was conscious that this was not one of his best rhymes, but it did not matter, for everyone's attention was now fixed on the horse. Little Billy raised his head, looked about him, and then heaved himself up onto his legs. The crowd, vastly relieved, broke into loud applause.

'When you have seen all my Bill's expresst,'

Astley shouted into the uproar,

'My wife, to conclude, performs the rest.'

Billy went through his repertoire of tricks, and finally Mrs Astley made her dramatic appearance standing on the backs of two horses. With her long golden hair floating out behind her, and her long skirts flying around her ankles, she looked like some windborne sprite. In

The astonished crowd saw the Learned Horse count to six with his hoof.

one frail feminine hand, however, she clutched a loaded pistol, which she boldly fired into the air as she galloped past the shilling places.

This was the climax and finish of the show. The boy with the drum slithered down from the pigeon house; the crowd broke up and began to drift out of the field. Astley and his wife sat in the saddle room counting the takings. A satisfying pile of coins lay on the table between them.

'And this is only the beginning.' Astley was already seeing his fortune made. 'As time goes on, it will get better.'

★   ★   ★   ★

As the news of Astley's skill and activities spread, he began to see the first results of all his efforts. People came to Halfpenny Hatch in ever-increasing numbers. At the height of the season he was taking as much as forty guineas a day at the entrance. His faith in his own abilities had been justified.

The first season of the new riding school in the Westminster Bridge Road opened with a bang. This was Mrs Astley beating the drum. Escorted by two men blowing shrill tunes on pipes, she paraded up and down the road followed by Astley and the white charger, complete with trumpet, sword and handbills.

'Walk up! walk up! One shilling for a seat, sixpence standing,' his old cry made itself heard through the clamour of the band. 'Children and servants threepence!'

The combined noise of drum, pipes and the sergeant major's voice attracted a large crowd, who paid their money and went in. This year he was giving them a bigger and better performance. Mrs Astley and Little Billy had learned new tricks. There were other improvements also: Astley had done away with the odd-job boy and the drum, and engaged proper musicians. Even now those two harassed gentlemen, who had been bursting their lungs up and down the road all the morning, were scrambling onto the wooden platform in the middle of the arena, to be a two-man band.

The pattern of the performance was much the same as before. Astley gave his display of 'attitudes' on the saddle, and made his horses leap a bar. After this Little Billy came into the arena to perform the

'Sham Death of Little Military Learned Horse', by now firmly established as a favourite. Then Mrs Astley made her entrance. She went through her tricks with all her old skill and vigour, while their son John, born a few months earlier, slept on peacefully unaware that his mother was risking her neck on the backs of two galloping horses.

'We have only these 'ere two horses to ride,' Astley's booming voice announced. 'So we shall ride together until Mrs Astley chooses to alight at full speed with elegance and ease.' He vaulted up behind her.

'And this time, don't push me,' she hissed over her shoulder at him as they stood together on the saddles, smiling to the crowd, while the white charger and his stable companion cantered placidly round the ride.

'Now! Jump!' Astley nudged her as they circled towards the shilling seats for the second time.

'Mind your own business.' She stamped on his foot, nearly overbalanced, and then deliberately waited until they were passing the sixpenny places.

Striking a graceful attitude, which was the signal for a roll on the drum, she gritted her teeth and jumped to the ground. The well-trained horses carried Astley out of the arena while she picked up her skirts and acknowledged the applause with a graceful curtsey and a modest smile. The reckoning would come later. Astley scowled furiously at her as she tripped jauntily past him, while he led Little Billy into the arena for his second appearance.

He had spent many patient hours teaching his horse new tricks. Little Billy could now nod and shake his head to order. Obeying a private system of signals he followed Astley round the arena sorting out ladies from gentlemen to the giggling delight of the crowd.

Astley then announced that his Learned Horse would tell the time; and the astonished crowd saw Billy strike six o'clock on the ground with his hoof while Astley's loud running commentary drowned the small click of thumb and finger nail which was the signal for each stroke. After this, he proceeded to go lame and hobbled about on three legs.

'My horse is sick,' Astley shouted, and gave Billy the signal to shake his head. 'He has a pain in his head,' he explained, and went on, in a burst of rhyme, to tell Billy that, although he was sick, he must go and fight for the Spaniards. But Billy, who had been taught to be a loyal British horse, promptly grew worse. He lay down and died, and remained dead until the last lines of the poem, when Astley told him he must go and fight for England with General Eliott's Dragoons. This at once brought Billy to life again. He got onto his feet, and, obeying another click, fired off a pistol with his hoof to the cheering delight of the crowd.

Little Billy's clever tricks were a great attraction. The fame of the Little Military Learned Horse spread, and people from all over London began flocking to the Westminster Bridge Road to see him.

In Pentonville, Zucker's Little Learned Horse might gnash his teeth in rage, for whatever he did the Little Learned Military Horse in Lambeth went one better. When the Learned Horse carried a loaded tea tray about, the Military Learned Horse picked a kettle of boiling water from the fire, in his mouth, to make the tea which he then served on a tray.

Astley was also quick to see the possibilities in other types of entertainment. For some time he had had his eye on another place of amusement in Islington that seemed to have discovered the secret of permanent popularity.

For nearly a hundred years Sadler's Wells had been attracting people. They had come first in the reign of King Charles to drink the waters of its famous wells; later to drink tea and listen to music. Now the place had been turned into a theatre, and people went there to be entertained by clowns, singers, tumblers and acrobats. This gave Astley the idea of adding other attractions to his own show.

Mrs Astley's voice became shrill when she discovered that he was also planning to spend all their profits on improvements to the showground.

'You have a child to support, so how can you risk all our hard-earned money on this place,' she said angrily. At that moment she hated the place, and looked with disgust at the trail of disorder; the jumbled benches, the trampled grass strewn with orange-peel and litter.

'It is getting late, let us go to bed.' Astley took his wife's arm. But she had not finished yet.

'What improvements are you planning?' she persisted.

'Covered seats for everyone,' his hand circled the whole arena. 'A proper entrance, stabling, and a gallery for the nobility.' He was determined to attract society to his establishment. 'With proper shelter we can give the performance even if there is a shower of rain.'

'So the people can sit and watch us getting soaked to the skin, risking our necks on slippery saddles! You would do better to spend the money putting the shelter over our heads,' she added sarcastically.

Astley did not reply. He looked up at the clear sky over the open field, and perhaps it was his wife's angry words that first gave him the vision of the day when he would build a roof to span the whole of his riding school, turning it into one great amphitheatre: Astley's Amphitheatre!

★　　　★　　　★　　　★

Over the next twenty years, despite keen competition from his rivals, Astley went from strength to strength. In 1779 he opened Astley's Amphitheatre Riding-House, the first modern circus building in the world. He took his show on tour in Europe, and in 1785 opened the first circus in Paris, the *Amphitheatre Anglaise*. In 1786 the London amphitheatre was completely refurbished, and renamed The Royal Grove, and the pattern of the next few years was set. Winters in Paris, summers in England, with John managing the Royal Grove, and Philip travelling and building. He even crossed the Irish Channel to establish Astley's Amphitheatre in Dublin.

In the end he left a trail of seventeen Amphitheatres strung across the provinces. These, with the establishments in London and Paris, made a grand total of nineteen amphitheatres built with the money, brains and energy of one man. It earned him the nickname of Amphi-Philip. No one, however, dared to use it to his face, for Astley would not tolerate such lack of respect. His success had made him very grand.

★　　　★　　　★　　　★

The French Revolution of 1789 forced him to give up the Paris building, and then, in 1793, a series of events took place that shocked and outraged the whole of England. On 21 January, King Louis XVI was guillotined in Paris. A month later the aggressive new Republic of France, announcing that it would carry its revolutionary ideas into other countries, invaded Belgium and declared war on Holland and England.

The English, who had at first cheered and approved of the French people's gallant struggle for freedom, were furious and resentful. The Duke of York immediately set about raising an army. In London the streets began to echo to the drums of the recruiting sergeants and to the tramp marching feet. These stirring military sounds reached Astley's ears and made him fret like an old war horse, and when he saw the proud uniforms and regimental colours parading through the city he could bear it no longer. He shook off his fifty years, and hurried away to offer his services to his King and country.

There were many things to arrange before he left. A soldier going on a campaign might be away a long time. He decided to give his son a seven-year lease on the amphitheatre.

In the middle of the activity Abraham Saunders arrived one day to see Astley and beg a special favour. Astley had known Saunders for many years. He had run a prosperous place of entertainment in Whitechapel. Then a run of bad luck had hit him. First a fire had completely destroyed his theatre, and then all his horses and his company had been drowned in the Irish Channel. Saunders had been struggling to build up his fortunes ever since, and Astley felt sorry for him. He was ready to help with money, but that was not what Saunders wanted. He was asking to borrow the Little Military Learned Horse.

'With that little horse of yours I can draw in the public,' Saunders pleaded. 'It'll turn the tide in my favour again.'

Astley was deeply distressed. He offered Saunders the choice of any other horse in his stable, but it seemed that Little Billy with his famous reputation was the only one who would do.

'You shall have him back safe and sound within a week,' Saunders promised. So, reluctantly, Astley allowed Little Billy to be taken out of his stall and led away.

'I don't like it, Johnny.' He shook his head unhappily. 'I don't like it at all.' Staring at the empty stall he could not shake off his feeling of uneasiness.

A week passed with no further news of Billy. Astley, arriving home at the end of the day, handed over his horse to an ostler and strode into the stables where John was in conference with Mr Smith, their chief rough rider.

'Is he back?' This was Astley's regular question the moment he got in.

'No, Father,' John replied. This had become a regular answer, but this time there was a difference. Astley frowned, aware suddenly of a strange tense silence that was spreading through the place like a chill wind.

'What's the matter?' he challenged. 'You have had news of my horse? Come now, out with it,'

'I'm afraid, Father, that Billy has been lost.' John paused, waiting for an outburst of violence. Instead he saw his father stagger, and reach out to grip a stall post.

'What do you mean?' The loud voice was strangely subdued.

'It appears that Saunders was heavily in debt,' John told him. 'Only three days after you saw him he was seized by his creditors and thrown into prison. They held a sale of all his possessions, including the horses. Billy was sold along with the rest.'

Astley turned abruptly, and without saying a word walked out of the stables.

'The old man's taken it hard,' Smith shook his head.

'I've never seen him like that before,' said John in a quiet voice. They were both silent, wondering if it had been their imagination, or a trick of the candlelight, or had they really seen old Astley's eyes fill with tears.

*   *   *   *

It was a warm sunlit afternoon in September. Two of Astley's equestrian performers were strolling through a cobbled street in the East End of London on their way back to the Amphitheatre for the evening performance. A church clock struck.

'That's the half-hour, Tom.' One of the men quickened his pace.

'It's too warm to hurry,' the other yawned. At that moment he would gladly have exchanged his strenuous life in the riding arena for the placid existence of the old men he saw sitting in their doorways puffing at long clay pipes. Even this dingy East End street looked pleasant enough with that sunlight slanting down between the huddled houses; shining on the cobbles where the sparrows pecked; warming the back of an old brown horse dozing in the shafts of a rickety cart. Tom gave the horse a casual glance, and then suddenly he stopped, and stood staring.

'What's the matter with you?' The other pulled impatiently at his arm.

'I say, Jack, I'm a Dutchman if that ain't our Billy.'

'Impossible,' said Jack. It was three years since Billy had been given up as lost, and he had almost forgotten what the little horse looked like.

'I tell you it is.' Tom shook himself free and strode across the street. There was something about this sad-looking brown horse in its shabby harness that convinced him it was indeed their Billy.

'It is his size and colour,' Jack admitted as he had a closer look. 'But how can we be certain?'

'I'll try him.' Tom knew the signals Astley used for some of Billy's tricks. He began to click the nails of his thumb and forefinger. In the quiet street the sound carried clearly. The horse suddenly jerked up his head. They saw him prick his ears, and then, as though obeying some half-forgotten instinct, he arched his neck and began to caper.

'It is him! It's our Billy!' Both men rushed forward, and the next moment the horse was rubbing his head against them.

'He remembers us.' Tom had his arms round Billy's neck.

'Think of the old man's face when we tell him,' said Jack.

'When he sees him, you mean.' Tom plunged his hands in his pockets to discover how much money he had about him. 'We must find his owner without delay.'

It was not difficult. They found Billy's owner in the nearest pub sitting behind a large tankard of ale. He was astonished when he learned that these two prosperous-looking men were interested in buying his old horse, but he was always ready to make a bargain, and so a price was agreed upon and the money paid. The three of them then went out together.

'He's a monstrous good-tempered creature,' the man told them as he took off Billy's harness, 'but he's got such odd antics we call him the Mountebank.' He slipped a rope halter over Billy's head. 'There you are gentlemen.' He handed over their bargain, and the two men led him triumphantly away.

Astley was changing into his best boots ready for the evening performance when Mrs Connell, the housekeeper, tapped on the door.

'There's two men downstairs to see you, sir.'

'I haven't time to see anyone,' Astley growled. 'What do they want?'

'It's a very important matter, sir,' she insisted. 'I think you should go.'

Astley didn't see the twinkle in her eyes. Grumbling and grunting he pulled on his boots and stumped away.

'You'll find them outside in the road,' she called over the banisters.

'Eh? Why don't they come in?'

Mrs Connell did not reply. She was hurrying to the landing window to watch the scene. Astley thumped into the hall. The front door stood wide open. Through it he caught sight of two of his performers standing in the road. He scowled. Someone was playing a joke.

'What does this mean?' He strode out of the house ready to blast the smiles off the men's faces. 'What are you . . .' he broke off staring, for they had led forward a small brown horse.

'We've found him,' they said simply.

'Billy!' At the sound of that well known voice calling his name the horse pricked up his ears and whickered. The next moment Astley was beside him and Billy was rubbing his head against his master and nuzzling at his pocket as though he had never been away. Astley's hand shook as he fondled his old favourite, and this time there was no mistaking the tears in his eyes. He listened to the men tell how they had found him, then swiftly he ran his hand over the horse's legs and body to reassure himself that Billy was fit and well.

'Wherever he has been these past three years they've taken good care of him,' was Astley's verdict, and pulling out a handkerchief he blew his nose loudly. He was deeply moved. All his fortunes were bound up with the life of this little horse. Billy had been lost, and fire had destroyed his theatre. Now the new Royal Amphitheatre had opened, and Billy had miraculously returned to ensure its success.

'Never again does this 'ere horse go out of my stables,' Astley declared, and he himself led Billy to the stall that was to be his home for the rest of his life.

'I shall have to see if he's forgotten his tricks,' Astley said. Billy hadn't. Twenty years' training had stamped itself indelibly on his memory. He responded at once to all his master's signals. The very next evening Astley announced that by special request, the Little Military Learned Horse would appear, and into the lighted arena trotted the small brown horse that two days before had been hauling a cart through the east end streets of London. The public had not forgotten their old favourite. Billy went through his tricks with all his usual lively assurance, and Astley, watching him take off his saddle, wash his feet in a pail of water, lift a boiling kettle in his mouth and play the waiter, felt a surge of pride and a deep reassurance. Billy was back, and from now on good fortune would go with them.

THE HUNTING OF THE WHITE WHALE

Herman Melville

Moby Dick, Herman Melville's extraordinary, rich and poetic novel of the sea, tells the story of Captain Ahab's obsession with the great white whale who was responsible for the loss of his leg. Through the South Seas the Pequod *and her crew search for Moby Dick. Captain Ahab nails to the ship's mast a gold doubloon, which will be given to the man who first spies the white whale. At last Moby Dick is sighted by the Captain himself, and a chase begins.*

That night, in the mid-watch, when the old man—as his wont at intervals—stepped forth from the scuttle in which he leaned, and went to his pivot-hole, he suddenly thrust out his face fiercely, snuffing up the sea air as a sagacious ship's dog will, in drawing nigh to some barbarous isle. He declared that a whale must be near. Soon that peculiar odour, sometimes to a great distance given forth by the living Sperm Whale, was palpable to all the watch nor was any mariner surprised when, after inspecting the compass, and then the dog-vane, and then ascertaining the precise bearing of the odour as nearly as possible, Ahab rapidly ordered the ship's course to be slightly altered, and the sail to be shortened.

The acute policy dictating these movements was sufficiently vindicated at daybreak by the sight of a long sleek on the sea directly and lengthwise ahead, smooth as oil, and resembling in the pleated watery wrinkles bordering it, the polished metallic-like marks of some swift tide-rip, at the mouth of a deep, rapid stream.

'Man the mastheads! Call all hands!'

Thundering with the butts of three clubbed handspikes on the forecastle deck, Daggoo, the negro harpooner, roused the sleepers with such judgment claps that they seemed to exhale from the scuttle, so instantaneously did they appear with their clothes in their hands.

'What d'ye see?' cried Ahab, flattening his face to the sky.

'Nothing, nothing, sir!' was the sound hailing down in reply.

'T'gallant-sails! stunsails alow and aloft, and on both sides!'

All sail being set, he now cast loose the life-line, reserved for swaying him to the mainroyal masthead; and in a few moments they were hoisting him thither, when, while but two-thirds of the way aloft, and while peering ahead through the horizontal vacancy between the maintopsail and topgallant-sail, he raised a gull-like cry in the air. 'There she blows!—there she blows! A hump like a snowhill! It is Moby Dick!'

Fired by the cry which seemed simultaneously taken up by the three lookouts, the men on deck rushed to the rigging to behold the famous whale they had so long been pursuing. Ahab had now gained his final perch, some feet above the other lookouts, Tashtego, the Red Indian harpooner, standing just beneath him on the cap of the top-gallant-mast, so that his head was almost on a level with Ahab's heel. From this height the whale was now seen some mile or so ahead, at every roll of the sea revealing his high sparkling hump, and regularly jetting his silent spout into the air. To the credulous mariners it seemed the same silent spout they had so long ago beheld in the moonlit Atlantic and Indian Oceans.

'And did none of ye see it before?' cried Ahab, hailing the perched men all around him.

'I saw him almost that same instant, sir, that Captain Ahab did, and I cried out,' said Tashtego.

'Not the same instant; not the same—no, the doubloon is mine, Fate reserved the doubloon for me. *I* only; none of ye could have raised the White Whale first. There she blows! there she blows!—there she blows! There again!—there again!' he cried, in long-drawn, lingering, methodic tones, attuned to the gradual prolongings of the whale's visible jets. 'He's going to sound! In stunsails! Down top-gallant-sails! Stand by three boats. Mr Starbuck, remember, stay on board, and keep the ship. Helm there! Luff, luff a point! So; steady, man, steady!

There go flukes! No, no; only black water! All ready the boats there? Stand by, stand by! Lower me, Mr Starbuck; lower, lower,—quick, quicker!' and he slid through the air to the deck.

'He is heading straight to leeward, sir,' cried Stubb, the second mate; 'right away from us; cannot have seen the ship yet.'

'Be dumb, man! Stand by the braces! Hard down the helm!—brace up! Shiver her!—shiver her! So; well that! Boats, boats!'

Soon all the boats but Starbuck's were dropped; all the boat-sails set—all the paddles plying; with rippling swiftness, shooting to leeward; and Ahab heading the onset. A pale, death-glimmer lit up the sunken eyes of Fedallah, the Indian; a hideous motion gnawed his mouth.

Like noiseless nautilus shells, their light prows sped through the sea; but only slowly they neared the foe. As they neared him, the ocean grew still more smooth; seemed drawing a carpet over its waves; seemed a noon-meadow, so serenely it spread. At length the breathless hunter came so nigh his seemingly unsuspecting prey, that his entire dazzling hump was distinctly visible, sliding along the sea as if an isolated thing, and continually set in a revolving ring of finest, fleecy, greenish foam. He saw the vast involved wrinkles of the slightly projecting head beyond. Before it, far out on the soft Turkish-rugged waters, went the glistening white shadow from his broad, milky forehead, a musical rippling playfully accompanying the shade; and behind, the blue waters interchangeably flowed over into the moving valley of his steady wake; and on either hand bright bubbles arose and danced by his side. But these were broken again by the light toes of hundreds of gay fowl softly feathering the sea, alternate with their fitful flight; and like to some flagstaff rising from the painted hull of an argosy, the tall but shattered pole of a recent lance projected from the white whale's back; and at intervals one of the cloud of soft-toed fowls hovering, and to and fro skimming like a canopy over the fish, silently perched and rocked on this pole, the long tail feathers streaming like pennons.

A gentle joyousness—a mighty mildness of repose in swiftness, invested the gliding whale. Not the white bull Jupiter swimming away with ravished Europa clinging to his graceful horns; his lovely, leering eyes sideways intent upon the maid; with smooth bewitching fleetness, rippling straight for the nuptial bower in Crete; not Jove did surpass the glorified White Whale as he so divinely swam.

On each soft side—coincident with the parted swell, that but once laving him, then flowed so wide way—on each bright side, the whale shed off enticings. No wonder there had been some among the hunters who namelessly transported and allured by all this serenity, had ventured to assail it; but had fatally found that quietude but the vesture of tornadoes. Yet calm, enticing calm, oh, whale! thou glidest on, to all who for the first time eye thee, no matter how many in that same way thou may'st have bejuggled and destroyed before.

And thus, through the serene tranquillities of the tropical sea, among waves whose hand-clappings were suspended by exceeding rapture, Moby Dick moved on, still withholding from sight the full terrors of his submerged trunk, entirely hiding the wretched hideousness of his jaw. But soon the fore part of him slowly rose from the water; for an instant his whole marbleized body formed a high arch, like Virginia's Natural Bridge, and warningly waving his bannered flukes in the air, the grand god revealed himself, sounded, and went out of sight. Hoveringly halting, and dipping on the wing, the white sea-fowls longingly lingered over the agitated pool that he left.

With oars apeak, and paddles down, the sheets of their sails adrift, the three boats now stilly floated, awaiting Moby Dick's reappearance.

'An hour,' said Ahab, standing rooted in his boat's stern, and he gazed beyond the whale's place, towards the dim blue spaces and wide wooing vacancies to leeward. It was only an instant; for again his eyes seemed whirling round in his head as he swept the watery circle. The breeze now freshened; the sea began to swell.

'The birds!—the birds!' cried Tashtego.

In long Indian file, as when herons take wing, the white birds were now all flying towards Ahab's boat; and when within a few yards began fluttering over the water there, wheeling round and round, with joyous, expectant cries. Their vision was keener than man's; Ahab could discover no sign in the sea. But suddenly as he peered down and down into its depths, he profoundly saw a white living spot no bigger than a white weasel, with wonderful celerity uprising, and magnifying as it rose, till it turned, and then there were plainly revealed two long crooked rows of white, glistening teeth, floating up from the undiscoverable bottom. It was Moby Dick's open mouth and scrolled jaw; his vast, shadowed bulk still half blending with the blue of the sea. The glittering mouth yawned beneath the boat like an open-doored marble tomb; and giving one sidelong sweep with his steering oar, Ahab whirled the craft aside from this tremendous apparition. Then, calling upon Fedellah to change places with him, went forward to the bows, and seizing Perth's harpoon, commanded his crew to grasp their oars and stand by to stern.

Now, by reason of this timely spinning round the boat upon its axis, its bow, by anticipation, was made to face the whale's head while yet under water. But as if perceiving this stratagem, Moby Dick, with that malicious intelligence ascribed to him, sidelingly transplanted himself, as it were, in an instant, shooting his plaited head lengthwise beneath the boat.

Through and through; through every plank and each rib, it thrilled for an instant, the whale obliquely lying on its back, in the manner of a biting shark, slowly and feelingly taking its bows full within his mouth, so that the long, narrow, scrolled lower jaw curled high up into the open air, and one of the teeth caught in a rowlock. The bluish pearl-white of the inside of the jaw was within six inches of Ahab's head, and reached higher than that. In this attitude the White Whale now shook the slight cedar as a mildly cruel cat her mouse. With unastonished eyes Fedallah gazed, and crossed his arms; but the tiger-yellow crew were tumbling over each other's heads to gain the uttermost stern.

And now, while both elastic gunwales were springing in and out, as the whale dallied with the doomed craft in this devilish way; and from his body being submerged beneath the boat, he could not be darted at from the bows, for the bows were almost inside of him, as it were; and while the other boats involuntarily paused, as before a quick crisis impossible to withstand, then it was that monomaniac Ahab, furious with this tantalising vicinity of his foe, which placed him all alive and helpless in the very jaws he hated; frenzied with all this, he seized the long bone with his naked hands, and wildly strove to wrench it from its gripe. As now he thus vainly strove, the jaw slipped from him; the frail gunwales bent in, collapsed, and snapped, as both jaws, like an enormous shears, sliding further aft, bit the craft completely in twain, and locked themselves fast again in the sea, midway between the two floating wrecks. These floated aside, the broken ends drooping, the crew at the stern-wreck clinging to the gunwales, and striving to hold fast to the oars to lash them across.

At that preluding moment, ere the boat was yet snapped, Ahab, the first to perceive the whale's intent, by the crafty upraising of his head, a movement that loosed his hold for the time; at that moment his hand had made one final effort to push the boat out of the bite. But only slipping further into the whale's mouth, and tilting over sideways as it slipped, the boat had shaken off his hold on the jaw; spilled him out of it, as he leaned to the push; and so he fell flat-faced upon the sea.

Ripplingly withdrawing from his prey, Moby Dick now lay at a little distance, vertically thrusting his oblong white head up and down in the billows; and at the same time slowly revolving his whole spindled body; so that when his vast wrinkled forehead rose—some twenty or more feet out of the water—the now rising swells, with all their confluent waves, dazzling broke against it; vindictively tossing their shivered spray still higher into the air. So, in a gale, the but half baffled Channel billows only recoil from the base of the Eddystone, triumphantly to overleap its summit with their scud.

But soon resuming his horizontal attitude, Moby Dick swam swiftly round and round the wrecked crew; sideways churning the water in his vengeful wake, as if lashing himself up to still another more deadly assault. The sight of the splintered boat seemed to madden him, as the blood of grapes and mulberries cast before Antiochus's elephants in the book of Maccabees. Meanwhile Ahab half smothered in the foam of the whale's insolent tail, and too much of a cripple to swim,—though he could still keep afloat, even in the heart of such a whirlpool as that; helpless Ahab's head was seen, like a tossed bubble which the least chance shock might burst. From the boat's fragmentary stern, Fedallah incuriously and mildly eyed him; the clinging crew, at the other drifting end, could not succour him; more than enough was it for them to look to themselves. For so revolvingly appalling was the White Whale's aspect, and so planetarily swift the ever-contracting circles he made, that he seemed horizontally swooping upon them. And though the other boats, unharmed, still hovered hard by, still they dared not

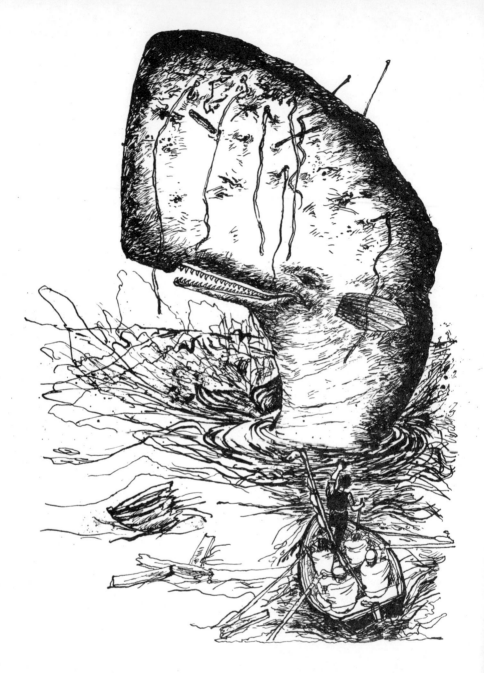

He raised his pale, bleached body and towered menacingly over us.

pull into the eddy to strike, lest that should be the signal for the instant destruction of the jeopardized castaways, Ahab and all; nor in that case could they themselves hope to escape. With straining eyes, then, they remained on the outer edge of the direful zone, whose centre had now become the old man's head.

Meantime, from the beginning all this had been descried from the ship's mastheads; and squaring her yards, she had borne down upon the scene; and was now so nigh, that Ahab in the water hailed her;— 'Sail on the'—but that moment a breaking sea dashed on him from Moby Dick, and whelmed him for the time. But struggling out of it again, and chancing to rise on a towering crest, he shouted,—'Sail on the whale!—Drive him off!'

The *Pequod's* prows were pointed; and breaking up the charmed circle, she effectually parted the White Whale from his victim. As he suddenly swam off, the boats flew to the rescue.

Dragged into Stubb's boat with bloodshot, blinded eyes, the white brine caking in his wrinkles; the long tension of Ahab's bodily strength did crack, and helplessly he yielded to his body's doom: for a time, lying all crushed in the bottom of Stubb's boat, like one trodden under foot of herds of elephants. Far inland, nameless wails came from him, as desolate sounds from out ravines.

But this intensity of his physical prostration did but so much the more abbreviate it. In an instant's compass, great hearts sometimes condense to one deep pang, the sum-total of those shallow pains kindly diffused through feebler men's whole lives. And so, such hearts, though summary in each one suffering; still, if the gods decree it, in their lifetime aggregate a whole age of woe, wholly made up of instantaneous intensities; for even in their pointless centres, those noble natures contain the entire circumferences of inferior souls.

'The harpoon,' said Ahab, half-way rising, and draggingly leaning on one bended arm—'it is safe?'

'Aye, sir, for it was not darted; this is it,' said Stubb, showing it.

'Lay it before me;—any missing men?'

'One, two, three, four, five;—there were five oars, sir and here are five men.'

'That's good.—Help me, man; I wish to stand. So, so, I see him! there! there! going to leeward still; what a leaping spout!—Hands

229

off from me! The eternal sap runs up in Ahab's bones again! Set the sail; out oars; the helm!'

It is often the case that when a boat is stove, its crew, being picked up by another boat, help to work that second boat; and the chase is thus continued with what is called double-banked oars. It was thus now. But the added power of the boat did not equal the added power of the whale, for he seemed to have treble-banked his every fin; swimming with a velocity which plainly showed, that if now, under these circumstances, pushed on, the chase would prove an indefinitely prolonged, if not a hopeless one; nor could any crew endure for so long a period, such an unintermitted, intense straining at the oar; a thing barely tolerable only in some one brief vicissitude. The ship itself, then, as it sometimes happens, offered the most promising intermediate means of overtaking the chase. Accordingly, the boats now made for her, and were soon swayed up to their cranes—the two parts of the wrecked boat having been previously secured by her—and then hoisting everything to her side, and stacking her canvas high up, and sideways outstretching it with stunsails, like the double-jointed wings of an albatross; the *Pequod* bore down on the leeward wake of Moby Dick. At the well-known, methodic intervals, the whale's glittering spout was regularly announced from the manned mastheads; and when he would be reported as just gone down, Ahab would take the time, and then pacing the deck, binnacle-watch in hand, so soon as the last second of the allotted hour expired, his voice was heard.— 'Whose is the doubloon now? D'ye see him?' and if the reply was, 'No, sir!' straightway he commanded them to lift him to his perch. In this way the day wore on; Ahab, now aloft and motionless; anon, unrestingly pacing the planks.

As he was thus walking, uttering no sound, except to hail the men aloft, or to bid them hoist a sail still higher, or to spread one to a still greater breadth—thus to and fro pacing, beneath his slouched hat, at every turn he passed his own wrecked boat, which had been dropped upon the quarter-deck, and lay there reversed; broken bow to shattered stern. At last he paused before it; and as in an already over-clouded sky fresh troops of clouds will sometimes sail across, so over the old man's face there now stole some such added gloom as this.

The day was nearly done; only the hem of his golden robe was rustling. Soon, it was almost dark, but the look-out men still remained unset.

'Can't see the spout now, sir;—too dark'—cried a voice from the air.

'How heading when last seen?'

'As before, sir,—straight to leeward.'

'Good! he will travel slower now 'tis night. Down royals and top-gallant stunsails, Mr Starbuck. We must not run over him before morning; he's making a passage now, and may heave-to a while. Helm there! keep her full before the wind!—Aloft! come down!—Mr Stubb, send a fresh hand to the foremast head, and see it manned till morning.'—Then advancing towards the doubloon in the mainmast— 'Men, this gold is mine, for I earned it; but I shall let it abide here till the White Whale is dead; and then, whosoever of ye first raises him, upon the day he shall be killed, this gold is that man's; and if on that day I shall again raise him, then, ten times its sum shall be divided among all of ye! Away now!—the deck is thine, sir.'

And so saying, he placed himself half-way within the scuttle, and slouching his hat, stood there till dawn, except when at intervals rousing himself to see how the night wore on.

HE FLOATS THROUGH THE AIR

Virginia S. Newlin

There were four of us guys who had saved the money to buy one, but only three of them, almost grown, playing around their mother. I already knew the one I wanted. The littlest. Grey-brown fur, a long fluffy tail, and curly fingers on his hands and feet. He was playing keep-a-way with a raisin, and when Robert said, 'I have a rabbit cage for mine, Sir,' he stopped tossing it and put his head on one side, looking at Robert with eyes like chocolate smartees, as if he were considering what a rabbit cage might be.

'They can't be kept outdoors. They catch cold easily,' said Mr Woolard.

'But flying squirrels live outdoors in Pennsylvania.'

'These have been raised in captivity. They're delicate, Robert.'

Captivity. I hated that word. My little fellow wasn't going to be in captivity—except from Growltiger, my sister's cat. He would live in my room and be my buddy.

'I'm going to put mine in a box,' said Ted.

'A cage is better,' said Wooly. 'They have sharp squirrel teeth.'

'Do they bite, then?' George asked.

'Not these.' Wooly reached into the cage and picked out my squirrel, put him into George's hand.

'He's soft,' George said.

All of us wanted to hold him, and he was passed around. I could see he didn't like it. I wanted to yell at them, take him away before he got frightened. 'He's afraid. Let's put him back,' I said.

'Could we see him fly, first?' asked Robert.

'They don't really fly, they glide,' said Mr Woolard. 'There's a membrane, running from wrist to foot to base of the tail on each side of a flying squirrel's body, that he stretches out into a kind of parachute. He can glide as far as eighty feet.'

Wooly put him up on his shoulder, where he sat, his little hands folded on his chest, looking at first one of us and then another, exactly like our Headmaster. We all laughed, he was so tiny there, no more than six inches long, I thought, and didn't look a bit impressed by us, as if he were the King of the Lilliputians deciding to make pets out of a posse of Gullivers. Then, all of a sudden, he took off. He spread out his arms and legs and the skin between them and flew through the air, landing on my shoulder. Out of all the guys, he picked me. Maybe even then he knew.

He landed on my shoulder, up against my ear, so soft there. I got a queer feeling down my back, but I laughed with the other guys, only quietly, so I wouldn't scare him. He wasn't scared. He jumped from me to Robert and then to Ted and back to me again and then just sat there. All the guys reached for him, asked if they could have him next.

'Please, Sir. He's the one I want if I get to keep one,' I said. 'I have an old aquarium I can use.'

'How big?' asked Wooly.

I held out my arms to show him the size.

'He seems to have chosen you too, Jeff. You'll have to make a lid for the aquarium, out of screening to let in air, and you, Robert will have to move your rabbit cage indoors and be sure that the mesh is fine enough for such a small animal.

'You, George and Ted, will have to get busy and fix a suitable home if you want one of the squirrels. The first three boys ready will get them. If you're all ready, we'll draw lots. You'll have to bring the homes in for me to see and demonstrate that you understand the proper care of a small animal.'

'Do they have to be caged all the time, Mr Woolard?' asked George.

'Not all the time. They love exercise, and, if you're careful, you can let your squirrels play in your room. You may find he's most playful when you're ready for bed, since flying squirrels are nocturnal, but he'll soon adjust to your habits. There's one thing you must remember, though. Flying squirrels are not like dogs and cats that can safely be left alone in the house.'

I won't keep you caged all the time, but you'll be safe with me, I promised him, as Mr Woolard put him back with the others.

As soon as I got home, I went down in the cellar to make a lid for the aquarium. I used to keep fish in it, but, if they were goldfish, they were forever floating belly-up, and if they were guppies and survived our water, they did what guppies do and I ran out of containers for them. At one time, I had the aquarium and three fish bowls full of guppies sitting on my windowsill. It was too much work, so, when spring came, I set up a guppy stand on the road, sold them off as if they were lemonade, and was glad to forget them.

But I wouldn't forget my squirrel, I promised myself, as I measured the aquarium for a lid, sawed four pieces of wood to the right size, nailed them together into a rectangle, and cut screening to fit. Of course, I didn't do it as fast as it sounds. Even though I'm good at carpentry, I made mistakes.

While I nailed the screening to its wooden frame, I thought of names. Squirrel Nutkin. My mother used to read me that book. And there was Sammy Squirrel, but my squirrel needed his own name. I thought of Fluffy Tail and Bright Eyes and Fly Boy, and then I remembered how much he looked like the Headmaster, so I called him Mr Merryweather. That was a good name. When I looked at the Headmaster, it would make me laugh inside, too.

After the lid was finished, I decided I would make him a little house, so he would have some privacy. That took quite a while. I worked after sports every day, made a little wooden house, with a door and a window he could look out of. Mr Woolard said that squirrels can see colours, so I painted it red. It had a roof but no floor. I put wood shavings and grass thickly on the bottom of the aquarium and set his house on top of that so he'd have a comfortable bed. Then I carried the whole business up to the windowsill in my room until it was time. At the end of the week I would find out if I got him or not.

My mother bought a wheel for him so he could exercise, and Wooly gave us each a list of things that flying squirrels like to eat: apples and raisins and nuts, bird seed, particularly sunflower seed, greens like lettuce or celery leaves and bits of carrot. Hamster food was okay too. I'd forgotten a water bottle. I went to the pet shop and bought one that would fit, and then, on the right day, I took the aquarium to school. Mother would pick me and Mr Merryweather up at four o'clock. If I got him.

I did. Mr Woolard loved his home. 'Good work, Jeff,' he said. And Robert and George got the others, because Ted had nothing to keep one in but a cardboard box. I felt sorry about that and so did Wooly; but then, Ted could have tried harder.

When we got home, I put Mr Merryweather up on my windowsill, close to my desk where I could watch him. He went into his house and stuck his head out the window and then out the door. I gave him some raisins, and he carried them inside one by one. I couldn't tell if he ate them or not, he was so quick about it. I did more watching than homework until supper, and, after supper, I brought him down for the family to meet.

'Where's Growltiger?' I asked Susie, my little sister, as I was carrying him down the stairs.

'On my bed,' she said.

'Well, be sure the door's shut tight.'

Everybody loved him. He jumped from my shoulder to Susie's and then to the curtain and then to Dad. Mother said that she felt left out, and then he jumped from Dad to the curtain to Mother to the mantlepiece, hid behind a candlestick and peered at us.

'He's lovely,' Mom said.

And my Dad sang, 'He floats through the air with the greatest of ease, the daring young man on the flying trapeze.'

Dad is funny. He made that Mr Merryweather's theme song, and I only minded it once.

We were still watching Mr Merryweather play peek-a-boo from behind the candlestick, so we didn't see Growltiger sneak into the room. The first thing we knew was when this big black shape hurtled through the air and landed on the mantel beside Mr

235

Merryweather, who leaped to the floor, the cat after him. Flying squirrels don't move very well on the ground, I could see that and so could Growltiger. I guess he thought he had him, but Mr Merryweather took off again, right from under his nose. Around the room they went, from floor to furniture to windowsill, while we all tried to grab Growltiger and Dad said, 'Damn that cat,' and Susie squealed. For some reason, Mr Merryweather wasn't doing his best flying. I thought the cat would get him, sure. They were both so fast that none of us could lay a hand on them.

Growltiger had Mr Merryweather backed into a corner on top of the bookcase, was switching his tail, waiting to pounce, and Dad was climbing up on a chair to grab him when my flying squirrel made his best flight. He soared through the air and landed on my shoulder, putting his little hands on my neck, close to my ear. I thought I heard a very small chattering, as if he was telling me about his escape. I gave Susie what for, and Growltiger was dumped outdoors.

Actually, after they got to know each other, the cat stopped looking at Mr Merryweather as if he were tabby treat. I tried to keep Growltiger out of my room, as you never know, but sometimes he would come in and climb up on the windowsill, sit beside the aquarium and stare at my squirrel. Mr Merryweather would run into his house and peer out the window at Growltiger. First the window and then the door and then the window again, as if it was a game.

I used to tell the other guys about his games. George said that his squirrel didn't play very much, and Robert's had already died, but Mr Merryweather loved games. When I was doing my homework, I would let him out of his aquarium to play around the room, making sure that the door was closed and that Growltiger wasn't hiding under anything. I would put raisins or bits of cookie or chocolate on my desk, and one of my squirrel's games was to steal them from me when I wasn't looking. Long afterwards, I found a pile of raisins in my closet. It made me feel really bad.

Another place he liked to play was the bathroom. I would take him in with me when I took a shower, make sure to close the toilet and open the closet door so he could play in the towels. He would hide under them, and you could see a tiny head peer at you from the yellow washcloths. Peer at you and then disappear and peer at you from

Mr Merryweather soared about the room while Jeff worked at his desk.

the blue bath-towels instead. When I got into the shower, I would sometimes find him clinging to the top of the curtain out of range of the water and jumping from there to the towel bar. One time he missed and slid down into the tub where he skidded all around trying to get out again. I put him up on the towel rack, where he shook himself and wriggled his little nose at me as if to say that squirrels hate baths more than anything.

Sometimes I'd leave him in the bathroom alone, since he liked it so much. He liked to pop out and surprise people from under the towels, and he liked to leap from the closet shelves to the basin to the shower curtain to the windowsill to the toilet seat. I always made sure it was closed, the window and the door too, and that there was no water in the tub. And I never went to bed leaving him there. Except once.

That once, I had a composition to hand in the next day. I hadn't done it when I should have, so I had to work late that night. Mom and Dad went out after saying, 'Do your homework, Jeff,' and Susie watched television and then went to bed.

I let Mr Merryweather out of the aquarium, but he had much too much energy. While I was working, he was playing around the room, and he kept running across the desk, rustling my papers, crawling under them even, and once carrying off my eraser. The composition was hard enough without him. I was making enough mistakes on my own, so I put him in the bathroom to play. Still I kept messing up, having to start over again, and it was very late when I finished. I guess I staggered to the bathroom, staggered back to my room and fell into bed, not remembering my squirrel at all. I was really tired, but that's no excuse.

Mr Merryweather must have been tired too, because when Mom and Dad came home and Mom started her bath, he didn't scramble out of the towels to greet her. She went back to her bedroom, where Dad was already asleep, and didn't know anything about my squirrel until she came in to take her bath and found him drowned in the tub.

I woke up with her shaking me. 'Mr Merryweather, Mr Merryweather. . . .'

'What . . . what. . . .' And then I remembered where he was.

'Drowned . . . in the bathtub. You forgot him.'

I ran into the bathroom, and he was lying on the bath mat, a heap of tiny wet-fur-covered bones. If his mouth had not been so small, I would have tried the mouth to mouth resuscitation that I'd learned in life-saving, but how do you breathe into a mouth as small as your little fingernail? Maybe I should have tried. I should have tried anything, but I just stood there looking at his limp body and saying, 'What happened? What happened?'

'I was running a bath,' Mother said. 'He must have fallen in.'

'Why didn't you save him?'

'I was in my room. . . . Oh, poor little fellow.'

'It's your fault! You didn't watch out for him.'

'I didn't know he was in here. The door wasn't even closed. Oh, Jeff, how could you have left him in the bathroom!'

'You could have thought! Why were you taking a bath so late anyway?' I hated her for it.

'Your poor little pet. Poor Mr Merryweather.' My mother was crying.

I went to my room, carrying him in my hand. He was so little and cold. I took a shirt from my drawer and wrapped him in it, laying him on the roof of his house, thinking, I guess, that if he was warmer and where he liked to be, he might come back to life. Then I got in my bed, trying not to picture how Mr Merryweather must have struggled to climb the sides of the bathtub, and cried into my pillow so my mother wouldn't hear me. But she came into my room and knelt by my bed and put her arm around my shoulders.

'It wasn't your fault, Jeff, or mine or anybody's. It's what happens when wild animals are taken from their habitat and kept as house pets. What you must remember, darling, is that, while Mr Merryweather was living here, you made him happy. That's the most you or anyone could have done.'

Still, I cried myself to sleep.

When Susie found out the next morning, she wouldn't speak to me or go to school. I went, though. I had to hand in that composition, even though I wanted to tear it up. I didn't tell anybody what had happened. I didn't want anybody to know, particularly Mr Woolard, who had congratulated me for being the only guy who had kept his flying squirrel alive.

All during school, I kept hoping that a miracle would have happened, that my little fellow would have come to life again while I was gone, but his body was still where I had left it, wrapped up on the roof of his house. Quite stiff.

I found a box for him and laid his body on some pretty material from Mother's scraps, and I went down in the cellar, got a board and made a marker for his grave. It took me till suppertime to burn in the words with my electric etcher:

'Here lies Mr Merryweather. Loved by all who knew him.'

After supper, we had his funeral. I dug a grave under the crab-apple tree and laid the box in it.

'We must sing a hymn,' Susie said.

'He floats through the air,' Dad suggested, laying his hand on my shoulder.

I was surprised at his bad taste.

'No,' I said. 'Now the Day is Over.'

So we sang, 'Now the day is over; night is falling nigh; shadows of the evening, creep across the sky.'

And Mom said, 'Rest in peace, Mr Merryweather.'

CHIA AND HER KITS

Joyce Stranger

Chia! is the sound a wildcat makes, as vituperative as a swearword; it is the name Fergus, the gamekeeper, gave to the heroine of Joyce Stranger's novel Chia, the Wildcat. *She lives in lonely places; she has no friends and her enemies are many—including Fergus and his dogs, Bran and Tim the Labradors, Jackie the Jack Russell terrier and Rob the sheepdog. After the death of her first three kittens Chia is much more careful with her second litter. . . .*

Chia watched her kittens grow; she noted each achievement; she guarded them as they played, stretching herself on a lichened rock where she could see everything that moved on either side and before her. She made certain that the wind was her watchdog and brought swift news of beasts behind her. The family was not yet old enough to take hunting.

Pride mastered her, and she purred softly to herself as the kits fought and bit, grappling together in feigned anger, sometimes in a tumble of paws and tails, at others two by two. Silver always struggled to overcome his smaller and more agile brother; Jade chased Amber, engaging her in trials of strength that lasted only seconds and ended with the two females pressed together, lying side by side, purring contentedly.

When play was over Chia leaped down beside them and led them into the den, dug deep beneath the tumbled rocks. Here all five curled close and slept through the bright hours of the day. Chia herself lay in a half-doze, aware of the albino stag, who avoided the herd and lived in loneliness among the bilberry bushes and the heather, and often grazed near the rocks; aware of the stoat slipping downhill on some urgent quest of his own; aware of the rustle of the wind in the shrubby undergrowth that masked the entrance to her lair.

She listened, always, for the thud of the man's boots on the ground, and the jingle of the tab on Bran's collar, inaudible to Fergus, but, to the wildcat, presenting a faint but insistent warning. Any unrecognized movement raced her heart and startled her to instant vigilance, which was only relaxed when the sounds were identified. She listened for the urgent yak yak from the birds that haunted the mountain. The threat might be from hunting hawk or prowling fox, or the eagle waiting to fill the maw of his growing youngster that screamed and opened its wide-gaped mouth for food and yet more food. The great bird knew where the wildkits hid. He wheeled in the air, a feathered presage of doom, and below him the creatures that laired on the hill trembled and crept out of sight, each one terrified of the winged death that swept pitilessly out of the sky.

Whenever the kits were playing and the eagle loured, Chia hissed them to safety. They learned to look up, and to fear him, although they did not yet know why. They had never witnessed his arrogant stoop. Always Amber was the last kit home, mesmerized by movement; by the shadows that fled over the ground as the wind tore the cloud shreds; by the entrancing dip and sway of a grass blade, asking to be tapped and caught and eaten; by the dancing wind-blown feathers that she could not resist chasing. Chia hissed, and slapped with an outraged paw, and caught her daughter by the scruff and carried her inside against her will, but still Amber tarried.

When the kits were six weeks old Chia left them, as usual, to go hunting. They taxed all her strength now that they were growing, and she was ravenous. The youngsters were already teasing at the mice and young rabbits that she brought, and she needed larger prey to fill her.

She saw the hare prancing in May-moon madness in the clearing beyond the burn. Twisting and turning, leaping sideways and bounding high, he performed by himself, unaware of passing time that lightened the sky with dawn, or eyes that watched him from the bushes. He was young and not yet wise.

Chia charged to protect her kit from the hungry weasel.

Belly low, crouching, Chia crept towards him, scarcely shivering the grasses. She had crawled beyond the wind and his scent was in her nose. Her scent was blown behind her, and the hare knew nothing of her presence. His final leap brought him to within five feet of her and she sprang. He died in a kick of legs and a sudden panic that was stifled before he had time to recognize the fate that had overtaken him. Chia dragged his body up the hill.

Dawn reddened the sky and sun trails shone in the burn. The kittens, waiting, were playing in the light of day, heedless and unaware. Silver and Fury chased each other's tails and sparred until they were breathless. Fury, suddenly angered beyond bearing, bit his brother's ear, drawing blood. Silver yowled and slashed at the smaller kit's nose. Seconds later the fight was forgotten and each was licking the other's wound.

Jade was watching for the wildcat. Always anxious, she had poised herself on the hillside, half hidden under a rock, so that she could be the first to see her mother return. She was aware of scent from the heather, and from bruised thyme trodden by a hind that had passed that way before the light betrayed her presence. There was a drift of sea-wrack on the air. Then, doom-laden, fright-provoking, death-threatening, came the throat-tightening tang and terrifying slither of weasel. Jade hissed. Her brothers heard her, obeyed the warning and ran to the den, where the three sheltered, ears flat, mouths snarling, small hearts thumping in painful fear.

Amber was playing with a trail of straw that had been blown for miles by the wind. It teased her and mocked her, mousetail straw, rattail straw. It was prey, it was victim, and her tapping paw would bring it death. She pounced as the wind snatched it from her, and grabbed, holding it down with both front paws. She took it in her teeth and, bewilderingly, there were two mousetails both twisting away from her, distracting her, so that she did not know which one to stalk.

She was overwhelmed by the sudden appalling weasel-scent as she darted after the nearest straw-tail. She leaped, twisting swiftly, electrified, as she saw the slender body, the bright wicked eyes and the eager many-toothed mouth that gaped at her in a grin of desire. The lolling tongue was wet. She dropped the straw and fluffed her fur until she was three times normal size, a-snarl with fury that was fed by terror, one clawed paw lifted ready to slash. The banshee squeal of enraged small cat fed the greedy air, and was blown on the whirling wind. Chia heard. She dropped the hare and raced up the hill on paws quickened by fear.

The weasel hesitated. Amber was armed, able to fight and bite although she was so small. The eagle saw them and his own heart thundered his excitement. He speeded his wingbeats and streamed down the sky, the air roaring behind him. Chia streaked towards her kit. Her screech of rage alerted the weasel. He turned his head. Amber fled for the rocks and Chia pounced, but missed the eel-like body that twisted away from her. The eagle was upon them, not having seen her come. The weasel hung from his talons as the huge bird struggled to rise. The unexpected trophy was larger than the wildkit and meant more food for the half-fledged creature that dominated the nest and shrieked when it saw its father riding the slipstream.

Chia drove Amber into the den, and returned to look for the dead hare. It had vanished, found by the vixen, running home, late and starving, to her own cubs. She had taken it, greedy for such unexpected largesse. Chia quartered the ground in vain, puzzled by its absence, then caught the foxscent and knew the search futile. That day the wildcat went hungry, hunting while the sky was light, feeding on tiny mice and a small bird that fluttered unwarily on a bush nearby. She leaped and knocked it out of the air as it flew. It was a meagre mouthful.

The kittens had learned a lesson. Amber, when night brought moonlight to flood the hill, had not yet recovered from fright. The weasel's teeth had been too near; the eagle, rushing through the air, had set her blood pumping fast, and even now, hours later, the fur of her tail was fluffed and when the other kits moved she hissed at them. She would never forget.

When her brothers and sister went out to play she crouched among the rocks, and every sound, and every hoofbeat, sent her further into the safety of darkness, into the quiet familiar lair where she listened and watched and sorted the scents on the wind, now warier even than Fury.

Twice Fury's warning sent the kits to shelter. Once a long-legged fox

245

raced by, intent on his own business; once a running deer, far away but plainly heard, roused their fears. They hid and waited for Chia to come.

Chia was no more merely hungry. She was ravenous. Her empty belly ached. Food was a driving urgency, a raging need, and to suffer longer was a penance she could not endure. Hares and rabbits were scarce on the ground and the hinds guarded the calves too well. There were now several new-born on the hill. There were roebuck kids, but the roe were clever and although she stalked one, a buck kicked her and her ribs were afire with bruises. A scant mile away Fergus kept his ducks and hens and geese. There were pheasant chicks in the pens and red grouse in the bushes.

She ran through tussocky heather and avoided the brambles that snatched at her fur. She found a dozy mouse and paused, and killed, and ate, but it was a pitiful thing, a mouthful that barely assuaged the pangs that ripped her. Saliva drooled on her lips and she licked them hastily.

She scented Fergus's cat Dragon, hunting on his own, revelling in the night. She waited, silent. If she went down the hill now he might attack her. The noise would betray her presence. Dragon had found a young rabbit that had never learned fear. The old cat washed the blood trace from his jaws with a careful paw and loped away. Chia finished the kill, but Dragon had left little. She stalked on, purposeful.

The stone house was silent, but the warm glow of an oil lamp spilled from the windows beside the front door. Tim, always conscious of telltale taint or movement, pricked his ears, uneasy, as the wind, unusually warm, drifted in through the window, redolent with scent. He gave a small half-bark to alert Fergus and Bran caught his excitement, and full of misguided enthusiasm chased to the window and barked joyously, glad of an opportunity to give tongue. Fergus quieted the dog. The Jack Russell listened, head cocked, ears pricked, intent. Rob sat, his eyes watchful.

The man stood by the open window. He heard nothing but the sough in the trees and, far away, the soft swell and suck of the waves on the beach of the loch. An owl whooped downwind. The wildcat was crouched in thick bushes, her eyes wide, watching the house. Chia was as silent as the shadows that sped across the ground, thrown by clouds that played beneath the moon, clouds that were building into rainstorm, and tattered by the wind that flung their streamers across the midnight sky.

There was a faint rustle, and Dragon came from the little garden behind the house, looked expectantly up at Fergus and jumped in through the window.

'It's only Dragon, you soft beasts,' the keeper said, and whistled the dogs upstairs. The dogs followed him, puzzled, knowing that the wildcat lurked in the darkness. They could not make the keeper understand and twice he quieted them, irritated.

The wildcat saw the glow die in the downstairs window. She heard the man's heavy footsteps and the following paws padding on the uncarpeted stone steps. She saw the brief glim that shone in the bedroom and was swiftly dowsed. Her fur was ruffled as the wind filled her nose with the taste of duck and chicken and pheasant and grouse and she could not control the slaver in her mouth. She licked her lips avidly, striving to master excitement that was mounting to a peak.

When darkness reassured her she glided through the shadows, using every scrap of cover. A thin rain began to fall, wetting her coat. She was aware of owlcall in the distance. She found a trace of Dragon on the ground and veered away from it, not wishing to meet him. The pens were at the back of the house. She leaped the garden wall and the smell of the fowl reeked all round her, the air thick and pungent, and saliva dripped from her mouth. She circled the pens. The wire was strong and firmly anchored. There was no way in.

She tried biting, tugging at the unrelenting caging, but the metal defied her teeth. She clawed, but although it moved to her muscular paw it did not give way. Fergus had reinforced all the fencing, until it was as safe as armour plating, and to make doubly sure he had bought a gander from the farm. The old bird heard her. He lifted his head. A moment later the wind betrayed the sound of her and told him that Chia was there, and the din he made startled the other birds to idiot clamour, set Bran and Tim barking, drove Jackie to the window to add his sharper note, and brought Fergus from his bed, half blind with sleep and yawning.

The wildcat did not wait. She knew the man would come and bring his gun. Long before the door was open she was away on the moors, her hunger greater than ever. She ran, bounding lightly, pausing at intervals to smell the wind and to listen. Rain lashed from the sky. Rain washed away the scent on the ground. Rain sent small beasts to shelter, mice into crannies and cracks and holes, rabbits to their burrows, hares to crouch in their forms, watching, ears fanned to detect the smallest sound. They would hear creak and rustle and whisper, no matter how faint.

At the edge of the moor was a young plantation. The conifers, no higher than a red stag's head, grew in formed and serried lines. A well-kept fence kept the deer from spoiling the young shoots. Chia circled the barrier, and then threw up her head. There was a deer crying, nearby. The sorrowing bleats called her on. She ran lightly.

A still-born calf lay on the ground. The hind mourned, unable to believe her loss or to reconcile herself to the fact that her baby was dead. Chia watched, but the wind betrayed her and, maddened by fear and grief, the bereaved hind raced towards her, standing on her hind-legs, intending to smash her forelegs on to the wildcat's back. Chia recognized her intention and fled. The deer returned to her calf and wailed to the heartless sky.

Chia hunted until daybreak, without success. The little creatures were wary. At dawn the hungry wildcat slipped quietly through the trees and crossed the moor. The kits were waiting for her. Jade ran to greet her, to fuss her, to welcome her with uplifted nose and frantic purr and a paw that patted Chia's face, as if the little beast had to make certain her mother was there, was real, had returned and was not the uncertain image of a dream. Amber waited in the shelter of the rocks. The eagle hung in the sky; although he was distant and intent on other prey, she had not forgotten her fright and at times her sleep was marred by the memory of his wings plunging towards her in a roar of sound, and she woke fear-filled and crept closer to her mother, and lay watchful, alert, listening to the daytime sounds that penetrated the lair.

Fury and Silver greeted Chia, fought amicably, and followed her inside. Day threatened their safety. Day showed them to the other creatures that hunted on the hills, Day was a traitor never to be trusted, though at times, when the sun was hot, the cat took the kits and they curled in a densely shrubby hollow, where the heat warmed a patch of soft earth and where, if murder came stalking, she could instantly hide in safety, running as soon as her senses warned of an enemy. The kits had now experienced danger and her quick hiss sent them into sanctuary, where they crouched, motionless, ready to spit defiance, to snarl in rage, to claw in desperate battle. Time passed, aiding her, ensuring that they were stronger, and already their claws were capable of inflicting severe damage.

That night Chia went to the moor, avoiding the manplace. She caught a large rat and four mice. She ate the rat but brought the mice home, one by one, without killing them. She freed them in front of the kittens, and watched as each played with a living trophy. They had never had live prey near them before. They were in a little clearing immediately below the entrance to the den.

Fury stretched his paw and tapped his mouse on the muzzle. It squealed in panic. Fury's eyes were bright, his head inquisitive. He sniffed the mouse, which ran, terrified, away from the reek of cat. The kitten tapped the warm body again. The game palled. He did not associate the living creature with food and let it run. Chia caught it, and brought it back to him and killed it in front of him. Then he recognized the taste and smell of warm blood, and began to lick at the dead body.

The other kittens were alerted by the tang and left their prey, and tried to take his from him. He was instant rage, snarling at them, justifying his name, so that they left him in peace. Chia killed the remaining mice and each kit took one, but Jade left hers and shared companionably with Amber. Chia ate the last, crouched over it, on the lookout rock. Not even while she was feeding did she relax, and as the old Scarface ran down the trail, his telltale aura betraying him, she hissed and the family fled to shelter, each kitten carrying a trophy. Fury had finished eating his mouse and retrieved his rabbit tail, filthy with age and licking, but still well-cherished. Jade carried a feather, leaving the mouse remains to Amber.

Deep beneath the rocks they slept, and Chia guarded them. Each hour of safety was a small triumph; each day gave her a stake for the future; each week brought new strength to her young. This time her kittens might survive. Her own store of wisdom was greater. She had experienced much since her first litter died and, although she was incapable of formulating thought, she had knowledge; she could learn and remember, and teach the kittens to avoid the pitfalls that trapped the unwary.

THE HAPPY FAMILY EXHIBITION

Henry Mayhew

In the nineteenth century Henry Mayhew and two collaborators went around the London streets interviewing thousands of ordinary people and taking down their life stories in their own words. The result of these researches, London Labour and the London Poor, *was first published in 1850s. Among the people interviewed was this street showman, whose 'Happy Family' show consisted of a collection of animals who would not normally get on, living peaceably together in one cage. He describes his exhibition and his life:*

'I have been three years connected with happy families, living by such connection. These exhibitions were first started at Coventry, sixteen years ago, by a man who was my teacher. He was a stocking-weaver, and a fancier of animals and birds, having a good many in his place—hawks, owls, pigeons, starlings, cats, dogs, rats, mice, guinea-pigs, jackdaws, fowls, ravens, and monkeys. He used to keep them separate and for his own amusement, or would train them for sale, teaching the dogs tricks, and such-like. He found his animals agree so well together, that he had a notion—and a snakecharmer, an old Indian, used to advise him on the subject—that he could show in public animals and birds, supposed to be one another's enemies and victims, living in quiet together. He did show them in public, beginning with cats, rats, and pigeons, in one cage; and then kept adding by degrees all the other creatures I have mentioned. His way of training the animals is a secret, which he has taught to me. It's principally done, however, I may tell you, by continued kindness and petting, and studying the nature of the creatures.

'Hundreds have tried their hands at happy families, and have failed. The cat has killed the mice, and the hawks have killed the birds, the dogs the rats, and even the cats, the rats, the birds, and even one another; indeed, it was anything but a happy family. By our system we never have a mishap; and have had animals eight or nine years in the cage—until they've died of age, indeed. In our present cage we have 54 birds and animals, and of 17 different kinds; 3 cats, 2 dogs (a terrier and a spaniel), 2 monkeys, 2 magpies, 2 jackdaws, 2 jays, 10 starlings (some of them talk), 6 pigeons, 2 hawks, 2 barn fowls, 1 screech owl, 5 common-sewer rats, 5 white rats (a novelty), 8 guinea-pigs, 2 rabbits (1 wild and 1 tame), 1 hedgehog, and 1 tortoise. Of all these, the rat is the most difficult to make a member of a happy family—among birds, the hawk. The easiest trained animal is a monkey, and the easiest trained bird a pigeon. They live together in their cages all night, and sleep in a stable, unattended by anyone. They were once thirty-six hours, as a trial, without food—that was in Cambridge; and no creature was injured; but they were very peckish, especially the birds of prey. I wouldn't allow it to be tried (it was for a scientific gentleman) any longer, and I fed them well to begin upon.

'There are now in London five happy families, all belonging to two families of men. Mine, that is the one I have the care of, is the strongest—fifty-four creatures: the others will average forty each, or 214 birds and beasts in happy families. Our only regular places now are Waterloo-bridge and the National Gallery. The expense of keeping my fifty-four is 12s. a-week; and in a good week—indeed, the best week—we take 30s.; and in a bad week sometimes not 8s. It's only a poor trade. Though there are more good weeks than bad: but the weather has so much to do with it.

'The first who ever took out a happy family to exhibit in the streets was a man of the name of John Austin, who lived in Nottingham. He was a very ingenious man indeed, and fond of all kinds of animals, and a fancier of all kinds of small birds. From what I have heard him say, he had a lot of cats he was very fond of, and also some white-mice, and the notion struck him that it would be very extraordinary if he could make his pets live together, and teach creatures of opposite natures to dwell in the same cage. In the commencement of his experiments he took the young, and learnt them to live happily together. He was a weaver by trade, was Austin—a stocking-weaver. He didn't exhibit for money in Manchester. It was his hobby and amusement, and he only showed it for a curiosity to his friends. Then he was persuaded to come to London to exhibit.

'There was no bridge to the Waterloo-road in those days, but he took up his pitch in Waterloo-road, close to the Feathers public-house, where the foot of Waterloo-bridge is now. He had a tremendous success. Everybody who passed gave him money. Noblemen and gentlepeople came far and near to see the sight. When first he went there he could go out at four o'clock in the afternoon, on any fine day as he thought proper to leave his work to go out, and he could take from his 14s. to £1. He stopped on this same spot opposite the Feathers public-house, from his first coming to the day he left it, a short space before he died, for 36 years all but 5 months. He's been dead for four years the 17th of last February, 1856, and then he wasn't getting 2s. 6d. a-day. Many had imitated him, and there were four happy family cages in London. He had never been a prudent man, so he never saved anything. He was too generous to his friends when they were distressed. If he made £5 in a week, there was money and food for them who wanted. He found that people were not so generous to him as he was to them; that he proved to his sorrow. He was a good man.

'In the year 1833 he had the honour of exhibiting before Her Majesty the Queen. She sent for him expressly, and he went to Buckingham Palace. He never would tell anybody what she gave him; but everybody considered that he had been handsomely rewarded.

'I was with him as assistant for eight years before he died, and a better master there could not be living in the world. I had been travelling with him through Kent, showing the happy family, and business run bad and did not meet his approbation, so he at last said he would return to his station on Waterloo-bridge. Then I was left in the country, so I started a collection of animals for myself.

'I came to London after working in the country. He was perfectly agreeable to my exhibiting in the streets. He was a good old man, and I wish I knew how to be as good, for I can't know how to be as good. I took the West-end, and he kept to the bridge. For a time

I did pretty well. I'd take about 6s. a-day, but then it cost me 1s. a-day for feeding the collection; and then I had a quantity of things given to me, such as bits of meat at the butcher's, and so on. In 1851 my stand was in Regent-street, by the corner of Castle-street. I did there very well when the Exhibition was open, and as soon as it was done I fell from taking about 8s. a-day down to 1s., and that's speaking the truth. Then I shifted my post, and went and pitched upon Tower-hill.

'I done pretty well for the first 18 months as I was there. The sailors was the most generous people to me, and those I had most to depend upon whilst I was on Tower-hill. Then I returns to the old man's original spot, on Waterloo-bridge, to try that; for the old man was dead. The first five or six weeks as I was there, during the summer, I got a tolerable good living, and I continued there till I wasn't able to get a crust for myself. I was obliged to leave it off, and I got a situation to go to work for a firework-maker in the Westminster-road. Now I only take to the streets when I have no other employment. It isn't barely a living.

'The animal that takes the longest to train is the ferret. I was the first that ever introduced one into a cage, and that was at Greenwich. It's a very savage little animal, and will attack almost anything. People have a notion that we use drugs to train a happy family; they have said to me, "It's done with opium"; but, sir, believe me, there is no drugs used at all: it's only patience, and kindness, and petting them that is used, and nothing else of any sort. The first ferret as I had, it killed me about £2 worth of things before I could get him in any way to get into the happy family. He destroyed birds, and rabbits, and guinea-pigs; and he'd seize them at any time, whether he was hungry or not. I watched that ferret till I could see that there was a better method to be used with a ferret, and then I sold my one to a rat-catcher, and then I bought two others. I tried my new system, and it succeeded. It's a secret which I used, so I can't mention it, but it's the simplest thing in the world. It's not drawing their teeth out, or operating on them; it's only kindness and such-like, and patience. I put my new ferrets into the cage, and there they have been ever since, as may have been seen on Tower-hill and such places as I've pitched on. My ferrets would play with the rats and sleep at night with them, while I've put them in the rat-box along with the rats, to carry

Everyday he wheeled his motley collection of animals to the usual spot.

them home together at night. My ferrets would come and eat out of my mouth and play with children. I compare my monkey to the clown of the cage, for he's mischievous, and clever, and good-natured.

'The cats and the birds are very good friends indeed; they'll perch on her back, and I've even seen them come on her head and pick up the bits of dirt as you'll generally find in a cat's head. I've tried a very curious experiment with cats and birds. I've introduced a strange cat into my cage, and instantly she gets into the cage she gets frightened, and looks round for a moment, and then she'll make a dart upon almost the first thing that is facing her. If it's the owl, monkey, small birds, or any thing, she'll fly at it. It's in general then that the monkey is the greatest enemy to the strange cat of anything in the cage. He'll go and bite her tail, but he won't face her. Then the other cats will be all with their hairs up and their tails swelled up to fly at the stranger, but then I generally takes her out, or else there would be a fight. All the rats will be on the look-out and run away from the strange cat, and the little birds fly to the top of the cage, fluttering chirriping with fear.

'The hawk I had a good deal of difficulty with to make him live happily with the small birds. When training a hawk, I always put him in with the large things first, and after he's accustomed to them, then I introduce smaller birds. He's always excited when he first comes amongst the smaller birds. I find Mr Monkey is always the guards, as he doesn't hurt them. When he sees the hawk fluttering and driving about after the small birds, Mr Monkey will go and pat him, as much as to say, "You musn't hurt them", and also to take his attention off. After Mr Hawk has been in the cage four, five, or six different times in training, the starlings gets accustomed to him, and will perch alongside of him; and it's as common as possible to see the starlings, when the hawk was feeding, go and eat off the same raw meat, and actually perch on his back and pick the bits off his bill as he is eating them.

'A good jackdaw, well trained to a happy family, is the life of the cage next to the monkey. He's at all the roguishness and mischief that it is possible for a man to be at. If he sees a cat or a dog, or anything asleep and quiet, he'll perch on its head, and peck away to rouse it. If there's a rat in his way, he'll peck at its nose till it turns round, and then peck at its tail. If Mr Rat gets spiteful he'll fly to the perches for it, and then hollow out Jack Daw, as much as to say, "I had the best of you". The people are very fond of the jackdaw, too, and they like putting their fingers to the wires, and Jack'll peck them. He's very fond of stealing things and hiding them. He'll take the halfpence and conceal them. He looks round, as if seeing whether he was watched, and go off to some sly corner where there is nothing near him. My monkey and the jackdaw ain't very good company. When Mr Jack begins his fun, it is generally when Mr Monkey is lying still, cuddling his best friend, that's one of the little dogs. If Mr Monkey is lying down with his tail out, he'll go and peck him hard on it, and he'll hollow out "Jackdaw", and off he is to the perches. But Mr Monkey will be after him, climbing after him, and he's sure to catch hold of him at last, and then Mr Jack is as good as his master, for he'll hollow out to attract me, and I have to rattle my cane along the wires, to tell them to give over. Then, as sure as ever the monkey was gone, the jack would begin to crow.

'I had a heron once, and it died; I had it about fourteen months. The way as he met with his death was—he was all well in the cage, and standing about, when he took a false step, and fell, and lamed himself. I was obliged to leave him at home, and then he pined and died. I fed my heron on flesh, though he liked fish best. It's the most daintiest bird that is in its eating.

'I had an old crow once, who was a great favourite of mine, and when he died I could almost have cried. To tell you what he could do is almost too much for me to say, for it was everything he was capable of. He would never stand to fight; always run away and hollow. He and the jackdaw was two birds as always kept apart from each other: they was both of a trade, and couldn't agree. He was very fond of getting on a perch next to any other bird—an owl, for instance—and then he'd pretend to be looking at nothing, and then suddenly peck at the feet of his neighbour on the sly, and then try and look innocent. After a time the other bird would turn round on him, and then he was off, screaming "Caw" at the top of his beak, as I may say. He was a general favourite with everybody.

'He knew me perfectly well, and would come and perch on my

shoulder, and peck me over the finger, and look at me and make his noise. As soon as he sees me going to fetch the food he would, if he was loose in the court where I lived in, run to me directly, but not at other times. He was a knowing fellow. I had him about one year and nine months. I used to call him the pantaloon to Mr Monkey's clown, and they was always at their pantomime tricks. Once an old woman came down our court when he was loose, and he cut after her and pecked at her naked feet, and she was so frightened she fell down. Then off he went, "caw, caw", as pleased as he could be. He always followed the children, picking at their heels. Nothing delighted him so much as all the roguishness and mischief as he could get into.

'For finding a happy family in good order, with 2 monkeys, 3 cats, 2 dogs, 16 rats, 6 starlings, 2 hawks, jackdaw, 3 owls, magpie, 2 guinea-pigs, one rabbit, will take about 1s. 4d. a-day. I buy leg of beef for the birds, about 1½lb., and the dogs have two pen'orth of proper dog's meat; and there are apples and nuts for the monkey, about one pen'orth, and then there's corn of different kinds, and seeds and sopped bread for the rats, and hay and sand-dust for the birds. It all tells up, and comes to about 1s. 4d. a-day.

'There are two happy families in London town, including my own. I don't know where the other man stands, for he moves about. Now I like going to one place, where I gets known. It isn't a living for any man now. People will come and stand round for hours, and never give a penny: Even very respectable people will come up, and as soon as ever I hand the cup to them, they'll be off about their business. There are some gentlemen who give me regularly a penny or twopence a-week. I could mention several professional actors who do that to me. I make the most money when the monkey is at his tricks, for then they want to stop and see him at his fun, and I keep asking them for money, and do it so often, that at last they are obliged to give something.

'My cage has wire-work all round, and blinds to pull down when I change my pitch. There are springs under the cage to save the jolting over the stones.

'I forgot to tell you that I've had cats, whose kittens have been taken from them, suckle rats which been put in their places when they are still blind, and only eight days old. She'll take to the rats instead of her kittens. I've not put them in the cage at this small age, but waited until they were old enough to run about. They'll keep on suckling at the cat till they get to a tidy size, till she gets annoyed with them and beats them off; but she'll caress them at other times, and allow them to come and lay under her belly, and protect them from Mr Monkey.

THE FISHERMAN AND THE TURTLE

Anthea Courtenay

This story is based on an ancient Japanese legend, of which there are many versions. It is said to be the origin of a dance called 'The Crane and Turtle Dance'.

If he had not been late that morning, Urashima Taro would never have met the turtle. In the ordinary way he was up and away in his boat at first light, ahead of the others—and last home, too, for he was a good son and a conscientious fisherman. And something else, besides.

Urashima Taro was special. Though he was poor and uneducated and had never left his village on the southern coast of Japan, he had always known that he was in some way exceptional. It was not that he was remarkably handsome and strong, for he cared nothing for appearances; it was not that he was extraordinarily kind-hearted, for his kindness came so naturally that he was unaware of it. It was not the pride of his name, which means 'Son of the Island'. It was a kind of inner knowledge, almost like a memory—the knowledge that for him some special destiny was reserved. It was this that drew him so early to the sea and kept him out so late. Alone in his little boat his knowledge echoed around him, whispered in the wind, repeated in the wavelets lapping at the sides of his boat, hinted in the seabirds' cries. 'Urashima Taro is not like other men—for him there is more, much more!'

He would gaze up at the sky, and his soul would expand to meet the distance. Or he would look down into the dark waters, and a curious urge would come over him to plunge into their depths, as if

THE FISHERMAN AND THE TURTLE

some answer lay in their mystery. He spoke of these things to no-one.

That morning his mother, as she served his breakfast, had delayed him. 'Urashima, I must talk to you seriously. You are twenty years old, you are a fine, handsome young man—oh, don't pretend—I've seen the way the girls look at you! It's high time you got married.'

A handful of rice halfway to his lips, Urashima paused. Patiently, for he had heard all this before, he answered her. 'Mother, I honour you far too much to wish to change my way of life.'

'You are my only son, born to me late in life, and it's many years since your father was drowned. Soon I shall be growing old, I shall need a pair of young hands to help me. And *you* won't be young forever— one day you will need a son to take your fishing boat out to sea.'

'Oh, not for many years yet, mother. I'm strong and healthy—'

'And you work too hard and you take risks. What if anything happened to you? I should be all alone!'

'Nothing will happen to me, you worry too much!'

'Urashima Taro,' said she a touch impatiently. 'I am your mother, and I tell you it is time you got married!'

He smiled his charming smile and said, 'Mother, how could I find a wife worthy enough, when for twenty years I have lived with the most perfect woman in the world?'

He meant it, too; he loved his mother deeply. But the other reason he could not speak of to her: simple woman that she was, how could she understand that he must remain free to meet his Destiny?

He rose, wiped his fingers, and embraced her. 'Mother, I promise I'll think about what you have said. You know I would never do anything to hurt you.'

His mother sighed. 'I know. You always were a dear, good boy. Now, be careful. The seas were high last night—'

'I'll come home especially early tonight,' he promised, and set off through the village streets down to the beach and his beloved boat. As he turned the corner he looked back at his home. His mother stood in the doorway, looking after him, a little woman in black, with a brown, wrinkled face.

At first he ignored the voices shouting on the beach and would have gone straight to his boat had he not detected in the cries a harshness, the unmistakeable tone of boys tormenting someone or something weaker than themselves. He walked across the sand to the group of youths who danced and circled, half-mocking, half-afraid, round something he could not see. As he approached, one or two of them fell back: the village boys respected Urashima.

'What's going on?' He stepped into the circle. In the centre lay the giant turtle, upturned in its huge, heavy shell, its flippers waving helplessly in the air, its wrinkled neck stretched in useless effort.

'It was stranded,' said a boy. 'The storm must have washed it up last night. It'll make good soup.'

'And is that a reason to torment it?' said Urashima Taro severely, looking at the sticks and stones in their hands. 'We should respect life, especially the life of the sea that gives us our living.'

A youth shrugged. 'What's the difference? It's going to die anyway.'

'Then we should ask the poor creature's forgiveness, and thank it for the life it gives us in losing its own.'

He looked down at the turtle which had stopped its flapping at the sound of his voice, and was looking at him from its small black eyes.

'And just to teach you—this one we will not kill.' He bent and talked gently to the turtle, while the boys watched in silence. Then he gave a heave to its shell. But even his strength was not enough. 'Who will help me?'

Several boys helped him to drag the creature to the water's edge, where they carefully tilted it over. 'How strange,' thought Urashima Taro as he watched it swim away, gathering speed and strength as it went. 'Such a look it gave me—as though it really wanted to thank me.'

Then he strode off to his boat, and forgot the incident.

$$\star \quad \star \quad \star \quad \star$$

He did not see the storm-clouds building on the horizon, nor become aware of the whirlwind until it was almost upon him. There was nothing he could do. He had truly intended not to be late; he had promised his mother, and he kept his promises. He had taken a good catch and could have returned. But some kind of daydream mood overtook him; he sat enjoying the silence and the loneliness, and wondering when and how his Destiny would come to him. He and his little vessel were flung this way and that; he felt as if a thousand boys with sticks were beating him on all sides. He clung to his boat until it shattered and was sucked down under the waves.

'Can this be my Destiny?' he cried aloud. 'To drown like so many others before me? If that's so, I refuse! I will live!'

'Yes,' said a voice beside him. 'Death is not for you. Come, quick, climb on my back.'

Swimming close to him was a turtle, the giant turtle of that morning. It did not surprise him that she should speak; he gripped the thick, solid shell above her neck and slid his body gratefully on to her back. Away they swam, away from the hurricane and away from the land. And from the turtle's wrinkled head the sweet, unearthly voice spoke. 'You saved my life, Urashima Taro. Such kindness must have its reward.'

And still he was not astonished that she spoke, only lulled and enchanted by the extraordinary beauty of her voice.

Without warning, the great creature dived. For a moment the fisherman's eyes, ears, nose, were full of salt water. A second or so later he found himself quite comfortable, not cold, not drowning, able to hear and answer the words of his strange mount.

As she swam effortlessly down and on, she spoke to him of the Kingdom under the sea from which she came, of the Sea God Ryugu, of the riches of his palace and the beauty of his daughter Otohime.

Was it really three days and three nights that they swam thus? So says the legend that they told afterwards. Time no longer existed. Urashima felt no hunger nor thirst, nor did he wish to sleep, though sometimes he had the sensation of a man returning from one dream only to lose himself in another. From time to time he wondered, 'Can this be my Destiny?' But the notion did not ring quite true, for he knew that when he met his Destiny he would be fully awake.

At last the towers and spires of the Sea God's palace rose before them, shimmering and glittering with a thousand precious stones, surrounded by underwater gardens: great banks of coral, from finger-nail pink to ruby red, sea anemones of every shape and hue, and great, tree-tall seaweeds, purple, blue and green, moved by the waters in a constant dance.

Through vast doors they swam into a great white hall glittering with crystal and mother-of-pearl, with pillars that soared so high it was hard to distinguish the curve of the roof. Among them moved fishes of every shade of the rainbow, a kaleidoscope of undulating colours that made Urashima gasp: never in all his life at sea had he seen such fish.

The turtle gently stopped and let him slide from her back.

'Wait here,' she said. 'I shall not be long.' And she left him.

While he waited some graceful blue and green fishes with long, feathery tails floated in, carrying in their mouths a kimono of the finest silk shot with gold and silver threads. They nudged him gently until he had discarded his coarse fisherman's tunic and put on the kimono. Looking at himself, he laughed.

'This is not for me—this is a garment for a prince!'

'And a prince you shall be,' said the sweet voice of his companion. He turned round and saw in a doorway framed with shells and pearls a young woman more beautiful than he could ever have imagined. On the thick black hair that framed her oval face she wore a silver crown. As she glided towards him she smiled.

'I am Otohime, the Sea God's daughter. Sometimes I take the form of a turtle to visit the world outside—and this last time I might never have returned, but for you. My father has therefore given you permission to marry me—if that is your wish.'

'Is it your wish, lady?'

'What better husband could I ask for?' she said. 'Let us be married and live in joy forever—for those who dwell in the Sea God's Kingdom never grow old.'

This, then, must be my Destiny, thought Urashima Taro: to marry the most beautiful woman in the world and live, forever young, as a prince in the Sea God's Kingdom. He stretched out his rough, work hardened hand and in it took her long-fingered white one.

So they were married, and each day was more full of enchantment, as Urashima and Otohime grew closer, delighting in each other's company. Together they danced and sang, together they explored the rooms of the palace, each one more beautiful than the last. All the time that he lived there, there were always undiscovered rooms for Urashima and his bride to explore.

264

He gripped the turtle's back tightly as they swam away from the hurricane.

Only two things troubled him. One was the box that stood on the bureau in Otohime's chamber: a large box, containing three drawers, it was lacquered the colour of blood, and into its surface were inlaid curious designs in mother-of-pearl. When he asked Otohime what it contained she laughed at first and said, 'A secret!' But when he pressed her she replied, 'It contains the most precious thing in the world. Oh, my love, may you never have to open it.'

And she suddenly looked so sad that he dared not ask her about it again.

The second cause of faint unease he could not at first put his finger on: then, alone one day in a crystal courtyard he had not visited before, he realized what it was. He missed the sound of bird-song.

But such tiny shadows could not dim his happiness.

So three years passed.

★   ★   ★   ★

'No!' He sat up in bed, wide awake. Beside him Otohime stirred and opened her dark eyes. 'What is it, my love? A nightmare?'

Urashima put his face in his hands. 'A dream! I dreamed of my mother, as she stood there looking after me the day I left home. Otohime, how could I? For three years I've lived here now, and I've never sent her a message, hardly given her a thought. Now she comes in my dreams to reproach me. I must go and see her!'

In the darkness he could not see the anxiety on his princess's face. Softly she stroked his brow and whispered, 'You have a new life now. . . . Are you not happy, here with me?'

'You know I am! But I have no right to happiness at her expense. My poor mother—I loved her so much, how could I have forgotten her? I must see her, reassure her.'

'Don't go! If you go, you will never come back.'

He turned and embraced her. 'Silly little one, of course I will. But I must go, just one visit to make sure she's all right, one visit, that's all. I can't be happy till I've seen her.'

'Ah, how is it that you men must always love the woman who is absent?' sighed Otohime. But she rose from their couch and went to her bureau. From it she took the lacquered box. 'If you must go,' she said,

'I will take you myself. Take this with you. Promise that you will only open it if you must.'

'Very well,' he said. He scarcely looked at the box now, his mind was all on his return.

'But I pray you may never have to,' she whispered.

He embraced her one last time. 'I'll come back safely, I promise. How could I ever leave you? My Destiny?'

But he felt a curious pang of doubt, as though, all unwillingly, he were lying.

★   ★   ★   ★

Three days and nights they travelled through the waters, Urashima Taro clinging to the back of his turtle princess. At last they broke surface and in the distance he could see the familiar outline of the shore, and his heart raced ahead of him so that he scarcely heard his wife's words or the sadness in her voice. At last they reached the sandy beach, and Urashima put his feet to the ground.

'You have the box?' she asked.

'I have it safe, don't worry.'

'I will wait for you here, then. Don't be too long.'

He patted the great domed shell affectionately. 'I won't, never fear.'

Eagerly he turned his footsteps to the village. As he walked, however, a strange uneasiness overcame him, a growing fear. For this was not his own village. Though the lines of the streets seemed the same, the houses were different; trees and gardens that he remembered well were no longer there. Had there been an earthquake in the last three years? A cold sensation gripped his stomach as he followed the line of the main street to where his home had stood. All he found was a patch of wild land strewn with rocks and stones; among them grasses and purple irises moved gently in the breeze.

'It is the wrong village,' he told himself, but he had already recognized the shape of the stone washbasin and the stepping stones of his mother's garden.

As he stood staring, an old peasant passed by.

'Good-day, father. Tell me—am I mistaken? I am looking for the house of Urashima Taro who left this village a few years ago. His mother—where is she?'

The old man's face creased in thought. 'Why, I remember that name,' he said. 'My grandmother used to tell me of an Urashima Taro who lived here once. Such a fine young man, he was quite a legend hereabouts. He was lost at sea one day—they never found his body, and his mother died soon after, of grief, they say. But that was—oh, that was three hundred years ago. You're a little late, young man.'

Three years . . . three hundred years! 'Oh, my poor mother!'

He sat down on the crumbling steps and began to weep. As he raised his sleeve to his eyes, his hand brushed against the princess's box. He took it in his hands: she had prayed he would never have to open it—was this what she had feared for him, known was in store for him—this stunning grief?

Three hundred years. . . . 'Only open it if you must!' Perhaps the box contained some magic spell that would wipe out those years, or perhaps enable him to see his mother one last time and ask her forgiveness. He only knew that he must open it.

In the velvet depths of the first drawer lay a white feather. He frowned; he knew it to be the feather of a crane, a symbol of long life. Was it there to mock him?

Anxiously he opened the second drawer; from it came a puff of smoke. As it coiled about him he felt a strange weakness overtake his limbs, his head felt too heavy for his neck, and his back began to curve forward. He looked at his hands and arms—but how wrinkled and dry they were, like the roots of dead trees. With what strength remained to him he opened the third drawer and drew from it the mirror that lay within, knowing the horror it would reveal. His face stared back at him, criss-crossed with a thousand lines, unrecognizable, the face of a man three hundred and twenty years old. He could never return to Otohime now.

'This, then, was my Destiny,' he thought. 'To have wounded and lost the two women I loved with all my heart.'

He cast the mirror from him. As it shattered on the stones, the crane's feather fluttered upwards, circled about him and came to rest on his shoulders.

Once more his limbs were transformed, long and slender his legs, his arms heavy with feathers. They began to beat, lifting him up, up, above the deserted garden and the ruined house. Light and urgent he flew, circling the garden three times, then higher, high above the village, above the seashore, his crane's wings gathering strength and skill, as he learned to rise and swoop with the wind.

Below him he saw the long stretch of sandy shore, children playing, a fisherman mending his nets. And the brown shape of a turtle, swimming slowly, sadly out to sea. He hovered above her until at last she dived.

Then he flew far out to sea, knowing that fatigue would not endanger him, that he had nothing to fear from winds and waves, that he would fly on forever, immortal. Urashima Taro had met his Destiny at last.

SREDNI VASHTAR

'Saki'

Conradin was ten years old, and the doctor had pronounced his professional opinion that the boy would not live another five years. The doctor was silky and effete, and counted for little, but his opinion was endorsed by Mrs De Ropp, who counted for nearly everything. Mrs De Ropp was Conradin's cousin and guardian, and in his eyes she represented those three-fifths of the world that are necessary and disagreeable and real; the other two fifths, in perpetual antagonism to the foregoing, were summed up in himself and his imagination. One of these days Conradin supposed he would succumb to the mastering pressure of wearisome necessary things—such as illnesses and coddling restrictions and drawnout dullness. Without his imagination, which was rampant under the spur of loneliness, he would have succumbed long ago.

Mrs De Ropp would never, in her honestest moments, have confessed to herself that she disliked Conradin, though she might have been dimly aware that thwarting him 'for his good' was a duty which she did not find particularly irksome. Conradin hated her with a desperate sincerity which he was perfectly able to mask. Such few pleasures as he could contrive for himself gained an added relish from the likelihood that they would be displeasing to his guardian, and from the realm of his imagination she was locked out—an unclean thing, which should find no entrance.

In the dull, cheerless garden, overlooked by so many windows that were ready to open with a message not to do this or that, or a reminder that medicines were due, he found little attraction. The few fruit-trees that it contained were set jealously apart from his pluck-ing, as though they were rare specimens of their kind blooming in an arid waste; it would probably have been difficult to find a market-gardener who would have offered ten shillings for their entire yearly produce. In a forgotten corner, however, almost hidden behind a dismal shrubbery, was a disused tool-shed of respectable proportions, and within its walls Conradin found a haven, something that took on the varying aspects of a playroom and a cathedral. He had peopled it with a legion of familiar phantoms, evoked partly from fragments of history and partly from his own brain, but it also boasted two inmates of flesh and blood. In one corner lived a ragged-plumaged Houdan hen, on which the boy lavished an affection that had scarcely another outlet. Further back in the gloom stood a large hutch, divided into two compartments, one of which was fronted with close iron bars. This was the abode of a large polecat-ferret, which a friendly butcher-boy had once smuggled, cage and all, into its present quarters, in exchange for a long-secreted hoard of small silver. Conradin was dreadfully afraid of the lithe, sharp-fanged beast, but it was his most treasured possession. Its very presence in the tool-shed was a secret and fearful joy, to be kept scrupulously from the knowledge of the Woman, as he privately dubbed his cousin. And one day, out of Heaven knows what material, he spun the beast a wonderful name, and from that moment it grew into a god and a religion. The Woman indulged in religion once a week at a church near by, and took Conradin with her, but to him the church service was an alien rite in the House of Rimmon. Every Thursday, in the dim and musty silence of the tool-shed, he wor-shipped with mystic and elaborate ceremonial before the wooden hutch where dwelt Sredni Vashtar, the great ferret. Red flowers in their season and scarlet berries in the winter-time were offered at his shrine, for he was a god who laid some special stress on the fierce impatient side of things, as opposed to the Woman's religion, which, as far as Conradin could observe, went to great lengths in the contrary direction. And on great festivals powdered nutmeg was strewn in front of his hutch, an important feature of the offering being that the nutmeg had to be stolen. These festivals were of irregular occurrence, and were chiefly appointed to celebrate some passing event. On one occasion, when Mrs De Ropp suffered from acute toothache for three days, Conradin kept up the festival during the entire three days, and almost succeeded in persuading himself that Sredni Vashtar was personally responsible for the toothache. If the malady had lasted for another day the supply of nutmeg would have given out.

The Houdan hen was never drawn into the cult of Sredni Vashtar. Conradin had long ago settled that she was an Anabaptist. He did not pretend to have the remotest knowledge as to what an Anabaptist was, but he privately hoped that it was dashing and not very respectable. Mrs De Ropp was the ground plan on which he based and detested all respectability.

After a while Conradin's absorption in the tool-shed began to attract the notice of his guardian. 'It is not good for him to be pottering down there in all weathers,' she promptly decided, and at breakfast one morning she announced that the Houdan hen had been sold and taken away overnight. With her short-sighted eyes she peered at Conradin, waiting for an outbreak of rage and sorrow, which she was ready to rebuke with a flow of excellent precepts and reasoning. But Conradin said nothing: there was nothing to be said. Something perhaps in his white set face gave her a momentary qualm, for at tea that afternoon there was toast on the table, a delicacy which she usually banned on the ground that it was bad for him; also because the making of it 'gave trouble', a deadly offence in the middle-class feminine eye.

'I thought you liked toast,' she exclaimed, with an injured air, observing that he did not touch it.

'Sometimes,' said Conradin.

In the shed that evening there was an innovation in the worship of the hutch-god. Conradin had been wont to chant his praises, tonight he asked a boon.

'Do one thing for me, Sredni Vashtar.'

The thing was not specified. As Sredni Vashtar was a god he must be supposed to know. And choking back a sob as he looked at that other empty corner, Conradin went back to the world he so hated.

And every night, in the welcome darkness of his bedroom, and every evening in the dusk of the tool-shed, Conradin's bitter litany went up: 'Do one thing for me, Sredni Vashtar.'

Mrs De Ropp noticed that the visits to the shed did not cease, and one day she made a further journey of inspection.

'What are you keeping in that locked hutch?' she asked. 'I believe it's guinea-pigs. I'll have them all cleared away.'

Conradin shut his lips tight, but the Woman ransacked his bedroom till she found the carefully hidden key, and forthwith marched down to the shed to complete her discovery. It was a cold afternoon, and Conradin had been bidden to keep to the house. From the furthest window of the dining-room the door of the shed could just be seen beyond the corner of the shrubbery, and there Conradin stationed himself. He saw the Woman enter, and then he imagined her opening the door of the sacred hutch and peering down with her short-sighted eyes into the thick straw bed where his god lay hidden. Perhaps she would prod at the straw in her clumsy impatience. And Conradin fervently breathed his prayer for the last time. But he knew as he prayed that he did not believe. He knew that the Woman would come out presently with that pursed smile he loathed so well on her face and that in an hour or two the gardener would carry away his wonderful god, a god no longer, but a simple brown ferret in a hutch. And he knew that the Woman would triumph always as she triumphed now, and that he would grow ever more sickly under her pestering and domineering and superior wisdom, till one day nothing would matter much more with him, and the doctor would be proved right. And in the sting and misery of his defeat, he began to chant loudly and defiantly the hymn of his threatened idol:

Sredni Vashtar went forth,
His thoughts were red thoughts and his teeth were white.
His enemies called for peace, but he brought them death.
Sredni Vashtar the Beautiful.

Through the window Conradin saw the woman enter the shed.

And then of a sudden he stopped his chanting and drew closer to the window-pane. The door of the shed still stood ajar as it had been left, and the minutes were slipping by. They were long minutes, but they slipped by nevertheless. He watched the starlings running and flying in little parties across the lawn; he counted them over and over again, with one eye always on that swinging door. A sour-faced maid came in to lay the table for tea, and still Conradin stood and waited and watched. Hope had crept by inches into his heart, and now a look of triumph began to blaze in his eyes that had only known the wistful patience of defeat. Under his breath, with a furtive exultation, he began once again the paean of victory and devastation. And presently his eyes were rewarded: out through that doorway came a long, low, yellow-and-brown beast, with eyes a-blink at the waning daylight, and dark wet stains around the fur of jaws and throat. Conradin dropped on his knees. The great polecat-ferret made its way down to a small brook at the foot of the garden, drank for a moment, then crossed a little plank bridge and was lost to sight in the bushes. Such was the passing of Sredni Vashtar.

'Tea is ready,' said the sour-faced maid; 'where is the mistress?'

'She went down to the shed some time ago,' said Conradin.

And while the maid went to summon her mistress to tea, Conradin fished a toasting-fork out of the sideboard drawer and proceeded to toast himself a piece of bread. And during the toasting of it and the buttering of it with much butter and the slow enjoyment of eating it, Conradin listened to the noises and silences which fell in quick spasms beyond the dining-room door. The loud foolish screaming of the maid, the answering chorus of wondering ejaculations from the kitchen region, the scuttering footsteps and hurried embassies for outside help, and then, after a lull, the sacred sobbings and the shuffling tread of those who bore a heavy burden into the house.

'Whoever will break it to the poor child? I couldn't for the life of me!' exclaimed a shrill voice. And while they debated the matter among themselves, Conradin made himself another piece of toast.

THE TRIUMPH OF BILL BROCK

Henry Williamson

Silence is never of earth or sky—even under the hills when the day and night are balanced in the still air, and blackbirds roosting in the hollies have ceased shrill cries at the passing shadowy owls; when the wintry moon is too wan for shining, and the chalk quarries grow grey in the dusk.

Always there is sound and movement. Worms are pushing out of their galleries, seizing fragments of dead leaves, and drawing them to their holes before roving again for others—always with their tails in the holes, for an instant return; slugs and beetles are abroad in the dewfall; sleepy birds·breathing softly through puffed feathers; rabbits lolloping along their runs in the stubble, pausing to nibble the young clover leaves; partridges, their wheezy dimmit-calling over, settling closer in mid-field; mice claws pattering on twigs and leaf-mould; slow sappy pulses of the still trees rising and falling along their cold grey boles. And from the tunnels of the badgers' earth come muffled sounds, and grunts, and the nearer noise of a mouth stretching. Quietness again, while a last leaf falls among the wandering mice, and the edges of black boughs begin to glisten. The wan air of dusk deepens into night, with star points flickering, and the moon lays the pale shadows of trunks and branches. All the while, by the glimmering badgers' earth, a noise is working at the smells of the air, and ears are harkening.

For a hundred and twenty yards along the top of the beech wood the ground was pressed into paths, and heaped in nine places with soil, as though cartloads had been tipped there. Some gleamed white, where tons of chalk had been thrown out. Tree trunks were buried five and six feet deep in the heaps, which were the mine-heads of the badgers' holt. They were always digging to extend their galleries among the roots, and carry their kitchens deeper into the chalk, which was dry.

An owl flew through the wood, alighting on a branch above the main opening. It listened and peered for a minute and a half, hearing the breathing of the badger, but unable to see its head. The moonlight made a blur of the trodden heap before the hole, with its scatter of chalk, and the white-arrowed head in the tunnel's dark opening was part of the blur. The owl flew on to its next perching place, and soon after it had gone the head withdrew, a grunt sounded down the tunnel, followed by the muffled thumping of broad paws.

★   ★   ★   ★

The hole, ragged with broken roots and hanging rootlets, was wider than the badger, yet he came out laboriously, with much scraping and grunting. He did not tread on his pads, but heaved himself along by the blunt black claws of his forepaws against the side of the tunnel. He moved like an immense mole. When his head and shoulders were outside he remained in his awkward position, his sharp nose pointing at the heap of earth. Then putting his nose between his paws he bent his thick neck and turned head over heels. Remaining on his back, he rolled until he had covered the area of the heap. Afterwards he got on his short legs and shook himself.

Every night he rolled like this, in case gins had been tilled there by day to catch him by the paw.

Four other badgers followed the old boar, rolling in the same manner. They followed him down a trodden path among the trees, indistinct in moonlight and shadow, one behind the other, and came to the streamlet at the bottom of the wood, where they drank.

The water was cold. The four smaller badgers lapped steadily, but the old boar drank with many pauses. He stood by the streamlet, lapping and pausing, nearly a minute after the others had gone to their prowling, one along a fox-path which lay straitly down the stubble field, another following up the water by its edge, a third going down the stream, the fourth returning into the wood. Thus they set about their night's work, each badger having its own ways.

The old boar lumbered after the badger in the wood, following by scent. He hastened in his waddling run, being hungry. He was always hungry.

The boar was many years older than the badger he followed. She and the other three had been born in the same farrow seven months before. During the summer her parents had been dug out by the badger-diggers, dropped into canvas bags, taken away, hit on the nose with spades, turned out, and stabbed. The old boar had followed the cubs home one morning, and curled up with them in their kitchen. Since he preferred to sleep warm, with much food inside him, he had remained there. From him the growing cubs had learned, unconsciously, by imitating his tumble, the way to spring gins, which the earth-stopper of the d'Essantville Foxhounds sometimes tilled outside the badger earths. The Hunt wished badgers destroyed, because their deep tunnels gave shelter to hunted foxes, and so spoiled many kills in the open.

Bloody Bill Brock waddled after the young badger among the trees, moving off her trail to gobble a big black slug he smelt two yards away. Then he picked up a couple of worms, rubbed his head against the trunk of a tree, and returned to the trail. He breathed heavily, grunting with exertion.

When he came upon the young badger, she was eating a dead wood-pigeon, one that had been shot in flight, its hard feathers having stopped the lead pellets; but a mile away it had fallen dead of the blow on the breast. The young badger's teeth, which could have bitten through a man's wrist, cracked the bones as though they were straw. Bill Brock, whose jaws were twice the size of her own, tried to pull the food from her mouth, and she let him have the wings and feet. He swallowed the reddish legs with wheezy gulps, while she was finishing the rest of the bird.

The two wandered over ten miles that night. Beside a hawthorn hedge the boar found a rabbit in a wire snare, set by the lime-burner who lived in the quarry beside the Colham road; and although he was hungry the smaller badger, who hurried round from the other side of the quarry when she heard the rabbit's last throttled cries, ate most of it.

The same thing happened with the next large meal he discovered. Thrusting his snout into a leaf-choked hole under a furze bush, the boar blew and sniffed, and then withdrew his snout, and began to dig. Earth, stones, rootlets, all were thrust behind him. At the end of the hole he found a heavy ball of dry leaves. Some of them were holly leaves, but more prickly than ever they had been when guarding the lower branches of their parent trees. Every leaf now bristled with spikes. Bill Brock grunted with pleasure, and rolled the leaf-ball into the open.

Turning it with snout and paws until he had determined, as it were, the axis on which the hedgehog had rolled itself, he then trod on it with a paw, using the paw as a wedge. His weight forced the ball open, and he bit its neck. He dropped it immediately.

When the young badger came she bared her teeth, drew back her tongue—as a horse crops furze—and bit through leaves, spines, and skin; and the hedgehog, which had slept through it all, died in a strange dream.

The young badger ate most of the hedgehog, and all the boar got was some of the skin.

Just before sunrise he followed the young badger into the holt in Rookhurst forest, not exactly famished, but hungry enough. Mice, worms, snails, slugs, pigeons' feet and feathers, dead leaves, hedgehog skin, rabbits' paws and pieces of fur, the core of an apple—poor fare with which to stay strength for the onslaught of seventeen dogs in the open.

★   ★   ★   ★

Already in the barrel room of The Rising Sun, five miles away, the foam of Mr Tinker's second-best ale was rising to the top of the first wicker-covered earthenware jars, and the servant-wench in the kitchen was cutting loaves and cheese into hunks and wedges, for the day's

Bill Brock grunted with pleasure, and rolled the leaf-ball into the open.

sport. Mr Tinker was snoring in bed, the water in his bedroom ewer as yet ungulped—for he had celebrated Christmas in proper style.

At the very moment that Mr Tinker became aware of daylight and an aching head, Bill Brock began to snore. He lay curled on top of two young boar badgers, who were sleeping in the main kitchen when he returned. By his side his young companion was curled, and the four were drowsing off when the fifth badger returned, and, after wiping his pads against a flint to get the mud off them, waddled down the tunnel and scrambled on their backs. Weary grunts greeted him, and then the five settled down, snug and warm, and fell asleep.

*   *   *   *

The annual badger-dig on 'the Day after Christmas Day', as that national holiday was always called by the inhabitants of Colham Old Town, was the biggest of the year. Badgers were always taken, owing to the numbers of labourers who came out to dig—and to get the free beer and food—bringing either pick or shovel or two-bill, and hoping for a large attendance of 'gentry' (a comprehensive term, including, for the occasion, all in brown boots) to swell the collection for diggers at the end of the day's sport.

They began digging at nine o'clock in the morning, after thrusting down slender sticks to discover the direction of the pipe, and encouraging, with horn and voice and patting, a couple of terriers into the tunnel. At one o'clock, the terriers still being underground, they stopped for lunch. For the sportsmen ('Messrs Tinker, Swidge, Potstacker, Corney, Dellbridge, Gammon, Ovey, and Krumm, no tyros at the game,' as the local paper described them) there was whisky. Mr Tinker's headache had gone, after an hour's strenuous digging; it would no doubt return before closing time that night.

At three o'clock in the afternoon—by which time six terriers had been put to ground, four of them creeping back bitten about the shoulders and jaws—Mr Tinker, kneeling at the main breach in the chalk, declared that another ten minutes would do it. He had already identified Bloody Bill Brock by the six-toed pad leading into the tunnel. The Master's teeth (made up by Mr Swidge, the quack dentist) dropped out in his excitement. They all laughed.

281

'Lucky for me Bloody Bill wasn't nearby!' said Mr Tinker jokingly. 'Well, gentlemen, I've carried the horn for eighteen years, and it looks as though we're going to get the old boar at last.'

He seized a pick from a labourer, and struck at the chalk. Five minutes of work made him wet and breathless, and he stood back, saying: 'To h-ll with that! Here, Jan, take a turn.'

Half an hour later the sportsmen, sitting or standing around and above the miniature quarry, saw a short tail poke out and disappear again.

'The Mullah!' they cried.

'I told you The Mullah'd hold'n,' said Mr Corney, a short man in clothes that looked and smelled as though they had been slept in for weeks. The pawnbroker rapidly brushed his drooping damp moustache with the back of one hand. 'I told you The Mullah'd have'n.'

The Mad Mullah was his terrier.

The tunnel had already been broken in two places, and dim daylight either way barred the escape. Colham Belle held the right entrance, Mad Mullah the left. Mr Tinker edged out of the group, got his badger-tongs, and asked them to stand back.

'As fine a bit of terrier work as I've seen in all the eighteen—yic—years I've carried the—yic—horn,' he announced.

'I'm sure of it,' exclaimed Mr Corney, spitting, or rather squirting tobacco juice and saliva accurately between his boots. 'I told you the Mullah'd have'n.'

The Mad Mullah hastily backed out of the tunnel, as though pushed by a narrow black pointed head, set with a white arrow. The small expressionless eyes glanced about, and the head retired, followed by the terrier, whose tail and hindquarters stuck out of the hole.

'They'm very near. Goo' boy, Mullah!' cried the Master.

'Don't forget Colham Belle,' suggested a voice.

'I'm not forgetting nothing,' replied the Master, shortly.

Mr Corney relit his pipe for the twentieth time, puffing out vast cheekfuls of rank smoke with immense satisfaction.

'Mullah's the boy,' he said. 'I wouldn't part with that dog for something. Noomye! Not if you was to offer me—'

The terrier backed again, and another face poked out. It was twice the size of the first white-arrowed head, and the short hair of the cheeks was grey instead of black. The Master said afterwards that he knew it was Bill, for the badger did what he had never known any other brock do during the eighteen years he had carried the horn—the badger came out to fight.

The sportsmen had been pressed tightly round the cavity. They scrambled back, pushing and pulling in their haste. The Master was unable to open the tongs in time to collar the boar as he waddled between his legs.

'Look out!' yelled Mr Corney. 'The b——'s loose!'

Bill Brock waddled on, the Mad Mullah retreating before him and making sudden rushes forward, but every time the terrier got within snapping distance the arrowed head turned at him and pierced his courage. Then, curiously, when he was about three yards outside the the hole, the boar stopped, opened his mouth as though in a yawn, and gave a prolonged groan. His tail stiffened and trembled. He stood there, with nose pointing to the ground, still except for the shudders that ran along his curved back. The Mad Mullah snarled at the air before him.

'Get the tongs round his neck—quick!' said the Master in a grating voice, as he pushed forward the long iron instrument. 'Quick—yic—get th' tongs round neck.'

Mr Swidge took them.

'Hold on to him tight,' said the Master, in glee, when this had been done easily. 'Hold his head down. Hold'm tight. Don't let'm get away, for God's sake. Gennulmen, I've carried the horn for—yic—eighteen year, and I've never seen a smarter bit of work.'

'The Mullah'd'v 'ad'n without the tongs,' grumbled Mr Corney.

'Not likely!' replied Mr Swidge, the owner of Colham Belle, promptly.

Bill Brock groaned.

★   ★   ★   ★

While Mr Swidge gripped the handles of the tongs with unnecessary strength, the potman called Jan fetched the bag. It was the size of a mail-bag, and the canvas was so stout that no badger teeth could bite through it. Many a badger, curled still in the bottom of that bag, had been bashed on the snout with a spade, and known nothing more.

The Master stooped down and gripped the trembling tail, and, holding his breath, lifted the boar up and dropped him into the bag.

'There,' he said. 'Bliddy William tailed at last!'

Several hands courageously helped to hold open the top of the bag, while peering heads craned over and bumped each other. The top of the bag was twisted, and fastened with cord. With slightly shaking hands the Master unhooked a spring-balance from his belt, where his hunting-knife hung, and hitched the cord to it.

'Two score and two pounds, gentlemen. The biggest brock I've ever dug out in all the eighteen—yic—'

'And yer woudden'v done that wi'out th' Mullah, noomye!' Mr Corney put in, kicking a piece of chalk violently with his boot. 'No other dog'd'v keppim from diggin' away, and I don't care who hears me say it!'

'No one's saying anything dissenting,' declared the Master. 'I think we're all sportsmen here, gentle—yic—'

All agreed to this immediately. Mr Corney muttered something, and looked surly as before.

While the boar lay still in the bag they had drinks all round. Afterwards they opened the bag, thrust in the tongs, encircled his neck with the iron collar, and drew him out. Then, while the Master pressed his weight on the handles so that the boar's chin was fixed on the ground, a young terrier was led forward and urged to attack the head. It whined and growled and snarled, but would not go near the white arrow and the small blinking eyes. Others were brought, and they all refused.

'I'll tell you what, gentlemen,' said the Master, looking over first one shoulder then the other. His voice became low. 'Yic,' he said, beckoning generally with his nose. 'We're all sports here, I think, gentlemen, and this won't go further, I'm sure. I've always tried to show good sport to the field. How about taking the boar down to the cover, and trying the terriers on him loose, a brace at a time?' This was badger-baiting, and illegal.

'Mullah'll 'ave'n, don't you worry,' muttered Mr Corney, looking at the ground and puffing out smoke violently.

The Master looked at the others, and winked.

So the boar was dropped in the bag again, and they took him down to the field. Here they spread out into a circle, holding their dogs on leash. The Master and the huntsman (Jan the potman) untied the bag, dropped it, and ran back. It heaved, and after a while the dreaded head poked out, sniffing the air. Two terriers were released. They ran at the badger, while every leashed dog sprang up and began to howl.

Slowly Bloody Bill Brock waddled out of the bag, and looked about him. When the two terriers were about a foot away he glanced at them, and did not otherwise appear to regard them; but when one of them came near enough to snap, he made a quick turn of his head; and its will broke.

'Try The Mullah,' shouted Mr Corney irritably. Without waiting for permission, he unleashed his terrier, but the dog would not, or could not, get within gripping distance of the boar's head. Mr Corney yelled at it in a bloodthirsty (whisky variety) voice.

★　　★　　★　　★

Bloody Bill Brock walked over the stubble and the clover, while the circle of men moved with him. Whenever he approached the shifting human group he was driven back with shouts and the banging of spades and picks. Up and down the field he walked, his head turning with instant swiftness at any terrier that dashed at him. He walked very slowly. The Master became impatient.

He blew his horn. 'Let every terrier loose!' he shouted, and waved the tongs in a semicircle.

Two of the labourers had brought their lurchers with them— long-legged hairy dogs, of mongrel greyhound strain, used for silent poaching—and these were loosed with the terriers.

'Get back!' yelled the Master, red in the face, to Mr Corney, who was running forward with raised pick. 'Let the terriers tackle him! We're all sports here, not—yic—bliddy rat-catchers!'

The terriers snarled and scrambled and screamed in a tusselling heap around the badger. Four of them—a Parson Jack Russell, two Sealyhams, and a Bedlington—got a grip on each other, and hung on grimly. A long-legged neurotic animal resembling a diminutive elderly sheep, called Trixie, who had been shrieking almost incessantly since the meet in the farmyard that morning, began a fight with one of the lurchers, and the fight spread to their respective owners, when Mr Potstacker kicked the lurcher in the ribs and was himself thumped on the ear by an enraged labourer. Shouts, oaths, drunken laughter, yelps, barks, growls; and in the centre of the confusion walked the old, old badger, opening his jaws slightly and thrusting his head at every snarling dog face. None dared to encounter the bite of the terrible boar.

At last the Master, having told anyone he could get to listen to him what he thought of the whole lot of dogs (he had no terrier of his own), decided to end it. He blew the recall on his horn, and bawled at them, asking if they knew what he was blowing?

One by one the dogs were gripped by their scruffs, and lugged away, collared, and held back on leashes. All became extremely bloodthirsty and leapt up to get at the boar again.

The boar was standing still, shuddering. The Master approached him from behind, and gripped his neck without the least difficulty.

'Keep terriers back! Jan, bring a spade!'

While the huntsman was bringing the spade, the Master said: 'Us'll make sure of ye this time, ye old—!' and with his right hand fumbled round his belt for his hunting knife.

A strange creaking noise was coming from the badger's throat. He gave a prolonged shudder, a feeble groan, and fell on his side. The Master pushed the limp body with his foot, and the head, with its filmy eyes, rolled loosely.

'Darn me if he isn't dead,' said the Master.

When the business of taking the trophies—the sporting term for hacking off head and pads—was done, Mr Tinker, before throwing the trunk to the terriers, thought he would try and find out what had caused the badger's death. He found, among other things, a piece of hedgehog skin with the prickles on it, the feet of a wood pigeon, and the core of an apple, all unchewed and undigested.

'Colic,' he said.

And when he opened the mouth of Bloody Bill Brock, the unconquerable, whose bite all his enemies had feared, he saw the reason of death: for not a tooth was left in the old jaws, but only brown stumps level with the gums.

BAMBI AND THE OLD STAG

Felix Salton

Bambi, the young faun, had to learn that growing up is not always easy. . . .

Bambi was often alone now. But he was not so troubled about it as he had been the first time. His mother would disappear and no matter how much he called her she wouldn't come back. Later she would appear unexpectedly and stay with him as before.

One night he was roaming around quite forlorn again. He could not even find his cousins Gobo and Faline. The sky had become pale grey and it began to darken so that the tree-tops seemed like a vault over the bushy undergrowth. There was a swishing in the bushes, a loud rustling came through the leaves and Bambi's mother dashed out. Someone else raced close behind her. Bambi did not know whether it was Aunt Ena or his father or someone else. But he recognized his mother at once. Though she rushed past him so quickly, he had recognized her voice. She screamed and it seemed to Bambi as if it were in play, though he thought it sounded a little frightened too.

One day Bambi wandered for hours through the thicket. At last he began to call. He simply couldn't bear to be so utterly lonely any more. He felt that pretty soon he'd be perfectly miserable. So he began to call for his mother.

Suddenly one of the fathers was standing in front of him looking sternly down at him. Bambi hadn't heard him coming and was terrified. This stag looked more powerful than the others, taller and prouder. His coat shone with a deeper richer red, but his face shimmered,

287

silvery grey. And tall black beaded antlers rose high above his nervous ears.

'What are you crying about?' the old stag asked severely. Bambi trembled in awe and did not dare answer. 'Your mother has no time for you now,' the old stag went on. Bambi was completely dominated by his masterful voice and at the same time, he admired it. 'Can't you stay by yourself? Shame on you!'

Bambi wanted to say that he was perfectly able to stay by himself, that he had often been left alone already, but he could not get it out. He was obedient and he felt terribly ashamed. The stag turned around and was gone. Bambi didn't know where or how, or whether the stag had gone slow or fast. He had simply gone as suddenly as he had come. Bambi strained his ears to listen, but he could not catch the sound of a departing footstep or a leaf stirring. So he thought the old stag must be somewhere close by and snuffed the air in all directions. It brought him no scent. Bambi sighed with relief to think he was alone. But he felt a lively desire to see the old stag again and win his approval.

When his mother came back he did not tell her anything of his encounter. He did not call her any more either the next time she disappeared. He thought of the old stag while he wandered around. He wanted very much to meet him. He wanted to say to him, 'See, I don't call my mother any more,' so the old stag would praise him.

But he told Gobo and Faline the next time they were together on the meadow. They listened attentively and had nothing to relate that could compare with this.

'Weren't you frightened?' asked Gobo excitedly.

O well,—Bambi confessed, he had been frightened. But only a little.

'I should have been terribly frightened,' Gobo declared.

Bambi replied, no, he hadn't been very much afraid, because the stag was so handsome.

'That wouldn't have helped me much,' Gobo added, 'I'd have been too afraid to look at him. When I'm frightened I have streaks before my eyes so that I can't see at all, and my heart beats so fast that I can't breathe.'

Faline became very thoughtful after Bambi's story and did not say anything.

But the next time they met, Gobo and Faline bounded up in great haste. They were alone again and so was Bambi. 'We have been hunting for you all this time,' cried Gobo. 'Yes,' Faline said importantly, 'because now we know who it was you saw.' Bambi bounded into the air for curiosity and asked, 'Who?'

Faline said solemnly, 'It was the old Prince.'

'Who told you that?' Bambi demanded.

'Mother,' Faline replied.

Bambi was amazed. 'Did you tell her the whole story?' They both nodded. 'But it was a secret,' Bambi cried angrily.

Gobo tried to shield himself at once. 'I didn't do it, it was Faline,' he said. But Faline cried excitedly 'What do you mean, a secret? I wanted to know who it was. Now we all know and it's much more exciting.'

Bambi was burning up with desire to hear all about it and let himself be mollified. Faline told him everything. 'The old Prince is the biggest stag in the whole forest. There isn't anybody else that compares with him. Nobody knows how old he is. Nobody can find out where he lives. No one knows his family. Very few have seen him even once. At times he was thought to be dead because he hadn't been seen for so long. Then someone would see him again for a second and so they knew he was still alive. Nobody had ever dared ask him where he had been. He speaks to nobody and no one dares speak to him. He uses trails none of the others ever use. He knows the very depths of the forest. And he does not know such a thing as danger. Other Princes fight one another at times, sometimes in fun or to try each other out, sometimes in earnest. For many years no one has fought with the old stag. And of those who fought with him long ago not one is living. He is the great Prince.'

Bambi forgave Gobo and Faline for babbling his secret to their mother. He was even glad to have found out all these important things, but he was glad that Gobo and Faline did not know all about it. They did not know that the great Prince had said, 'Can't you stay by yourself? Shame on you!' Now Bambi was very glad that he had not told them about these things. For then Gobo and Faline would have told that along with the rest, and the whole forest would have gossiped about it.

That night when the moon rose Bambi's mother came back again.

He suddenly saw her standing under the great oak at the edge of the meadow looking around for him. He saw her right away and ran to her.

That night Bambi learned something new. His mother was tired and hungry. They did not walk as far as usual. The mother quieted her hunger in the meadow where Bambi too was used to eating most of his meals. Side by side they nibbled at the bushes and pleasantly ruminating, went farther and farther into the woods.

Presently there was a loud rustling in the bushes. Before Bambi could guess what it was his mother began to cry aloud as she did when she was very terrified or when she was beside herself. 'Aoh!' she cried and, giving a bound, stopped and cried, 'Aoh! Baoh!' Bambi tried to make out the mighty forms which were drawing near as the rustling grew louder. They were right near now. They resembled Bambi and Bambi's mother, Aunt Ena and all the rest of his family, but they were gigantic and so powerfully built that he stared up at them overcome.

Suddenly Bambi began to bleat, 'Aoh! Baoh-baoh!' He hardly knew he was bleating. He couldn't help himself. The procession tramped slowly by. Three, four giant apparitions, one after the other. The last of them was bigger than any of the others. He had a wild mane on his neck and his antlers were tree-like. It took Bambi's breath away to see them. He stood and bleated from a heart full of wonder, for he was more weirdly affected than ever before in his life. He was afraid, but in a peculiar way. He felt how pitifully small he was, and even his mother seemed to him to have shrunk. He felt ashamed without understanding why and at the same time terror shook him. He bleated, 'Baoh! b-a-o-h!' He felt better when he bleated that way.

The procession had gone by. There was nothing more to be seen or heard. Even his mother was silent. Only Bambi kept giving short bleats now and then. He still felt the shock.

'Be still,' his mother said, 'they have gone now.'

'Oh, Mother,' Bambi whispered, 'who was it?'

'Well,' said his mother, 'they are not so dangerous when all is said and done. Those are your big cousins, the elk—they are strong and they are important, far stronger than we are.'

'And aren't they dangerous?' Bambi asked.

'Not as a rule,' his mother explained. 'Of course, a good many

Suddenly the Old Stag was towering over him.

things are said to have happened. This and that is told about them, but I don't know if there is any truth in such gossip or not. They've never done any harm to me or to any one of my acquaintances.'

'Why should they do anything to us?' asked Bambi, 'if they are cousins of ours?' He wanted to feel calm but he kept trembling.

'O, they never do anything to us,' his mother answered, 'but I don't know why, I'm frightened whenever I see them. I don't understand it myself. But it happens that way every time.'

Bambi was gradually reassured by her words but he remained thoughtful. Right above him in the branches of an alder, the screech-owl was hooting in his blood-curdling way. Bambi was distracted and forgot to act as if he had been frightened. But the screech-owl flew by anyhow and asked, 'Didn't I frighten you?'

'Of course,' Bambi replied, 'you always frighten me.'

The screech-owl chuckled softly. He was pleased. 'I hope you don't hold it against me,' he said, 'it's just my way.' He fluffed himself up so that he resembled a ball, sank his bill in his foamy white feathers and put on a terribly wise and serious face. He was satisfied with himself.

Bambi poured out his heart to him. 'Do you know?' he began slyly, 'I've just had a much worse fright.'

'Indeed!' said the owl, displeased.

Bambi told him about his encounter with his giant relations.

'Don't talk to me about relations,' the owl exclaimed, 'I've got relations too. But I only fly about in the daytime so they are all down on me now. No, there isn't much use in relations. If they're bigger than you are, they're no good to you, and if they're smaller they're worth still less. If they're bigger than you, you can't bear them because they're proud, and if they're smaller they can't bear you because you're proud. No, I prefer to have nothing to do with the whole crowd.'

'But I don't even know my relations,' Bambi said, laughing shyly. 'I never heard of them, I never saw them, before today.'

'Don't bother about such people,' the screech-owl advised. 'Believe me,' and he rolled his eyes significantly, 'believe me, it's the best way. Relatives are never as good as friends. Look at us, we're not related in any way but we're good friends, and that's much better.'

Bambi wanted to say something else but the screech-owl went on,

'I've had experience with such things. You are still too young but, believe me, I know better. Besides, I don't like to get mixed up in family affairs.' He rolled his eyes thoughtfully and looked so impressive with his serious face that Bambi kept a discreet silence.

★   ★   ★   ★

Another night passed and morning brought an event.

It was a cloudless morning, dewy and fresh. All the leaves on the trees and the bushes seemed suddenly to smell sweeter. The meadows sent up great clouds of perfume to the tree-tops.

'Peep!' said the field-mice when they awoke. They said it very softly. But since it was still grey dawn they said nothing else for a while. For a time it was perfectly still. Then a crow's hoarse rasping caw sounded far above in the sky. The crows had awakened and were visiting one another in the tree-tops. The magpie answered at once, 'Shackarakshak! Did you think I was still asleep?' Then a hundred small voices started in very softly here and there. Peep! peep! tiu! Sleep and the dark were still in these sounds. And they came from far apart.

Suddenly a blackbird flew to the top of a beech. She perched way up on the topmost twig that stuck up thin against the sky and sat there watching how, far away over the trees, the night-weary, pale-grey heavens were glowing in the distant east and coming to life. Then she commenced to sing.

Her little black body seemed only a tiny dark speck at that distance. She looked like a dead leaf. But she poured out her song in a great flood of rejoicing through the whole forest. And everything began to stir. The finches warbled, the little redthroat and the goldfinch were heard. The doves rushed from place to place with a loud clapping and rustling of wings. The pheasants cackled as though their throats would burst. The noise of their wings, as they flew from their roosts to the ground, was soft but powerful. They kept uttering their metallic splintering call with its soft ensuing chuckle. Far above, the falcons cried sharply and joyously, 'Yayaya!'

The sun rose.

'Diu diyu!' the yellow bird rejoiced. He flew to and fro among the branches, and his round yellow body flashed in the morning light like a winged ball of gold.

Bambi walked under the great oak on the meadow. It sparkled with dew. It smelled of grass and flowers and moist earth, and whispered of a thousand living things. Friend Hare was there and seemed to be thinking over something important. A haughty pheasant strutted slowly by, nibbling at the grass seeds and peering cautiously in all directions. The dark metallic blue on his neck gleamed in the sun.

One of the Princes was standing close to Bambi. Bambi had never seen any of the fathers so close before. The stag was standing right in front of him next to the hazel bush and was somewhat hidden by the branches. Bambi did not move. He wanted the Prince to come out completely and was wondering whether he dared speak to him. He wanted to ask his mother and looked around for her. But his mother had already gone away and was standing some distance off, beside Aunt Ena. At the same time Gobo and Faline came running out of the woods. Bambi was still thinking it over without stirring. If he went up to his mother and the others now he would have to pass by the Prince. He felt as if he couldn't do it.

'O well,' he thought, 'I don't have to ask my mother first. The old Prince spoke to me and I didn't tell mother anything about it. I'll say, 'Good-morning, Prince.' He can't be offended at that. But if he does get angry I'll run away fast.' Bambi struggled with his resolve which began to waver again.

Presently the Prince walked out from behind the hazel bush on to the meadow.

'Now,' thought Bambi.

Then there was a crash like thunder.

Bambi shrank together and didn't know what had happened. He saw the Prince leap into the air under his very nose and watched him rush past him into the forest with one great bound.

Bambi looked around in a daze. The thunder still vibrated. He saw how his mother and Aunt Ena, Gobo and Faline fled into the woods. He saw how Friend Hare scurried away like mad. He saw the pheasant running with his neck outstretched. He noticed that the forest grew suddenly still. He started and sprang into the thicket. He had made only a few bounds when he saw the Prince lying on the ground in front of him, motionless. Bambi stopped horrified, not understanding what it meant. The Prince lay bleeding from a great wound in his shoulder. He was dead.

'Don't stop!' a voice beside commanded. It was his mother who rushed past at full gallop. 'Run,' she cried. 'Run as fast as you can!' She did not slow up, but raced ahead, and her command brought Bambi after her. He ran with all his might.

'What is it, Mother?' he asked. 'What is it, Mother?'

His mother answered between gasps, 'It—was—He!'

Bambi shuddered and they ran on. At last they stopped for lack of breath.

'What did you say? Tell me what it was you said?' a soft voice called down from overhead. Bambi looked up. The squirrel came chattering through the branches.

'I ran the whole way with you,' he cried. 'It was dreadful.'

'Were you there?' asked the mother.

'Of course I was there,' the squirrel replied. 'I am still trembling in every limb.' He sat erect, balancing with his splendid tail, displaying his small white chest, and holding his forepaws protestingly against his body. 'I'm beside myself with excitement,' he said.

'I'm quite weak from fright myself,' said the mother. 'I don't understand it. Not one of us saw a thing.'

'Is that so?' the squirrel said pettishly. 'I saw Him long before.'

'So did I,' another voice cried. It was the magpie. She flew past and settled on a branch.

'So did I,' came a croak from above. It was the jay who was sitting on an ash.

A couple of crows in the tree-tops cawed harshly, 'We saw Him, too.'

They all sat around talking importantly. They were unusually excited and seemed to be full of anger and fear.

'Whom?' Bambi thought. 'Whom did they see?'

'I tried my best,' the squirrel was saying, pressing his forepaws protestingly against his heart. 'I tried my best to warn the poor Prince.'

'And I,' the jay rasped. 'How often did I scream? But he didn't care to hear me.'

'He didn't hear me either,' the magpie croaked. 'I called him at least ten times. I wanted to fly right past him, for, thought I, he hasn't heard me yet; I'll fly to the hazel bush where he's standing. He can't help hearing me there. But at that minute it happened.'

'My voice is probably louder than yours, and I warned him as well as I could,' the crow said in an impudent tone. 'But gentlemen of that stamp pay little attention to the likes of us.'

'Much too little, really,' the squirrel agreed.

'Well, we did what we could,' said the magpie. 'We're certainly not to blame when an accident happens.'

'Such a handsome Prince,' the squirrel lamented. 'And in the very prime of life.'

'Akh!' croaked the jay. 'It would have been better for him if he hadn't been so proud and had paid more attention to us.'

'He certainly wasn't proud.'

'No more so than the other Princes of his family,' the magpie put in.

'Just plain stupid,' sneered the jay.

'You're stupid yourself,' the crow cried down from overhead. 'Don't you talk about stupidity. The whole forest knows how stupid you are.'

'I!' replied the jay, stiff with astonishment. 'Nobody can accuse me of being stupid. I may be forgetful but I'm certainly not stupid.'

'O just as you please,' said the crow solemnly. 'Forget what I said to you but remember that the Prince did not die because he was proud or stupid, but because no one can escape Him.'

'Akh!' croaked the jay. 'I don't like that kind of talk.' He flew away.

The crow went on, 'He has already outwitted many of my family. He kills what He wants. Nothing can help us.'

'You have to be on your guard against Him,' the magpie broke in.

'You certainly do,' said the crow sadly. 'Goodbye.' He flew off, with his family accompanying him.

Bambi looked around. His mother was no longer there.

'What are they talking about now?' thought Bambi. 'I can't understand what they are talking about. Who is this "He" they talk about? That was He, too, that I saw in the bushes, but He didn't kill me.'

Bambi thought of the Prince lying in front of him with his bloody mangled shoulder. He was dead now. Bambi walked along. The forest sang again with a thousand voices, the sun pierced the tree-tops with its broad rays. There was light everywhere. The leaves began to smell. Far above the falcons called, close at hand a woodpecker hammered as if nothing had happened. Bambi was not happy. He felt himself threatened by something dark. He did not understand how the others could be so carefree and happy while life was so difficult and dangerous. Then the desire seized him to go deeper and deeper into the woods. They lured him into their depths. He wanted to find some hiding place where, shielded on all sides by impenetrable thickets, he could never be seen. He never wanted to go to the meadows again.

Something moved very softly in the bushes. Bambi drew back violently. The old stag was standing in front of him.

Bambi trembled. He wanted to run away, but he controlled himself and remained. The old stag looked at him with his great deep eyes and asked. 'Were you out there before?'

'Yes,' Bambi said softly. His heart was pounding in his throat.

'Where is your mother?' asked the stag.

Bambi answered still very softly, 'I don't know.'

The old stag kept gazing at him. 'And still you're not calling for her?' he said.

Bambi looked into the noble, iron-grey face, looked at the stag's antlers and suddenly felt full of courage. 'I can stay by myself, too,' he said.

The old stag considered him for a while; then he asked gently, 'Aren't you the little one that was crying for his mother not long ago?'

Bambi was somewhat embarrassed, but his courage held. 'Yes, I am,' he confessed.

The old stag looked at him in silence and it seemed to Bambi as if those deep eyes gazed still more mildly. 'You scolded me then, Prince,' he cried excitedly, 'because I was afraid of being left alone. Since then I haven't been.'

The stag looked at Bambi appraisingly and smiled a very slight, hardly noticeable smile. Bambi noticed it, however. 'Noble Prince,' he asked confidently, 'what has happened? I don't understand it. Who is this "He" they are all talking about?' He stopped, terrified by the dark glance that bade him be silent.

Another pause ensued. The old stag was gazing past Bambi into the distance. Then he said slowly, 'Listen, smell and see for yourself. Find out for yourself.' He lifted his antlered head still higher. 'Farewell,' he said, nothing else. Then he vanished.

Bambi stood transfixed and wanted to cry. But that farewell still rang in his ears and sustained him. Farewell, the old stag had said, so he couldn't have been angry.

Bambi felt himself thrill with pride, felt inspired with a deep earnestness. Yes, life was difficult and full of danger. But come what might he would learn to bear it all.

He walked slowly deeper into the forest.

THE DEATH OF WAHB

Ernest Thompson Seton

Everything has a smell of its own for those that have noses to smell. Wahb, the Grizzly, had been learning smells all his life, and knew the meaning of most of those in the mountains. It was as though each and every thing had a voice of its own for him; and yet it was far better than a voice, for every one knows that a good nose is better than eyes and ears together. And each of these myriads of voices kept crying, 'Here and such am I.'

The juniper-berries, the rosehips, the strawberries, each had a soft, sweet little voice, calling, 'Here we are—Berries, Berries.'

The great pine woods had a loud, far-reaching voice, 'Here are we, the Pine trees,' but when he got right up to them Wahb could hear the low, sweet call of the piñon-nuts, 'Here are we, the Piñon-nuts.'

And the quamash beds in May sang a perfect chorus when the wind was right: 'Quamash beds, Quamash beds.'

And when he got among them he made out each single voice. Each root had its own little piece to say to his nose: 'Here am I, a big Quamash, rich and ripe,' or a tiny, sharp voice, 'Here am I, a good-for-nothing, stringy little root.'

And the broad, rich russulas in the autumn called aloud, 'I am a fat, wholesome Mushroom,' and the deadly amanita cried, 'I am an Amanita. Let me alone, or you'll be a sick bear.' And the fairy harebell!

of the canyon-banks sang a song too, as fine as its thread-like stem, and as soft as its dainty blue; but the warden of the smells had learned to report it not, for this, and a million other such, were of no interest to Wahb.

So every living thing that moved, and every flower that grew, and every rock and stone and shape on earth told out its tale and sang its little story to his nose. Day or night, fog or bright, that great, moist nose told him most of the things he needed to know, or passed unnoticed those of no concern, and he depended on it more and more. If his eyes and ears together reported so and so, he would not even then believe it until his nose said, 'Yes; that is right.'

But this is something that man cannot understand, for he has sold the birthright of his nose for the privilege of living in towns.

While hundreds of smells were agreeable to Wahb, thousands were indifferent to him, a good many were unpleasant, and some actually put him in a rage.

He had often noticed that if a west wind were blowing when he was at the head of the Piney Canyon there was an odd, new scent. Some days he did not mind it, and some days it disgusted him; but he never followed it up. On other days a north wind from the high Divide brought a most awful smell, something unlike any other, a smell that he wanted only to get away from.

★   ★   ★   ★

Wahb was getting well past his youth now, and he began to have pains in the hind leg that had been wounded so often. After a cold night or a long time of wet weather he could scarcely use that leg, and one day, while thus crippled, the west wind came down the canyon with an odd message to his nose. Wahb could not clearly read the message, but it seemed to say, 'Come', and something within him said, 'Go'. The smell of food will draw a hungry creature and disgust a gorged one. We do not know why, and all that any one can learn is that the desire springs from a need of the body. So Wahb felt drawn by what had long disgusted him, and he slouched up the mountain path, grumbling to himself and slapping savagely back at branches that chanced to switch his face.

The odd odour grew very strong; it led him where he had never been before—up a bank of whitish sand to a bench of the same colour, where there was unhealthy-looking water running down, and a kind of fog coming out of a hole. Wahb threw up his nose suspiciously— such a peculiar smell! He climbed the bench.

A snake wriggled across the sand in front. Wahb crushed it with a blow that made the near trees shiver and sent a balanced boulder toppling down, and he growled a growl that rumbled up the valley like distant thunder. Then he came to the foggy hole. It was full of water that moved gently and steamed. Wahb put in his foot, and found it was quite warm and that it felt pleasantly on his skin. He put in both feet, and little by little went in farther, causing the pool to overflow on all sides, till he was lying at full length in the warm, almost hot, sulphur-spring, and sweltering in the greenish water, while the wind drifted the steam about overhead.

There are plenty of these sulphur-springs in the Rockies, but this chanced to be the only one on Wahb's range. He lay in it for over an hour; then, feeling that he had had enough, he heaved his huge bulk up on the bank, and realized that he was feeling remarkably well and supple. The stiffness of his hind leg was gone.

He shook the water from his shaggy coat. A broad ledge in full sun-heat invited him to stretch himself out and dry. But first he reared against the nearest tree and left a mark that none could mistake. True, there were plenty of signs of other animals using the sulphur-bath for their ills; but what of it? Thenceforth that tree bore this inscription, in a language of mud, hair, and smell, that every mountain creature could read:

My bath. Keep away!

(signed) WAHB.

Wahb lay on his belly till his back was dry, then turned on his broad back and squirmed about in a ponderous way till the broiling sun had wholly dried him. He realized that he was really feeling very well now. He did not say to himself, 'I am troubled with that unpleasant disease called rheumatism, and sulphur-bath treatment is the thing to cure it.' But what he did know was, 'I have dreadful pains;

I feel better when I am in this stinking pool.' So thenceforth he came back whenever the pains began again, and each time he was cured.

★ ★ ★ ★

Everyone knows that a Bitter-root Grizzly is a bad bear. The Bitter-root Range is the roughest part of the mountains. The ground is everywhere cut up with deep ravines and overgrown with dense and tangled underbrush.

It is an impossible country for horses, and difficult for gunners, and there is any amount of good bear-pasture. So there are plenty of bears and plenty of trappers.

The Roachbacks, as the Bitter-root Grizzlies are called, are a cunning and desperate race. An old Roachback knows more about traps than half a dozen ordinary trappers; he knows more about plants and roots than a whole college of botanists. He can tell to a certainty just when and where to find each kind of grub and worm, and he knows by a whiff whether the hunter on his trail a mile away is working with guns, poison, dogs, traps, or all of them together. And he has one general rule, which is an endless puzzle to the hunter: 'Whatever you decide to do, do it quickly and follow it right up.' So when a trapper and a Roachback meet, the bear at once makes up his mind to run away as hard as he can, or to rush at the man and fight to a finish.

The Grizzlies of the Bad Lands did not do this: they used to stand on their dignity and growl like a thunderstorm, and so gave the hunters a chance to play their deadly lightning; and lightning is worse than thunder any day. Men can get used to growls that rumble along the ground and up one's legs to the little house where one's courage lives; but bears cannot get used to 45–90 soft-nosed bullets, and that is why the Grizzlies of the Bad Lands were all killed off.

So the hunters have learned that they never know what a Roachback will do; but they do know that he is going to be quick about it.

Altogether these Bitter-root Grizzlies have solved very well the problem of life, in spite of white men, and are therefore increasing in their own wild mountains.

Of course a range will hold only so many bears, and the increase is crowded out; so that when that slim young Baldfaced Roachback found he could not hold the range he wanted, he went out perforce to seek his fortune in the world.

He was not a big bear, or he would not have been crowded out; but he had been trained in a good school, so that he was cunning enough to get on very well elsewhere. How he wandered down to the Salmon River Mountains and did not like them; how he travelled till he got among the barb-wire fences of the Snake Plains and of course could not stay there; how a mere chance turned him from going eastward to the park, where he might have rested; how he made for the Snake River Mountains and found more hunters than berries; how he crossed into the Tetons and looked down with digust on the teeming man colony of Jackson's Hole, does not belong to this history of Wahb. But when Baldy Roachback crossed the Gros Ventre Range and over the Wind River Divide to the head of the Greybull, he does come into the story, just as he did into the country and the life of the Meteetsee Grizzly.

The Roachback had not found a man-sign since he left Jackson's Hole, and here he was in a land of plenty of food. He feasted on all the delicacies of the season, and enjoyed the easy, brushless country till he came on one of Wahb's signposts.

'Trespassers beware!' it said in the plainest manner. The Roachback reared up against it.

'Thunder! what a bear!' The nose-mark was a head and neck above Baldy's highest reach. Now, a simple bear would have gone quietly away after this discovery; but Baldy felt that the mountains owed him a living, and here was a good one if he could keep out of the way of the big fellow. He nosed about the place, kept a sharp lookout for the present owner, and went on feeding wherever he ran across a good thing.

A step or two from this ominous tree was an old pine stump. In the Bitter-roots there are often mice nests under such stumps, and Baldy jerked it over to see. There was nothing. The stump rolled over against the signpost. Baldy had not yet made up his mind about it; but a new notion came into his cunning brain. He turned his head on this side, then on that. He looked at the stump, then at the sign, with his little pig-like eyes. Then he deliberately stood up on the pine root, with his back to the tree, and put his mark away up, a head at least above that of Wahb. He rubbed his back long and hard, and he sought

He could sense the presence of danger all round him.

some mud to smear his head and shoulders, then came back and made the mark so big, so strong, and so high, and emphasized it with such claw-gashes in the bark, that it could be read only in one way— a challenge to the present claimant from some monstrous invader, who was ready, nay anxious, to fight to a finish for this desirable range.

Maybe it was accident and maybe design, but when the Roachback jumped from the root it rolled to one side. Baldy went on down the canyon, keeping the keenest lookout for his enemy.

It was not long before Wahb found the trail of the interloper, and all the ferocity of his outside-the-park nature was aroused.

He followed the trail for miles on more than one occasion. But the small bear was quick-footed as well as quick-witted and never showed himself. He made a point, however, of calling at each signpost, and if there was any means of cheating, so that his mark might be put higher, he did it with a vim, and left a big, showy record. But if there was no chance of any but a fair register, he would not go near the tree, but looked for a fresh tree near by with some log or side ledge to reach from.

Thus Wahb soon found the interloper's marks towering far above his own—a monstrous bear evidently, that even he could not be sure of mastering. But Wahb was no coward. He was ready to fight to a finish any one that might come; and he hunted the range for that invader. Day after day Wahb sought for him and held himself ready to fight. He found his trail daily, and more and more often he found that towering record far above his own. He often smelled him on the wind; but he never saw him, for the old Grizzly's eyes had grown very dim of late years; things but a little way off were mere blurs to him. The continual menace could not but fill Wahb with uneasiness, for he was not young now, and his teeth and claws were worn and blunted. He was more than ever troubled with pains in his old wounds, and though he could have risen on the spur of the moment to fight any number of Grizzlies of any size, still the continual apprehension, the knowledge that he must hold himself ready at any moment to fight this young monster, weighed on his spirits and began to tell on his general health.

★   ★   ★   ★

The Roachback's life was one of continual vigilance, always ready to run, doubling and shifting to avoid the encounter that must mean instant death to him. Many a time from some hiding-place he watched the great bear, and trembled lest the wind should betray him. Several times his very impudence saved him, and more than once he was nearly cornered in a box-canyon. Once he escaped only by climbing up a long crack in a cliff, which Wahb's huge frame could not have entered. But still, in a mad persistence, he kept on marking the trees farther into the range.

At last he scented and followed up the sulphur bath. He did not understand it at all. It had no appeal to him, but hereabouts were the tracks of the owner. In a spirit of mischief the Roachback scratched dirt into the spring, and then seeing the rubbing-tree, he stood sidewise on the rocky ledge, and was thus able to put his mark full five feet above that of Wahb. Then he nervously jumped down, and was running about, defiling the bath and keeping a sharp lookout, when he heard a noise in the woods below. Instantly he was all alert. The sound drew near, then the wind brought the sure proof, and the Roachback, in terror, turned and fled into the woods.

It was Wahb. He had been failing in health of late; his old pains were on him again, and, as well as his hind leg, had seized his right shoulder, where were still lodged two rifleballs. He was feeling very ill, and crippled with pain. He came up the familiar bank at a jerky limp, and there caught the odour of the foe; then he saw the track in the mud—his eyes said the track of a *small* bear, but his eyes were dim now, and his nose, his unerring nose, said, 'This is the track of the huge invader.' Then he noticed the tree with his sign on it, and there beyond doubt was the stranger's mark far above his own. His eyes and nose were agreed on this; and more, they told him that the foe was close at hand, might at any moment come.

Wahb was feeling ill and weak with pain. He was in no mood for a desperate fight. A battle against such odds would be madness now. So, without taking the treatment, he turned and swung along the bench away from the direction taken by the stranger—the first time since his cubhood that he had declined to fight.

That was a turning-point in Wahb's life. If he had followed up the stranger he would have found the miserable little craven trembling, cowering, in an agony of terror, behind a log in a natural trap, a walled-in glade only fifty yards away, and would surely have crushed him. Had he even taken the bath, his strength and courage would have been renewed, and if not, then at least in time he would have met his foe, and his after life would have been different. But he had turned. This was the fork in the trail, but he had no means of knowing it.

He limped along, skirting the lower spurs of the Shoshones, and soon came on that horrid smell that he had known for years, but never followed up or understood. It was right in his road, and he traced it to a small, barren ravine that was strewn over with skeletons and dark objects, and Wahb, as he passed, smelled a smell of many different animals, and knew by its quality that they were lying dead in this treeless, grassless hollow. For there was a cleft in the rocks at the upper end, whence poured a deadly gas; invisible but heavy, it filled the little gulch like a brimming poison bowl, and at the lower end there was a steady overflow. But Wahb knew only that the air that poured from it as he passed made him dizzy and sleepy, and repelled him, so that he got quickly away from it and was glad once more to breathe the piney wind.

Once Wahb decided to retreat, it was all too easy to do so next time; and the result worked double disaster. For, since the big stranger was allowed possession of the sulphur-spring, Wahb felt that he would rather not go there. Sometimes when he came across the traces of his foe, a spurt of his old courage would come back. He would rumble that thunder-growl as of old, and go painfully lumbering along the trail to settle the thing right then and there. But he never overtook the mysterious giant, and his rheumatism, growing worse now that he was barred from the cure, soon made him daily less capable of either running or fighting.

Sometimes Wahb would sense his foe's approach when he was in a bad place for fighting, and, without really running, he would yield to a wish to be on a better footing, where he would have a fair chance. This better footing never led him nearer the enemy, for it is well known that the one awaiting has the advantage.

Some days Wahb felt so ill that it would have been madness to have staked everything on a fight, and when he felt well or a little better, the stranger seemed to keep away.

Wahb soon found that the stranger's track was most often on the Warhouse and the west slope of the Piney, the very best feeding-grounds. To avoid these when he did not feel equal to fighting was only natural, and as he was always in more or less pain now, it amounted to abandoning to the stranger the best part of the range.

Weeks went by. Wahb had meant to go back to his bath, but he never did. His pains grew worse; he was now crippled in his right shoulder as well as in his hind leg.

The long strain of waiting for the fight begot anxiety, that grew to be apprehension, which, with the sapping of his strength, was breaking down his courage, as it always must when courage is founded on muscular force. His daily care now was not to meet and fight the invader, but to avoid him till he felt better.

Thus that first little retreat grew into one long retreat. Wahb had to go farther and farther down the Piney to avoid an encounter. He was daily worse fed, and as the weeks went by was daily less able to crush a foe.

He was living and hiding at last on the Lower Piney—the very place where once his mother had brought him with his little brothers. The life he led now was much like the one he had led after that dark day. Perhaps for the same reason. If he had had a family of his own all might have been different. As he limped along one morning, seeking among the barren aspen groves for a few roots, or the wormy partridge-berries that were too poor to interest the squirrel and the grouse, he heard a stone rattle down the western slope into the woods, and a little later, on the wind was borne the dreaded taint. He waded through the ice-cold Piney—once he would have leaped it—and the chill water sent through and up each great hairy limb keen pains that seemed to reach his very life. He was retreating again—which way? There seemed but one way now—towards the new ranch-house.

But there were signs of stir about it long before he was near enough to be seen. His nose, his trustiest friend, said, 'Turn, turn and seek the hills,' and turn he did even at the risk of meeting there the dreadful foe. He limped painfully along the north bank of the Piney, keeping in the hollows and among the trees. He tried to climb a cliff that of old he had often bounded up at full speed. When halfway up his footing gave way, and down he rolled to the bottom. A long way round was now the only road, for onward he must go—on—on. But where? There seemed no choice now but to abandon the whole range to the terrible stranger.

And feeling, as far as a bear can feel, that he is fallen, defeated, dethroned at last, that he is driven from his ancient range by a bear too strong for him to face, he turned up the west fork, and the lot was drawn. The strength and speed were gone from his once mighty limbs; he took three times as long as he once would to mount each well-known ridge, and as he went he glanced backwards from time to time to know if he were pursued. Away up the head of the little branch were the Shoshones, bleak, forbidding; no enemies were there, and the park was beyond it all—on, on he must go. But as he climbed with shaky limbs, and short uncertain steps, the west wind brought the odour of Death Gulch, that fearful little valley where everything was dead, where the very air was deadly. It used to disgust him and drive him away, but now Wahb felt that it had a message for him; he was drawn by it. It was in his line of flight, and he hobbled slowly towards the place. He went nearer, nearer, until he stood upon the entering ledge. A vulture that had descended to feed on one of the victims was slowly going to sleep on the untouched carcass. Wahb swung his great grizzled muzzle and his long white beard in the wind. The odour that he once had hated was attractive now. There was a strange biting quality in the air. His body craved it. For it seemed to numb his pain and it promised sleep, as it did that day when first he saw the place.

Far below him, to the right and to the left and on and on as far as the eye could reach, was the great kingdom that once had been his; where he had lived for years in the glory of his strength; where none had dared to meet him face to face. The whole earth could show no view more beautiful. But Wahb had no thought of its beauty; he only knew that it was a good land to live in; that it had been his, but that now it was gone, for his strength was gone, and he was flying to seek a place where he could rest and be at peace.

Away over the Shoshones, indeed, was the road to the park, but it was far, far away, with a doubtful end to the long, doubtful journey. But why so far? Here in this little gulch was all he sought; here were peace and painless sleep. He knew it; for his nose, his never-erring nose, said, '*Here! here now!*'

He paused a moment at the gate, and as he stood the windborne fumes began their subtle work. Five were the faithful wardens of his life, and the best and trustiest of them all flung open wide the door he long had kept. A moment still Wahb stood in doubt. His lifelong guide was silent now, had given up his post. But another sense he felt within. The Angel of the Wild Things was standing there, beckoning, in the little vale. Wahb did not understand. He had no eyes to see the tear in the angel's eyes, nor the pitying smile that was surely on his lips. He could not even see the angel. But he *felt* him beckoning, beckoning.

A rush of his ancient courage surged in the Grizzly's rugged breast. He turned aside into the little gulch. The deadly vapours entered in, filled his huge chest and tingled in his vast, heroic limbs as he calmly lay down on the rocky, herbless floor and as gently went to sleep, as he did that day in his mother's arms by the Greybull, long ago.

TO SAVE THE TIGER

Chris Spencer

An April wind scudded low across the ground, rustling ferns and setting the first bluebells nodding in welcome to a new day. High on a rise a sudden group of silver birches huddled defiantly like comrades of war settled in for the last stand. At their feet, lying as still as death across their roots, a stranger looked out, his eyes flickering in recognition of far-off sounds borne on the wind. The yapping of excited hounds mingled with the urgent voices of men, and though the stranger did not understand the words, he knew their meaning as clearly as if he spoke the language. 'Hurry!' they are saying. 'He went this way. Look, the dogs have found the scent. Come on, there's no time to lose!'

The tiger yawned and bent to wash a paw, his coarse tongue rasping over golden fur. The pursuit could wait a little longer. He was tired. Tired and hungry. It had been a long night of seeking and failing to find food. Not that food hadn't been available—the English countryside abounds with potential meals, albeit small ones, for a tiger on the loose— but a young tiger whose instinct to hunt has been dulled by captivity and regular mealtimes cannot expect to be instantly successful in finding its own food in the wild. But give it time. . . .

He winced as a strange hollow feeling growled at him from deep within his stomach—a feeling as unwelcome as the growing sense of alarm triggered by the advancing dogs. He longed to close his heavy eyes and slip into the land of distant adventures—after all, daytime was made for sleeping as surely as night was meant for prowling— but the wind was beginning to bring the scent as well as the sound of his pursuers, and instinct was stirring his tired bulk. It was best to move now, before the dogs and their handlers came over that next hill. Best to keep ahead, to hold on to the advantage. And no sooner had he thought it than he had risen to his feet and vanished as silently as a shadow into the thick-knitted undergrowth. Welcome protection for the tiger, the brambles and twisting shoots would slow down the men long enough for the big cat to put miles between them.

Out in the open again at the other side of the thicket, powerful legs rhythmically pounded the carpet of leaf-mould, carrying the tiger on and on, his unfamiliar form and speed sending birds clattering upwards from the trees with great cries of alarm. Beneath his feet, woodland creatures scurried out of the way of this hulk of charging thunder.

As he ran, the need to keep ahead was joined by the exhilaration of freedom—of knowing no bounds and no master. But as quickly as this sunshine broke through into his racing mind, so clouds hurried across with the dark reality of his loneliness. For the broken ties with confinement and keeper meant broken ties with his family. His pace slowed as his mind became crowded with memories of his brother, always game for a rough-and-tumble on the old log; of his sisters, sweet as honeycomb to your face but as spiteful as any she-cat when your back was turned; and of his mother—so gentle yet so firm a tutor, so sweet yet so sharp a guardian, with paws that could caress or cuff with equal measures of love and correction. . . .

This vision of his mother grew until, almost overwhelmed by the icy harshness of separation, he began to lose his incentive to move on. Padding to a halt in a copse of beech and oak, he looked all around, almost expecting to hear his mother's voice, so strong was the impression of her face upon his mind.

But the vision was snatched away by a movement in the distance, away across the open ground which stretched beyond the trees. There were people—only one or two—but wasn't there also water?

★　　★　　★　　★

'In Surrey the search is still going on for the young Indian tiger which escaped when the lorry in which it was being transported overturned in a crash on the A25 near Dorking. Although capable of travelling many miles at night—the time when tigers are most active—the animal is thought still to be in the area, which offers good cover with its hundreds of acres of woodland. There are few homes in the vicinity— just a few large, detached properties on the edge of Surrey's executive belt—but police are concerned for the safety of people who use the woods for recreational purposes. The message to them is: stay away until the tiger has been found. Zoo officials are backing this advice. They say that although the tiger is not fully grown and not necessarily dangerous (in the wild tigers prefer to steer well clear of man), it is nevertheless unpredictable, particularly in its present state of confusion and possible hunger. Under no circumstances should it be approached. Anyone who thinks he spots the tiger should inform his local police station immediately.

'Now sport, and in today's home match against—'

Click! A woman's fingers switched off the portable radio and she muttered nervously as she bit into a sliver of toast, best butter oozing around gold-capped teeth.

'Goodness, I hope they hurry up and catch that animal. I don't feel safe here on my own.'

Across the table, his head embedded in a copy of the *Financial Times,* her husband grunted, then cursed. He folded the newspaper expertly and threw it down on the table with an air of finality.

'Well, that's Cobrax Castings up the spout.'

He looked up, realising his wife had spoken.

'Er, what was that, dear?'

She rolled her eyes in a gesture of hopelessness.

'Talk to a brick wall. I said I wish they'd hurry up and catch that tiger. They think it's still in the area, or weren't you listening?'

But even now he wasn't listening. His gaze had fixed on something beyond his wife, something outside the picture window at which they sat, and his eyes were widening in apparent disbelief. His mouth fell open, and he blurted out:

'Good grief! The—the tiger! Damn it, the thing's in the swimming pool!'

The woman turned, shrieked, dropped her toast, jumped up, fled out of the room, and raced upstairs, whimpering.

'Magnificent!'

The man was now on is feet, transfixed by the majestic orange-white head skimming across the pool not thirty feet from where he stood. Then, as though snapped from his trance, he said aloud:

'Camera. Where's my camera?'

His mind turning over like a fruit machine, he tore upstairs, just in time to hear his wife slam and bolt the bathroom door as he rushed into his bedroom. He grabbed his camera—the best money could buy—and snatched a glance out of the window to make sure his latest business venture was still in the swimming pool before bounding back down the stairs, skidding like a schoolboy on the parquet flooring in the hall.

The tiger watched warily from the corner of his eye as a one-eyed black metal box with a man behind it came cautiously through sliding doors on to the patio and across to the edge of the pool. Then there was a click and a 'Fabulous!' and the tiger tossed his proud head in the air, turned to the sound of another click and paddled regally to the far end of the pool where he climbed agilely from the water. Far above, clouds parted and streams of golden sunlight fell on orange and black fur as the tiger shook a small storm of crystal beads from his coat. He turned to see the black box coming towards him and remembered how many of these intimidating objects had been pointed at him through the chain-link fencing of his enclosure. Angered by the memory, he began pacing towards the box, letting out a bone-trembling roar that seemed to come all the way up from the pit of his stomach. The black box retreated to its cover. Satisfied, the tiger stopped. As glass doors slid shut, the man's voice rang through the house.

'Darling, you should see the shots I got of that thing! The papers will positively snap them up. You'll be able to get that new fur you keep on about.'

His muscles rippling like waves beneath his shining coat, the tiger padded leisurely to the distant seven-foot fence and sprang up and over, into a green sea of gently waving grasses.

He felt good in the long grass, as though this was where he was meant to be. It pleased him to be able to twist his supple body through the tall blades, and he began to play a game—no, it was more serious than a game: a test—to see if he could squeeze between certain blades without touching them. He found to his pleasure that he could. What more was this lithe, powerful, obedient body capable of he wondered? What other skills, suppressed by the lazy, undemanding life of captivity, lay dormant deep within, just waiting, like a tightly-wound spring, to be triggered into action?

A movement just a few yards ahead froze him in mid-step, a front paw seizing up only inches from the ground, his head suddenly cast as bronze, not a whisker moving in the warm air. The only sign of life in this instant statue was a white tail-tip, fluttering excitedly like a butterfly over nettles.

At last, fifty feet ahead, a rabbit showed itself, looked at the tiger unseeing, turned and began to hop away. The turning of its back was like the breaking of a spell to the big cat. Muscles bunched, and then as smoothly as running water the tiger was flowing through the grass. Sensing but not daring to see its enemy, the rabbit scooted away, its tiny heart pounding, its eyes popping. The tiger flashed on, his great, silent bulk throwing an early morning shadow of death over its helpless prey. . . .

And then the rabbit was out of the long grass and into open farmland. What happened next was a confusion of sound, sight and movement as a thunder-crack sent the little animal catapulting to a sudden, bloody standstill. The tiger, his liquid energy flowing too readily to stem, bounded on over his lifeless, bulge-eyed prey, himself now knowing the fear of death as another thunder-crack made earth spray up into his face.

Excited voices carried across the furrowed earth.

'The tiger! Get it, Jack! Get it while I reload!'

'Don't be a fool, you can't gun down a tiger!'

'You watch me! Here, give me that and reload for me.'

Another bullet smacked into chocolate earth, and a third whistled over the tiger's ears. Urged by the taste of terror, the big cat pounded faster and faster to the top of the field and into a thicket, leaves spraying around him as another thunder-crack sent its singing missile overhead.

'Missed! Blast it! I should have got the beggar, I was that close!'

'Be thankful you didn't. I doubt if you'd have killed it, and if you'd wounded it, it would have turned on us. A right mess it would have made of us, too.'

'Aw, you're just chicken.'

'I'd rather be chicken than dead. Come on, we'd better get back and report this. You go on; I'll get the rabbits.'

But what rabbits the two men had shot that morning were not to be found under the bush where they had been left. A hundred yards away, in cover of thick woodland, a young tiger sank his teeth into cold fur and warm blood.

With food inside him and the warm April sun filtering down through the trees on to his back, the tiger felt a drowsiness washing over him—a drowsiness with which he struggled, instinct pressing him to move on, to keep ahead, but his body welcoming the comfortable sleepiness that weighed on his eyelids. At last he gave up struggling and let himself slide into a contented doze.

★　　★　　★　　★

The noise that woke him burst rudely in upon his dream, dragging him reluctantly from a fairer land where he had been lord of all, strolling through his kingdom to the obedient acknowledgement of every living thing. How annoying to be roused from such a splendid world to find the real one crashing down around him. At first he didn't dare move, unsure of his foe in every way except its song and its strength. What earthly beast was this that buzzed like a million bees in a cave, having buzzed, knocked down full-grown trees with such a snapping and crashing that the blood of every woodland creature froze in its veins?

More buzzing, more crashing, but at last there came a clue: the voice of man. His enemy identified, he moved out, slipping sinuously between the saplings until, on the edge of his wood, he spied the scene of slaughter. Men with gleaming white heads wielded buzzing knives that spat in the eye of a hundred years of magnificent growth.

The deeper truth dawned upon his mind. In killing the trees they were killing *him*, for he could not survive without the cover of the woodland. His eyes flaming in anger, and with the terrifying roar of a wounded beast—wounded in soul if not in body—he turned, unleashed his coil-spring of power, and became a striped blur, hurrying far, far away from the cruel scene and all the raging senses it stirred within him.

★   ★   ★   ★

The man with the camera had reported his visitor to the police, and his evidence, backed up by the exaggerated claims of the rabbit-hunter, had brought the pursuit back to the trail which the dogs had lost at a stream crossed by the tiger shortly after he had emerged from the bramble thicket. The big cat still had a good lead on them, though, and he felt quite secure as, having run off his fury, he came to rest in a cluster of bushes perched high on a hill—a fine vantage point from which he could survey his new territory.

The sun was now high overhead, flaming down out of a cloudless sky with a warmth more befitting June, soothing him into a comfortable laziness that took him back to idle days in the enclosure when the heat stole away his strength so that he hadn't the energy even to brush the flies from his nose. When the heat became unbearable there was nothing for it but to flop into the water trough. On the very hottest day the keeper would come and hose them down—a spectacle which delighted the humans who came to stare and point, but a far more serious act, as necessary almost as breathing, for the steaming tiger.

The image of his mother came drifting back, and he recalled how, together with the others in the litter, he had lain curled up and wide-eyed in the moonlight as the big tigress recounted stories of long-ago—stories of adventure, of daring, of narrow escapes; stories that sent ripples of icy shivers down the little cats' spines as they shuffled closer to the big, protective paws, frightened to hear more and yet eager for the next scare. The stories his sisters had liked best were the sad ones, especially the one which told how the family came to be there in that small world of water-trough, logs and wire fencing: a story of a day in the Indian grasslands that began as a dream, so perfect did it seem in every way, and ended as a nightmare. It was the day when, in a moment's carelessness, the young tigress had walked into a trap laid by men; the day that ended a life of freedom and began an existence of captivity.

Her own mother had told her about man, warning that he was the tiger's only real enemy. Countless tigers had died by his hand, she had said. The lucky ones were captured and taken alive across a wide water, but where to no one knew. Now she knew her mother had been wrong: the lucky tigers were the dead ones. Death set the spirit free. But here, on the other side of the wide water, freedom was a dream.

His wet, pink nose twitched and he gave a gruff, snorty bellow, blowing away flies that buzzed around his eyes and landed, springing, on his whiskers.

The stories *he* had liked best were those which told of his fathers: of the Indian tiger's proud reign as the fierce and feared ruler of his kingdom—a beast so powerful it could bring down a gaur—India's giant wild ox—or leap high into a tree to snatch a monkey; so brilliantly marked it could stand motionless in a bed of swamp-reeds and never be seen; so cunning, so fast it could lure or chase to its death almost any creature it chose as its next meal. . . .

But the story didn't end there. The days of glory were destined to disappear with the arrival of man. He came with his thunder-stick and effortlessly stilled tiger after tiger. He came with bottles of death, poisoning carcasses of cattle which in turn poisoned the tiger so that man could steal his coat. And he came with long knives, killing the forests which were the tiger's home and taking the land for himself. With the forests had died the tiger's prey, and with its prey died the. . . .

The truth came upon him slowly, as though the sun had risen in his mind. Man *still* was killing the tiger; *still* was using him. The man with the black box—what had he wanted with him? And the man with the thunder-stick which in one noisy moment drove the life-blood from the rabbit—that was no friend, either. And those men who killed trees amid the deafening buzzing of a million bees—what of them? He had known they were destroying his home, but only now did he realize they had been doing it for ages past, doing it to his fathers, driving them to their deaths as surely as if they had used the thunder-sticks. . . .

He stirred from his reverie, lifting his head erect and gazing across the woodland below him. Death to the tiger. That was what man was saying. He would kill all tigers—all except the few he could catch and put away for other men to approach with courage as thin as the wire behind which they stood. How they did it did not matter. What mattered, it was clear, was that the tiger died. Why should the tiger pay so dearly for being what he was? Well, *he* would not pay the price. He would survive!

He wondered where they had been taking him when that bone-jarring jolt had tossed him through the darkness of his small enclosure, and then, with another mighty crash, had let him loose into this new world of space and air. From one place of captivity to another, most likely. But no matter, for he was free now, and free he would stay.

★   ★   ★   ★

'Now!'

He leapt to his feet, turning this way and that, but they were all around him. There was a gap, though—there, between those two men. Muscles bunched, and he sprang for the opening—but realized it was a trap as the men rushed in, casting a giant spider's web into the air. Twisting lithely, he darted away, the sprawling net brushing his tail. With the speed of fear he raced on, but then—

'Use the gun!'

—and a thunder-crack exploded, driving a pain—like a red-hot claw —deep into his side. His eyes flashed in anger and he bounded on, crashing through the undergrowth, his strong shoulders snapping saplings like matchwood.

'Good shot, John. After him now. He won't get far.'

His mind was racing, then reeling, then swirling as the world began turning upside down. His head started to hurt, but then pain gave way to a strangely pleasant sensation of drowsiness. Suddenly—as quickly as night comes to distant forests—a black curtain was being drawn across behind his eyes. He knew no more.

★   ★   ★   ★

They found him lying on his side at the foot of a silver birch about two hundred yards away.

'Sorry to have to use the rifle, old boy,' said a voice to closed ears.

The man bent and gently pulled the tranquiliser dart from the tiger's flank while another man checked him for any injuries sustained in his

The tiger vanished as a shadow into the thick-knitted undergrowth.

panic run. There were none. Two other men were making the tiger comfortable with a pillow of twigs and leaves, ensuring that he wouldn't inhale dust from the woodland floor.

The leader of the hunt—a big man with a scar on his chin—turned to a man with a walkie-talkie set.

'Okay, I think we'll get the lorry up here now. We'll have to hack down some of this undergrowth, but we've got a bit of time while it's under the drug.'

He turned to another man.

'Good idea of yours to leave the dogs behind, Brian. Still, they did their job.'

A policeman came running up, red-faced and puffing and clutching his helmet under his arm. He went across to the big man, casting a surprised look at the tiger, its eyes wide open, seemingly awake.

'Everything under control here, sir?'

The man nodded.

'Thank you, Sergeant.'

'The lorry's on its way. You'll soon have this blighter back in the zoo. Best place for it, if you ask me. Nasty thing. Vicious.'

He glanced at the tiger again.

'Look at it. "Death in fancy dress" they call it. Have your leg off as soon as look at you.'

The big man's cheeks flushed and he was about to say something but thought better of it. Instead he said, 'It isn't going back to a zoo, this one.'

'Oh?'

'No, this is a lucky one. It's been selected for the rehabilitation project—reintroducing animals born in captivity into the wild.'

The policeman looked blank for a moment, then said, 'Oh yes, it was on its way back to India when the accident happened, wasn't it.'

'Nepal, actually. There's a protected wildlife reserve there—three hundred and fifty square miles of it. Like others, this tiger will be retrained to adapt to its natural habitat and to use its instincts. It's still young enough.'

The policeman shook his head and said emphatically:

'Waste of money. I've got a boy studying all this conservation lark at school. Getting really interested in it, he is. Reckons he might even get a job working with animals. Well, I told him: forget that nonsense. Get yourself into a nice, steady, secure job—something with a decent pension. There's no future in animals, I said. No offence, of course, but—'

'But you've hit the nail on the head!' said the big man. 'There *is* no future for our wildlife—unless *we* do something about it. Take the tiger. Fifty years ago there were a hundred thousand tigers in Asia. Today there are less than *three* thousand. Some of the sub-species are already extinct.'

He looked across at the unconscious big cat.

'He'll go the same way, unless. . . .'

He turned back, looking the policeman squarely in the eye.

'Believe me, he needs all the friends he can get.'

The officer was silent, looking down at the ground and nudging a twig with the dust-covered toe-cap of his boot.

The big man left him with his thoughts and went to the tiger, but soon the policeman was beside him again. He coughed nervously, almost apologetically.

'Well—is there anything I can do to help, sir?'

For the first time the big man smiled.

'Quite a lot, actually. You could start by telling your boy you've had second thoughts. . . .'

FRIEND MONKEY HELPS THE SAILORS

P.L. Travers

There is no one kinder or more helpful than Monkey, but somehow other people don't always appreciate his help, and his kind deeds tend to end up in chaos—as in this episode, where he finds himself aboard a ship. His full story is told by P. L. Travers in Friend Monkey, *about which Margery Fisher has written: 'There is so much in this incomparable book. It is comedy on the highest plane—that is comedy with the indispensable note of amazement and melancholy. Above all it is grounded on myth. The elusive beauty and disturbing puzzles of Hindu myth have enriched the story of* Friend Monkey *and have made it a piece of literature to be enjoyed by young and old alike. Pamela Travers shows triumphantly in this book what she means when she says she does not only write for children.'*

The ship swung to and fro on the water, her white sails flapping in the breeze, like washing on a line.

'Ahoy, there!' bellowed the sailor's mates, as his laden boat drew nearer.

'Ahoy, yourselves, and let down the rope! My cargo's about to sink the boat.'

A rope ladder came snaking down, and up it, hand over hand, went the natty navy-blue figure. Two fat bundles were tumbled aboard, and the sailor began to huff and puff as he laboured up with the third.

'Funny,' he thought, as he heaved and panted. 'I'd have said they all weighed about the same, but this one—whew!—it's a blooming millstone. Out of my way, Young Napper,' he warned. 'If this load falls on top of you, we'll be short of a cabin-boy!'

But the skinny, gangling lad at the rail made no attempt to move. He was staring over the sailor's shoulder.

'W-what you got there, Mr Hawkes?' he stammered, pointing towards the sack.

'Yes, Barley,' echoed Fat Harry, the cook. 'What you been up to now, mate? I thought you was sent for cocoa-nuts.'

'And cocoa-nuts, Harry, is what I got. Round green fruit off a cocoa-nut tree, in case you never saw one!' Barley Hawkes was sarcastic.

'Well, take a look behind you, mate. You'll find you've got more than nuts.'

'More than nuts?' He turned his head. 'Well, I'll be—' But what he was going to be no one knew, for as he lowered the sack to the deck, Monkey came sidling from behind it, extending his paw palm-downward.

'So that's where you were!' said Barley Hawkes. 'And me thinking you'd hopped it! Well, you've got a cheek, I must say, boarding my boat without a ticket. And who requested your company, if I might be so bold to ask?'

Young Napper thrust himself between them.

'Don't go hurting him, Mr Hawkes! He's only a beast. He knows no better!'

'Yes, Barley. You let him be!' Fat Harry grabbed him by the arm. 'He's not done anyone any harm. Give him half a chance!'

'Hurt him? Me?' roared Barley Hawkes. 'You gone crazy, the two of you? Why should I hurt him? He's my pal!' He flung Fat Harry and Napper aside and bent to receive Monkey's proffered paw.

But Monkey was there no longer.

He was busily emptying the sacks and tossing cocoa-nuts into the air. Fat Harry caught one in his apron. Napper tucked two inside his blouse. The rest of the crew came running up, and Monkey darted about among them scattering nuts in all directions. One fell into the sea with a splash, another was caught in a coil of rope, and another tripped the Captain up as he entered on the scene.

'What's going on?' the Captain demanded. 'This is a ship, not a football field.' He glanced round disapprovingly at the litter on the deck. Then his eye fell on the furry shape, a whirling thing with a long tail and a cocoa-nut in its arms.

The Captain's face was a sight to see. He was both surprised and indignant.

'I sent you for cocoa-nuts, Mr Hawkes, not apes! You know the company's regulations. No pets allowed on the high seas!'

'Ay, ay, Captain. I know the rules. And I went for nuts, just like you said. It was him—' He jerked his head at Monkey. 'It was him that got them for me.'

'What? That hairy creature?' The Captain frowned.

'He did, sir, honest and hope to die. Shook the cocoa-nuts down from the trees when they wouldn't budge for me. But I never meant to bring him aboard. He must have stowed away on the boat when I turned my head away.'

'Well—' The Captain bent down to stare at Monkey and touched the outstretched paw. And Monkey, taking this for a welcome, thrust the cocoa-nut into his arms.

'Hurrrumph! Well, the thing seems to be tame enough. I'll make an exception just this once. But he'd better behave—I warn you, Hawkes —or he'll find himself stowed away right there!' He pointed downwards with his thumb. 'Right there in Davy Jones's Locker.'

Davy Jones's Locker is down at the bottom of the sea. All drowned things go there at last, men and ships and chests of gold. There is nothing deeper in the world than Davy Jones's Locker.

'Cross my heart,' said Barley Hawkes. 'He'll be helpful, sir, I promise!'

Oh, the rash promises of sailors! But how could Barley Hawkes have known—no tiger was there to bid him heed, no cautionary mynah bird—that the time would come when he would wish that Monkey had helped a little less?

★   ★   ★   ★

Meanwhile, Monkey was all agog and delighted with his new world. Fat Harry searched through his dwindling stores and found him a ripe banana. Young Napper sewed him a blue serge cap with half the name of the ship round the rim. '*London Ex—*' was all it said. For Monkey's head was far too small to accommodate the whole word. Not that it mattered, the men agreed. An animal, since it could not read, would never know the difference.

'There you are!' Young Napper exclaimed, as he set the cap at a jaunty angle. 'Now you're one of us. You're a sailor!'

Monkey, overwhelmed with joy, was about to reward him with half the banana, when the Captain's voice called from the stern and Napper was hailed to more pressing duties.

'Anchors aweigh!' the Captain ordered. And at once there was a rattle of chains, the pounding of feet along the deck, the thunder of sails as they took the wind—the usual orderly confusion of a vessel resuming her voyage.

But where was Monkey?

Everywhere!

The new sailor worked with a will, hiding things that everyone needed, dragging out others that nobody wanted. Once, he got under the Captain's feet, but the Captain mistook his leg for a rope and pitched him into a corner.

The ship moved, giving herself to the sea, her timbers creaking rhythmically like the sound of somebody breathing.

'Take a last look at your island, pal,' said Barley Hawkes to Monkey. 'We shan't get another sniff of land till we dock in London River.'

He turned to gaze at the sandy shore, edged with its shawl of jungle green and the hills rising behind it. But, to his surprise, he could not see them. There was nothing but endless ocean.

'Captain! There's something wrong to starboard. That cocoa-nut island—it's disappeared! Take a squint through the spy-glass, sir! Maybe you can see it.'

'Disappeared? Ridiculous!' The Captain put his glass to his eye. He took it away, rubbed the lens, and peered through it again.

'Preposterous! It must be there! And yet—' The Captain's voice was quiet. 'You're right! That island's gone.'

'But where would it go, sir? It couldn't just blow away—like smoke!'

'Wherever it's gone, I don't like it. It wasn't on the chart, remember. We came on it unexpectedly. I used to hear tales,' the Captain brooded, 'of islands that came and went. But I took them simply as sailors' yarns. It's a bad omen, Hawkes,' he said, as he swung his glass in a wide circle, searching the empty sea. 'Great Stars!' he cried. 'What's that up there!'

'Not the island, sir, surely?' An island in the sky, thought Barley, was as useless as one that disappeared.

'No, no!' said the Captain, testily. 'There's something up there on top of the mast.'

It was Monkey.

He had seen Young Napper run up the rigging and—anxious, as always, to render assistance—had scrambled after him. Now he was hanging, feet over head, apparently urging his sailor friend to work in the same position.

'Stop it! Let go!' Young Napper yelled. 'You'll have us overboard!'

But Monkey clasped him around the waist and swung him away from the mast. Together they dangled aloft for a moment, with only the sea beneath them. But Napper, alas, was too heavy.

'I'm gone! I'm lost! Oh, me poor old mother!' He slipped from Monkey's circling arm and hurtled towards the water.

The Captain and Barley Hawkes waited, helplessly flinging out their arms, for the end of their cabin-boy. But just then the ship gave a lurch to starboard, a sail swung out in a puff of wind and caught him in its lap.

With a horrible screech of tearing canvas. Napper slid down the slope of the sail and landed on the deck. Monkey, with a single leap, was waiting there to greet him.

'Oh, let me die,' Young Napper moaned. 'All me bones are broken!' He pressed himself against the deck, grateful for its solidity after the nothingness of air.

'Well—if there's a bone that isn't broken, I'll break it myself, Young Napper!' The Captain, relieved of anxiety, could now give vent to his anger. 'Look at that sail, all ripped to ribbons! Bully beef and water for you, until it's properly patched. And don't let me find you wasting time playing with that ape. Get a rope and tie him up or we'll have him wrecking the ship!'

'Oh, please, sir, not to tie him up! Wild beasts don't like it. They pine away.'

'That wouldn't worry me,' said the Captain.

'But he's not to blame—it was me, Captain!' Young Napper searched for a plausible phrase. 'I was trying to be a monkey.'

'Then try to be a cabin-boy.' The Captain turned away.

'Ay, ay, then, sir.' Young Napper snivelled, scrambling to his feet. He searched through the treasures in his pocket and fished up a piece of string. Then he put out his hand for Monkey.

But Monkey had left the scene of disaster and was now perched on the ship's side, gazing at the sky.

'Leave it loose,' whispered Barley Hawkes, as they tied one end of the string to the rail and the other to Monkey's ankle. 'Don't let him think he's a prisoner.'

Monkey, however, had no such thought. The string, he assumed, was another gift. And since his friends were tying knots, it was clearly his duty to help them. So, in spite of their efforts to dissuade him, he lashed his own foot to the rail as though his life depended on it.

Having done that to his satisfaction, he turned to the sky again.

'What's he staring at?' said Napper, tilting back his head.

A shadow was moving over the ship, blotting out the sun.

'An albatross!' The sailors cheered. For to meet an albatross at sea is considered great good fortune.

'A lucky omen!' the Captain cried, his anger visibly melting.

'An omen with a catch though, sir. It's lucky, they say, unless you feed them. Once they've eaten the food of land—' Barley Hawkes gave a shudder. 'They follow and follow after the ship, till somebody from the land joins them. I know it, Captain! I've seen it happen.'

'Nonsense, Hawkes! That's an old wives' tale.' The Captain believed in old wives' tales, but he did not like to admit it. 'And who would feed it, anyway? An albatross gets its food from the sea.'

The great bird glided over the ship, dipping and swerving above the sailors in a kind of skiey dance. Now and then he would turn away as though he had seen enough. But each time he came winging back, swooping lower and lower. Then, suddenly, with a determined movement, he folded his black and white wings together and landed on the rail.

'He's looking for someone!' said Barley Hawkes. as the bird turned his head from side to side.

Fat Harry gave a sudden cry. 'He's looking for me! I know him now. It's my old mate, Sim Parkin! We lost him overboard in a gale, down by Santiago.'

Albatrosses, seamen believe, are really the souls of drowned sailors. The bodies of men who are lost at sea go down to Davy Jones. But the rest of them, their own true selves, fly up to the air as birds. How this happens nobody knows. And sailors, being superstitious, do not like to enquire.

'It *is* you, Sim—isn't it?' Fat Harry lumbered towards the rail.

'Of course it's not Sim Parkin, Harry!' The Captain stamped with impatience. 'Nor Tom Smith, nor anyone else. Now, all of you, get back to work. You're sailors, men, not bird collectors. I tell you, this will bring us luck. Fair winds. Smooth waters. You'll see.' He strode off down the deck.

The Captain had spoken no more than the truth, at least as far as he knew it. He had met with many an albatross. And each time the meeting had brought them luck.

But he had not reckoned with Monkey. There he sat, lashed to the rail, his dark glance moving back and forth from the cook to the brooding bird.

'I know you, Sim!' Fat Harry whispered. 'I know the squint in your left eye.'

The bird's slanting eyes flickered, and he reached out with his beak.

'No, no! You keep off, boy!' Fat Harry took a step backwards.

'If I let you touch me, that's the end. I'll find myself down there.' He nodded darkly at the sea.

The albatross withdrew his beak and hung his head on his breast.

'Don't take it hard,' Fat Harry pleaded. 'I can't help liking my bit of life. You did, too, remember, mate? But if you're lonely—well, I'm here. You can always drop in when you're passing. Hi! Hold off! You leave him be!' Fat Harry let out a warning yell.

Monkey—having decided, apparently, that the albatross was in need of help—was now helping the albatross. One paw was stroking the drooping head, the other pressing upon the beak a morsel of banana.

'Don't eat it, Sim!' Fat Harry wailed. But the warning came too late.

The albatross had sniffed the fruit and was gobbling it down. It seemed to satisfy something in him, for his head went up with a lordly

329

toss. His squinting eye fell on Fat Harry with a dark, significant glance. His beak, half open, seemed to smile. Then, with a lift of his great wings, he gave himself back to the air. Once more he circled about the ship, his shadow falling on every face. And then he turned away. The sailors watched, half bewitched, as his shape grew small in the distance.

'He's had what he came for,' Fat Harry moaned, blubbering into his apron. 'A bit of food from the land he wanted. And why? Because he wants me, too.'

'Shut up, Harry, you're not dead yet. And maybe it's just a seaman's yarn.' Barley Hawkes tried to reassure him.

'No, no, it's only a matter of time. And it's him!' He shook his fist at Monkey. 'It's that dumb thing as who's to blame. Him and his old banana!'

'You won't tell the Captain?' implored Young Napper.

'Of course he won't tell,' said Barley Hawkes. 'Harry's a gentleman.'

'What? Me split on anyone to the Captain?' Fat Harry was deeply offended.

So they buttered him up and smoothed him down, and soon he was laughing again. Fat Harry was an optimist. His mate, Sim Parkin, would surely get him—of that he had no doubt. But not today. Tomorrow, perhaps. And tomorrow, he reminded himself, is something that never comes. So he waddled off to the ship's galley, planning a new kind of stew for supper—salt-beef, hard biscuits, and cocoa-nuts.

It was a success. Everyone had a second helping.

There was even a saucerful for Monkey, which he picked at, not because he liked it, but simply to gratify Young Napper.

They sat together in companionable silence, Monkey secure in his knots of string, Young Napper untidily sprawled beside him.

The constellations were out in the sky. The North Star, that brings all sailors home, was shining in the Great Bear's tail. A following wind filled the sails, and the labouring ship creaked and groaned as she thrust the waves behind her. It was a moment—such a one comes in every voyage—when sea and sky, ship and men were part of a single whole.

As for the Captain, he was full of high spirits. Up and down the deck he went, shouting important orders. 'Trim the sails! Square away!

Put the helm down! Put the helm up!' and other nautical expressions.

'You see, Hawkes, I was right!' He laughed. 'The bird has brought us luck!'

'Ay, ay, sir,' answered Barley Hawkes, exchanging a glance with Young Napper and hoping that this was indeed the case.

The Captain had forgotten—if he ever knew—that luck, like fruit, takes time to ripen. It doesn't happen all at once.

With ill luck it is just the same. . . .

★   ★   ★   ★

Hour by hour, on their steady course, the constellations moved. The sailors alternately slept and watched, as they ran before the wind.

But towards morning the wind fell. There was not a pocket of air in the sails. The ship lay becalmed upon the water, motionless as a model ship inside a whiskey bottle.

And to make matters worse, a thick mist rose up out of nowhere. No man could see his own hand. The sailors spoke to each other in whispers, like ghost talking to ghost.

The Captain took this sudden change as a personal affront. He had praised the weather and called it lucky, and the weather, far from appearing grateful, had turned and flouted him.

He stumbled along the invisible deck giving orders in a loud voice that the mist absorbed and muffled.

Once, something moved swiftly by him, brushing against his arm.

'Is that you, Hawkes?' he called sharply.

'No, Captain, I'm up in the bow.'

And again, as he passed beneath some rigging, his glass was knocked from his hand.

'Is that you, Napper?' the Captain bawled.

'No, sir, I'm in the galley with Harry.'

'Then who keeps bumping me, confound it?'

Barley Hawkes made a move in the mist. He would have to go and help the Captain. He put out a hand to feel his way and found in it a small warm paw.

And within the paw was the Captain's spy-glass.

Monkey had wearied of sitting still, gazing at the sea. It was all very well when the stars were out. But now it was dark and misty. He knew —he had learned it in the jungle—that mist was tricky, not to be trusted. And where were his friends? In danger, perhaps? If so, they would surely need his help. So he quickly untied the string from his ankle and went to look for them.

Up and down the ship he hunted, using his tail as a sounding line. He banged into this and knocked down that. And at last, after a long search, he came upon one of his cronies.

'So it was you! I might have known it! Don't you ever know when to stop? How can I save you from Davy Jones if you gallivant about like this?' Barley Hawkes, exasperated, felt around in the dark with his foot and came on a coil of rope. He seized Monkey by the scruff of the neck and dumped him down inside it. 'Now you stay there!' he whispered hoarsely. 'Or I'll scalp you—that's a promise!'

The coil of rope was like a nest, cleaner than the mynah bird's, and not a sign of an egg. Monkey settled himself serenely, taking it for granted that, as he had helped the mynah bird, he was now helping the sailor. All that could be seen of him—if any eye could have pierced the mist—was the flat top of his blue serge cap and the letters *London Ex—*.

Barley Hawkes felt his way forward.

'Your spy-glass, sir!' he said smartly, as the Captain loomed up beside him.

'Great heavens, Hawkes, a glass can't fly! How did it get up here?'

'Dunno, sir.' Barley Hawkes was stolid. 'Funny things happen in the mist.'

'Far too many funny things, if you ask me, Mr Hawkes.'

'But it's lifting, sir. I can see you clear.'

And, indeed, the mist, having done its worst, was now giving way to the dawn. Ship and sailors appeared again as though from a conjurer's hat.

'And about time, too,' The Captain grumbled. 'Now we must whistle for a wind.'

Landlubbers find it hard to believe that a wind may be called as one calls a dog. But for sailors it is a fact.

Barley Hawkes pursed his lips and whistled. And it seemed that the sky sent back the sound—a high, shrill, screaming echo that ended in a loud bang as something hit the deck.

It was a cannonball.

'Steady, lads!' the Captain shouted, as the seamen set up a wild commotion. 'Somebody's making a big mistake. They can't do this to us, men. We're not armed, we're a trading ship. Run up the white flag—that'll show them!'

'Shippa ahoy-a! Heave-a to-a!' Voices were calling across the water.

'What do they mean—Heaver Toer! We're hove to already! Where's my glass?'

'There's a ship standing off on the port side, sir. By the look of the crew, I think they're pirates.'

'Pirates, Hawkes? Have you gone mad? This is eighteen hundred and ninety-seven. There haven't been pirates in these seas for over fifty years!'

'Well, they're flying the Skull and Crossbones, sir. And they're putting off a boat—'

'You're right! It's unbelievable! My thundering stars, they're boarding us. All hands on deck!' the Captain roared, as a dozen pirates, brandishing knives, came swarming over the side.

'At 'em, boys!' the Captain ordered, seizing a pirate by the waist and sending him sprawling across the deck.

'Ay, ay, sir!' willing voices answered. And then the rumpus began. Bumps, bangs, curses, groans—all the pandemonium of a hand-to-hand shipboard battle. And the sailors got the best of it. They were all unarmed, but their blood was up. Pirates, indeed! They'd pirate them!

So the raiders were flung this way and that, into the scuppers, against the masts, moaning and sobbing and rolling their eyes. Daggers and cutlasses slipped from their hands, the deck resounded with falling bodies. At the end of the fray there was not one pirate standing upright. The sailors tied their hands with rope, propped them against the ship's side, and regarded them triumphantly.

They were, indeed, a poor lot—shabby, toothless, and skinny. A tatterdemalion remnant, perhaps, of the buccaneers of long ago.

The Captain eyed them with contempt. 'Well, what have you got to say for yourselves?'

'Notta spikka Angliss,' a pirate muttered, dejectedly shaking his head.

Not speak English? Great gods! Bad enough to be a pirate, worse

The monkey was perched on the ship's side, gazing at the sky.

to board a British vessel lawfully plying her proper trade, but not to speak English—! What could the world be coming to, the Captain clearly wondered.

'We'll deal with this riff-raff later, lads! In the meantime, we must celebrate. Harry, splice the mainbrace!'

Splicing the mainbrace on board ship means doubling each man's ration of rum. The custom is highly esteemed by sailors.

And soon there came from the ship's galley such a sound of junketing, such roars of laughter, such jollification, that a passer-by, had there possibly been one, would have said that the mainbrace had been spliced many times more than once.

'Down with all pirates!' the Captain was shouting. 'We'll take their ship in tow, hearties. It's treasure-trove and prize money for every man of the crew.' A loud cheer greeted the good tidings.

'Well, fill up once more and then to work!' The Captain held out his pannikin. And something that looked like a very small sailor filled it with rum from a keg.

The Captain stared. Was it possible? Apparently, it was.

'It's that ape again!' he said wrathfully. 'I thought I gave orders to tie him up! How did he get in here?'

Nobody knew—except Monkey.

Sitting in his coil of rope, he had heard the panting battle cries and assumed that the sailors and their friends were playing a rowdy game. Such things happened daily in the jungle. And so he joined the fun. He was here, he was there, he was everywhere. But in all that skelter of arms and legs no one had noticed an extra pair. And later, amid the jubilation, no one had noticed the extra sailor. So the extra sailor had busied himself with pouring out the rum.

'Well?' said the Captain, ominously.

'He *was* tied up, Captain, sir! I did it myself,' Young Napper declared.

'It's true, sir,' put in Barley Hawkes.

This rosy vision so cheered the Captain that he burst into a sailing song and held out his cup again.

'Cross my heart,' Fat Harry added. 'Trussed him up like a roast duck.'

'Then it must have been those damned pirates. They'll have set him free as they came aboard.' Napper, Hawkes, and Fat Harry glanced at each other but said nothing. There was nothing to be said.

'Well, he seems to be making himself useful. And he'd jolly well better, or there'll be trouble!' The Captain's voice sounded ferocious, but for once his bark was worse than his bite. He was far too full of his own good fortune to be worried by a mere monkey.

Think of it! He had captured a gang of bloodthirsty villains—not single-handed, but that was a detail—the last pirates, perhaps, in the world. And now he was a hero. Maybe, as well as the prize money, someone would give him a silver medal. They might even make a waxwork of him and put him in Madame Tussaud's.

This rosy vision so cheered the Captain that he burst into a sailing song and held out his cup again.

But Monkey was no longer there to fill it. He was now searching through the ship, looking for other friends to help.

And very soon he found them.

They were sitting on the deck in a row, each with his head on the next man's shoulder, dejected and forlorn.

Their eyes brightened when Monkey appeared, for any pirate, like any sailor, knows a keg of rum when he sees it. And since, to Monkey, a pirate was as thirsty as the next man, their spirits were shortly as bright as their eyes. Up and down the row he went, tipping the rum to every mouth until the keg was empty.

The strangers were obviously grateful. They nodded and smiled at him toothlessly and held out their fettered hands. And Monkey, at once, knew what was needed. He had been tied up himself.

So he quickly unloosed the knotted ropes, eagerly glancing from pirate to pirate, hoping to be of further service. But his new friends, it seemed, were about to depart. The only help they needed—or wanted—was a leg-up over the side. One by one, they tottered shakily to their feet and, with Monkey giving a heave and a push, clambered to the top of the rail and disappeared from view.

'Farewell and adieu to you, sweet Spanish ladies,' came the Captain's voice from the galley.

> 'Farewell and adieu to you, ladies of Spain!
> Until we strike soundings in the channel of old England,
> From Ushant to . . .'

The last words were drowned in a burst of applause. 'Up with the Captain!' somebody shouted. 'Down with the pirates!' cried another. And they clapped the Captain so hard on the back that they pushed him out of the crowded galley and followed him on to the deck.

It was just at this moment that the last pirate, courteously assisted by Monkey, clambered on to the rail.

Suddenly the rumpus ceased. The shouts died on the sailors' lips as they took in the situation. Even the sea was quiet.

For a second that seemed as long as a year, sailors and pirate stared at each other. Then the pirate took off his greasy cap and made a mocking bow.

'Gooda-bye-a! Olly vore! Ta ta!' He smirked. And with a hearty shove from Monkey, he was over and out of sight.

From below came the clonk and rattle of oars and a cackle of laughter, most un-English, as the pirates pulled away.

'Hawkes!' The word rang out like a shot from a gun.

'Ay, ay, sir,' muttered Barley Hawkes, who thought he knew what was coming.

The Captain pointed a trembling finger. His body shook with rage.

'Irons!' he spluttered. 'Put him in irons! Get that brute out of my sight. Take him below and clap him in.'

'Oh, not irons!' Young Napper wailed.

'It's that or drowning. Take your choice.'

'I could sew him up in a hammock, sir. He wouldn't escape, I promise.' Barley Hawkes reached out his arm for Monkey.

'TAKE HIM AWAY!' the Captain yelled. He was clearly beside himself. 'Sew him up, for all I care. Put him in chains! Strangle him! But if I set eyes on him again, you know what will happen, I warn you! He's brought nothing but trouble, trouble, TROUBLE, since the moment he came aboard.'

One cannot really blame the Captain. Being spick and orderly himself, he felt he had a right to expect that life should be orderly, too. Yet, here it was, all ups and downs, like a game of Snakes and Ladders.

He had found fresh cocoa-nuts, it was true, but he had lost an island. An albatross had brought him luck in the shape of a gang of pirates, and a wild beast, a thing from the jungle, had set the pirates free. No sooner, it seemed, was he up a ladder than he was down a snake. No one would give him a medal now, nor make a waxwork of him. The ill luck had indeed ripened.

As a last straw, it sent him a wind. Barley Hawkes had whistled for it, and the Captain had confidently expected a well-behaved, dependable breeze that would blow him gently home.

But what he got was a tornado.

It rose up out of nothingness, bellowing rudely through the rigging, ripping the sails into tatters. It flung the waves on top of each other till the sea, like a great watery whale, alternately swallowed the *London Exporter* and spat it out again. It even broke off the top of an iceberg and sent it into the Bay of Biscay, just where the ship was passing.

And always at the edge of the weather, round and round tirelessly, a dark shape flew and hovered. The sailors knew it was watching and waiting. But they did not tell the Captain.

Then, just as they entered the English Channel, the wind broke open the door to the galley where Fat Harry, bouncing from wall to wall, was trying to make a pudding. It sucked him out of his warm shelter and swept him on deck, shrieking for help. Then it picked him up, pudding and all, and tossed him into the sea.

'He should have been lashed to the stove,' said the Captain, as the waves closed over his body.

But no rope on earth, the sailors knew, could have lashed Fat Harry tightly enough to save him from his fate.

They were silent, staring down at the water. And the sea was suddenly silent, too. The wind changed from a roar to a whisper, the watery mountains flattened out, the iceberg turned tail and floated away. And the flying shape that had watched and waited lifted its wings triumphantly and flew towards the horizon.

'He knew it would happen, Harry did.' Young Napper wiped his nose on his sleeve. 'That there banana it was, what done it. And now Sim Parkin's got him.' He had no chance to finish what was evidently intended to be a long lament, for Barley Hawkes's hand was over his mouth.

'Hold your gob or I'll spiflicate you! Do you want the Captain to hear?'

He was thinking, of course, of Monkey and trying to save him, if he could, from Davy Jones's Locker.

But what was Monkey thinking?

There he lay, sewn up in his hammock, looking like an Egyptian mummy, with only his head uncovered. All through the storm, as the ship rolled over on her side or spun like a merry-go-round in the waters, he had seen the sailors tossed hither and thither and had longed to rush to their aid.

But no amount of twisting and turning could set him free from his canvas shroud. Barley Hawkes had done the job well. He couldn't even bite his way out, no matter how hard he tried.

Why had this happened, he asked himself. He had thought he was helping his new friends, and those same friends, far from being pleased, had sewn him up like a parcel.

He had never heard of Snakes and Ladders. But, nevertheless, it seemed to him that life was full of surprises. Up one minute and down the next with no one to tell him why.

So, since there was nothing else to do, he lay quite still and wondered.

And while he was busy doing this, the ship, egged on by a kindly breeze, came safely into port. . . .

FOUR SAINTS

Helen Waddell

Helen Waddell's Beasts and Saints *is a collection of stories about the co-operation between saints and beasts, from the end of the fourth to the end of the twelfth century, translated from the original Latin, They include tales of the Desert Fathers like St Jerome, saints of the West like St Werburga and St Godric, and the saints of Ireland, like St Moling.*

Impossible and long it would be to unfold all that might be told of that great man and his austere life and ways. Yet one miracle about this monastery there is, like those of old time, that oblivion hath not yet stolen from memory, for it is handed down from one to another, and told by holy men that lived in Bethlehem for love of the heavenly fatherland: and it I now weave into this compendious discourse.

Upon a certain day as evening drew on, and the blessed Jerome sat with the brethren, as is the way of the monk, to hear the reading of the lesson and to speak good words, lo of a sudden, limping on three paws and the fourth caught up, came a mighty lion into the cloister. At sight of him a good many of the brethren fled in terror, for human frailty is but timorous. But the blessed Jerome went out to meet him as one greets an incoming guest.

And while the distance between them was shortening, the lion who had no way of speaking, it not being his nature, offered the good father as best he might his wounded paw: and the Saint, calling the brethren, gave instructions that the wounded paw should be bathed, to find why the lion went thus limping. Upon close examination, they found that the paw had been pierced by thorns. Fomentations were applied with all diligence, and the wound speedily healed.

And now, all wildness and savagery laid aside, the lion began to go to and fro among them as peaceable and domestic as any animal about the house. This the blessed Jerome observed, and spoke as follows to the brethren: 'Bring your minds to bear upon this, my brethren: what, I ask you, can we find for this lion to do in the way of useful and suitable work, that will not be burdensome to him, and that he can efficiently accomplish? For I believe of a surety that it was not so much for the healing of his paw that God sent him hither, since He could have cured him without us, as to show us that He is anxious to provide marvellous well for our necessity.'

To which the brethren gave concerted and humble response: 'Thou knowest, father, that the donkey who brings us our wood from the forest pasture needs someone to look after him, and that we are always in fear that some naughty beast will devour him. Wherefore if it seem to thee good and right, let the charge of our donkey be laid upon the lion, that he may take him out to pasture, and again may bring him home.'

And so it was done: the donkey was put in charge of the lion, as his shepherd: together they took the road to the pasture, and wherever the donkey grazed, there was his defender: and a sure defence he was. Nevertheless, at regular hours, that he might refresh himself and the donkey do his appointed task, the lion would come with him home.

And so for long enough it was: till one day, the donkey duly brought to his pasture, the lion felt a great weight of sluggishness come upon him, and he fell asleep. And as he lay sunk in deep slumber, it befell that certain merchants came along that road on their way to Egypt to buy oil. They saw the donkey grazing, they saw that no guardian was at hand, and seized by sudden wicked greed, they caught him and led him away.

In due course the lion roused up, knowing nothing of his loss, and set out to fetch his charge at graze. But when he was not to be seen in the accustomed pasture, constricted with anxiety and in deep distress the lion went roaring up and down, hither and thither, for the remainder of the day, seeking what he had lost. And at last, when all hope of finding the donkey was gone, he came and stood at the monastery gate.

Conscious of guilt, he no longer dared walk in as of old time with his donkey. The blessed Jerome saw him, and the brethren too, hanging about outside the gate, without the donkey, and long past his usual hour: and they concluded that he had been tempted by hunger to kill his animal. In no mind, therefore, to offer him his wonted ration, 'Away with you,' said they, 'and finish up whatever you have left of the donkey, and fill your greedy belly.' And yet even as they spoke, they were doubtful as to whether he had indeed perpetrated this crime or no.

So finally the brethren went out to the pasture whither the lion was wont to bring the animal aforesaid, and up and down they scoured, to see if they could find any trace of the slaughter. No sign of violence was to be seen: and turning home they made haste to bring their report to the blessed Jerome. He heard them, and spoke. 'I entreat you, brethren,' said he, 'that although ye have suffered the loss of the ass, do not, nevertheless, nag at him or make him wretched. Treat him as before, and offer him his food: and let him take the donkey's place, and make a light harness for him so that he can drag home the branches that have fallen in the wood.' And it was done.

So the lion did regularly his appointed task, while the time grew on for the merchants to return. Then one day, his work done, he went out, inspired as I believe, brute beast though he was, by some divine prompting, and made his way to the field. Up and down, hither and thither in circles he ran, craving some further light on the fate that had befallen his comrade. And finally, worn out but still anxious, he climbed to a rising above the highway where he might look all around him. A great way off he spied men coming with laden camels, and in front of them walked a donkey. So far off was he that he could not recognize him. None the less he set out, stepping cautiously, to meet them.

Now it is said to be the custom in that part of the country that whenever men set out with camels on a long journey, a donkey goes in front, with the camel's halter on its neck, and the camels follow after. And now the merchants came nearer, and he recognized his donkey. With a fierce roar he charged down upon them, making a mighty din, though doing no damage to any. Crazed with terror, as they might

Daily, the lion shepherded the donkey out to pasture.

well be, they left all they had and took to their heels, the lion meantime roaring terribly and lashing the ground with his tail: and so he drove the affrighted camels, laden as they were, back to the monastery before him.

So when this surprising sight met the brethren's gaze, the donkey pacing in the van, the lion in like fashion marching in the rear, and the laden beasts in the middle, they slipped quietly away to inform the blessed Jerome. He came out, and benevolently bade them to set open the monastery gate, enjoining them to silence. 'Take their loads off these our guests,' said he, 'the camels, I mean, and the donkey, and bathe their feet and give them fodder, and wait to see what God is minded to show His servants.'

Then, when all instructions as to the camels had been obeyed, began the lion as of old to go here and there in high feather through the cloister, flattening himself at the feet of each several brother and wagging his tail, as though to ask forgiveness for the crime that he had never committed. Whereupon the brethren, full of remorse for the cruel charge they had brought against him, would say to one another, 'Behold our trusty shepherd whom so short a while ago we were upbraiding for a greedy ruffian, and God has deigned to send him to us with such a resounding miracle, to clear his character!' Meantime the blessed Jerome, aware of things to come, spoke to the brethren, saying, 'Be prepared, my brethren, in all things that are requisite for refreshment: so that those who are about to be our guests may be received, as is fitting, without embarrassment.'

His orders duly obeyed, and the brethren chatting with the blessed Jerome, suddenly comes a messenger with the news that there are guests without the gate, desirous to see the Father of the community. At this, the already frequently named Father commanded that the doors of the monastery be opened, and the visitors brought to him. They, however, in spite of this invitation, came in blushing, and prostrated themselves at the feet of the blessed Jerome, entreating forgiveness for their fault. Gently raising them up, he admonished them to enjoy their own with thanksgiving, but not to encroach on others' goods: and in short to live cautiously, as ever in the presence of God. And this marvellous discourse ended, he bade them accept refreshment, and take again their camels and go their way.

344

Then with one voice they cried out, 'We entreat you, Father, that you will accept, for the lamps in the church and the necessity of the brethren, half of the oil that the camels have brought: because we know and are sure that it was rather to be of service to you than for our own profit that we went down into Egypt to bargain there.' To which the blessed Jerome replied, 'This that you ask is indeed not right, for it would seem a great hardship that we who ought to have compassion on others and relieve their necessities by our own giving, should bear so heavy on you, taking your property away from you when we are not in need of it.'

To which they answer: 'Neither this food, nor any of our own property do we touch, unless you first command that what we ask shall be done. And so, as we have said, do you now accept half of the oil that the camels have brought: and we pledge ourselves and our heirs to give to you and those that come after you the measure of oil which is called a hin in each succeeding year.'

So therefore, constrained and compelled by the violence of their entreaties, the blessed Jerome commanded that their prayer should be fulfilled. They partook of refreshment, and after receiving both benediction and camels, they returned exultant and jocund to their own people. But that these things were done at Bethlehem, and the fashion of their doing, is confidently related among the inhabitants of that place until this day.

ST GODRIC AND THE HUNTED STAG

In the time of Rainulf, Bishop of Durham, certain of his household had come out for a day's hunting, with their hounds, and were following a stag which they had singled out for its beauty. The creature, hard pressed by the clamour and the baying, made for Godric's hermitage, and seemed by its plaintive cries to beseech his help, The old man came out, saw the stag shivering and exhausted at his gate, and moved with pity bade it hush its moans, and opening the door of his hut, let it go in. The creature dropped at the good father's feet, but he, feeling that the hunt was coming near, came out, shut the door behind him and sat down in the open: while the dogs, vexed at the loss of their quarry, turned back with a mighty baying upon their masters. They, none the less, following on the track of the stag, encircled about the place, plunging through the well-nigh impenetrable brushwood of thorns and briars; and hacking a path with their blades, came upon the man of God in his poor rags. They questioned him about the stag: but he would not be the betrayer of his guest, and he made prudent answer, 'God knows where he may be.' They looked at the angelic beauty of his countenance, and in reverence for his holiness, they fell before him and asked his pardon for their bold intrusion. Many a time afterwards they would tell what had befallen them there, and marvel at it, and by their oft telling of it, the thing was kept in memory by those that came after. But the stag kept house with Godric until the evening: and then he let it go free. But for years thereafter it would turn from its way to visit him, and lie at his feet, to show what gratitude it could for its deliverance.

ST WERBURGA OF CHESTER AND THE WILD GEESE

It was in the city of Chester that the girl Werburga, daughter of Wulfhere, King of Mercia, and Ermenhild . . . took her vows and her goodness shone for many years. The story of one miracle done by her I now shall tell, which made a great stir and was long told about the countryside. She had a farm outside the walls, where the wild geese would come and destroy the standing corn in the fields. The steward in charge of the farm took all shifts to drive them off, but with small success. And so, when he came to wait upon his lady, he added his complaint of them to the other tales he would tell her of the day. 'Go,' said she, 'and shut them all into a house.' The countryman, dumbfounded at the oddness of the command, thought that his lady was jesting: but finding her serious and insistent, went back to the field where he had first spied the miscreants, and bade them, speaking loud and clear, to do their lady's bidding and come after him. Whereupon with one accord they gathered themselves into a flock, and walking with down bent necks after their enemy, were shut up under a roof. On one of them however, the rustic, with no thought of any to accuse him, made bold to dine.

At dawn came the maid, and after scolding the birds for pillaging other people's property, bade them take their flight. But the winged creatures knew that one of their company was missing: nor did they lack wit to go circling round their lady's feet, refusing to budge further, and complaining as best they could, to excite her compassion. She, through God's revealing, and convinced that all this clamour was not without cause, turned her gaze upon the steward, and divined the theft. She bade him gather up the bones and bring them to her. And straightway, at a healing sign from the girl's hand, skin and flesh began to come upon the bones, and feathers to fledge upon the skin, till the living bird, at first with eager hop and soon upon the wing, launched itself into the air. Nor were the others slow to follow it, their numbers now complete, though first they made obeisance to their lady and deliverer. And so the merits of this maid are told at Chester, and her miracles extolled. Yet though she be generous and swift to answer all men's prayers, yet most gracious is her footfall among the women and boys, who pray as it might be to a neighbour and a woman of their own countryside.

ST MOLING AND THE FOX

The blessed bishop Moling used to keep animals both wild and tame about him, in honour of their Maker, and they would eat out of his hand. And among these was a fox. Now one day the fox stole a hen that belonged to the brethren and ate it. The brethren brought their complaint, and the man of God scolded the fox and accused him of being perfidious above other animals. The fox, however, seeing his master wroth with him, gazed upon him with solicitude, and made off to a convent of nuns that were under St Moling's care, captured a hen by guile, and bringing her to his lord, presented her safe and sound. And the saint, smiling, said to him: 'Thou hast offered rapine to atone for theft. Take back this hen to her ladies, and deliver her to them unharmed: and hereafter do thou live without stealing, like the rest of the animals.' Hearing this, the fox took the hen between his teeth and deposited her unharmed in her ladies' cloister. And those

347

who saw so great a marvel wrought in either place, made merry over it and blessed God.

Another time another fox stole a book from the brethren, and carried it off to hide it in one of his earths, intending to come back shortly and gnaw it there. But on his return to the monastery, he was found stealing and eating a honeycomb. Whereupon the brethren laid hold on him and brought him to St Moling, and accused him of stealing the book. And the holy old man bade the brethren to let him go free. And when he was released, the Saint said to him, 'O wise and crafty one, be off, and bring me back that book unharmed, and quickly.' At that, off went the fox, and hasted to bring the book from his cave, and set it down dry and unharmed before the holy bishop. And then he lay upon the ground before the man of God, as if seeking forgiveness. And the Saint said, 'Get up, you wretch, and fear nought: but never touch a book again.' And the fox got up rejoicing, and fulfilled in marvellous wise the Saint's behest: for not only did he never touch books again, but if any one would show him a book in jest, he took to flight.

ON A WING AND A PRAYER

Alan Coren

The largest known creature ever to have flown, an extinct reptile with an estimated wingspan of fifty-one feet, has been discovered by fossil hunters in West Texas. The creature had twice the wingspan of the biggest previously known pterodactyl.

The Times

From a hole in a rock just outside what was to become Sevenoaks, Homo Britannicus slowly emerged into the grey morning. A single snowflake floated down and settled on his forearm, paused, and dissolved among the thick, matted hair. He watched it disappear, his thin rim of forehead wrinkling.

A second landed on his broad flat nose. He squinted at it until it became a droplet, and until that droplet vanished.

'What's it like out?' called his wife, from the dark recess of the cave. H. Britannicus shivered.

'Bloody freezing,' he said. 'Also, promise you won't laugh, the rain is coming down in bits.'

His wife scuttled out, her lovely knuckles skimming the ground.

'What?' she said.

'Look,' he said. 'Bits.'

She looked at the snow, and she looked at the leaden sky.

'That'll be the Ice Age coming, then,' she said.

'Here,' said H. Brittanicus, 'what's that grey coming out of your mouth?'

349

'It's coming out of yours as well,' she snapped. 'How do I know what it is, I've never been in an Ice Age before, have I?'

H. Britannicus shook his head slowly. Tiny Pleistocene items flew out of his thatch, and hitting the chilly air, immediately became extinct.

'What's it all coming to?' said H. Britannicus. 'Where will it all end? When I was a kid, the summers we had!'

'I blame,' said his wife, 'the tool. All these bone needles, all these flint hammers, it's not natural.'

'Progress,' said her husband. 'You got to have progress.'

He tried to stand a little more erect. It wasn't easy.

'I'm off for a bit of a stroll,' he said. 'I'll catch me death standing here.'

★   ★   ★   ★

It was just outside what is now the subsoil of Canterbury that Homo Britannicus glanced up through his rime-hung eyebrows and noticed a figure shambling towards him. It had a pterodactyl on its arm.

'Morning,' said Homo Britannicus, taking a firmer grip on his club, just in case.

'Bonjour,' said the figure.

H. Britannicus raised his club slightly.

'What?' he said.

'Mah nem,' said the figure, 'eez Omo Gallicus. 'Ow eez eet going?'

'Mustn't grumble,' said Homo Britannicus. 'Where are you from?'

Homo Gallicus pointed behind him with his free hand, towards France.

'Ah 'ave walk many days,' said Homo Gallicus, 'wiz a proposition.'

'It looks like an ordinary bloody pterodactyl to me,' said Homo Britannicus. 'And what's that round your neck?'

'Wi call zem onions,' said Homo Gallicus.

Homo Britannicus reached out and felt one, cautiously.

'You'll never kill nothing with that, son,' he said. 'Too soft.'

'Wi eat zem,' said Homo Gallicus.

Homo Britannicus looked at him.

'It takes all sorts,' he said. 'What's the pterodactyl for?'

'Where can wi talk?' replied Homo Gallicus.

e years they fed it, while it grew bigger and bigger. The
at continued to blow through Europe having taken its
the vegetation was now so sparse that the family of
nicus spent its every waking hour in scouring the white
pterosaur fodder, they themselves subsisting on grubs and
nd anything else the pterosaur could not use.
l it be big enough?' they would plead of the manufacturers,
be ready? When will it all end? When will the miracle

anufacturers, by now mere hirsute skeletons themselves,
oon, soon.'
in the bleak autumn of the tenth year, when its wingspan
fifty-one feet, and its sleek giant body was consuming a
and its insistent 'ERK! ERK!' had reached a pitch and
would start avalanches rolling a dozen leagues away, they
Gallo-Britannic pterosaur out of its enormous cave, and
hat it was ready.
head West,' cried Homo Gallicus, 'to zer sun and zer

itannicus clubbed his wife for the last time, tenderly.
wo shakes,' he said, and gathering the mangy ratskins about
ones, he and his colleague climbed aboard.
t wings flapped, and the pterosaur lumbered down the
trail of webby pot-holes, and took off.
thing they saw, before the freezing snow-clouds enfolded
he pitiful little knot of rags beneath, staring upwards.
med to be praying.

*   *   *   *

m in the place that was subsequently Dallas.
of fat, balding hominids were sitting around a triceratops-
l, examining a roughly circular rock that Homo Texus was
nd down.
said Homo Oklahomus, who had made the trip especially
could be very big. It could be, like, very big indeed.'
e right packaging,' said Homo Arkansus.

They found a small cave, and crept inside, and sat down. Homo
Britannicus blew on his fingers.
'I wish we had a couple of sticks,' he said.
'What for?'
Homo Britannicus thought for a while.
'I'm not sure,' he said, at last. He nodded towards the pterodactyl.
'What about him, then?'
'In mah country,' began Homo Gallicus, 'wi 'ave no dinosaurs. Zer
dinosaur eez—'ow you say?'
'Extinct.'
'Exactement! 'Owevaire, wi 'ave zer pterodactyl. You, on zer uzzer
'and, 'ave no pterodactyl, but you 'ave zer dinosaur, n'est-ce pas?'
'Just a few,' said Homo Britannicus. 'They're a bit bloody ropey,
mind. Past their best, know what I mean? We've let 'em run down,
werl, there's no call for 'em these days, is there?'
'Ah beg to diffaire,' said Homo Gallicus. He bent forward, and his
black eyes glittered. 'Mah plan eez to mate zer Gallic pterodactyl wiz
zer Brittanic dinosaur! Wi will produce zer Gallo-Britannic pterosaur,
mon vieux! Eet weel be zer biggest flying objeck evaire seen!'
'So what?'
'Zer Ice Age is coming, hein?' said Homo Gallicus. 'In an eon or two,
eet will be 'ere. Wi weel 'ave to find warmaire climate, or . . .' he drew
a thick finger across his imperceptible neck. 'Wi cannot walk, eet eez
too far; so wi weel climb aboard zer giant pterosaur—*an' wi weel fly
there!*'
'Gerroff!' cried Homo Britannicus.
'Also,' continued Homo Gallicus, unruffled, 'wi weel rule zer worl'!
Everyone weel want one. Wi weel clean up zer pterosaur market.'
Homo Britannicus, to be fair, did all he could to fathom this
momentous idea: he furrowed his millimetric brow, he scratched his
craggy head, he sucked his great green teeth. But it was not until Homo
Gallicus began to draw upon the cave-wall with his easy, flowing line,
that his partner-to-be was really convinced.
It looked wonderful, in the picture.

*   *   *   *

Over the next five years, the innumerable, unforseeable technological problems came forth and multiplied.

For two years alone, the dinosaur and the pterodactyl could not be persuaded to mate at all, and the wretched co-partners were forced to stand by while the two halves of the project shrieked and bit one another. But in the third year, by a process of strategic starving, feeding and cajoling, the message got gradually through, and the dinosaur fell pregnant.

Ultimately giving birth to an enormous saurian cylinder with six legs and two very small wings. It flapped these latter for a few impotent beats, fell over, and expired.

'Ah well,' said Homo Gallicus, 'back to zer cave-wall!'

Which was all very well, except that the family of Homo Britannicus was finding it more and more difficult to make ends meet: it was not merely that most of their breadwinner's time was spent in husbanding the animals involved, but also that those animals were consuming a vast amount of food. They were being saved from natural extinction only at the expense of the unfortunate hominids who had been forced to cast their lot with them.

'You never told us it would cost this much,' was how Homo Britannicus's wife put it, over and over again.

Whereupon her husband would flatten her with his club, a gesture which over the years was becoming less and less affectionate.

But towards the end of the fifth year (by which time the temperature had dropped to a constant ten below zero, and the emaciated families of the luckless inventors reduced to gnawing for nourishment upon the misshapen bones of past failed experiments), a small pterosaur was produced of rather pleasing proportion. Even more encouraging was the fact that when it flapped its large feathery wings, it actually took off, flew for a few yards, and landed again without breaking anything.

'It works!' shrieked the two Homos, hugging one another and dancing great whorls in the encircling snow. 'A new dawn is breaking!'

'Erk,' went the baby pterosaur. It opened its mouth wide. 'Erk.'

'Eet wants,' said Homo Gallicus, 'to be fed.'

⋆　　⋆　　⋆　　⋆

The two of them rejoiced whe[...]

For five mor[...]
cold wind th[...]
constant toll[...]
Homo Brita[...]
landscape for[...]
bits of bark [...]

'When wi[...]
'when will i[...]
begin?'

And the [...]
would say '[...]

And then,[...]
had reached[...]
field a day,[...]
volume that[...]
trundled th[...]
announced [...]

'Wi wee[...]
fleshpots!'

Homo B[...]

'Back in t[...]
his jutting [...]

The grea[...]
runway in [...]

The last [...]
them, was [...]

They see[...]

It was war[...]

A group[...]
shaped po[...]
rolling up[...]

'I agree,[...]
to see it,'[...]

'With t[...]

'With the right packaging,' said Homo Oklahomus, nodding.

It was at that point that the sun was blotted out.

'What the—!' cried Homo Texus, letting the wheel roll from his fingers.

They leapt up, as the pterosaur came in to a perfect two-point landing, and ran across. Homos Gallicus and Britannicus jumped down.

'This is private property, buddy!' shouted Homo Texus.

'And this,' cried Homo Britannicus, 'is the Gallo-Britannic pterosaur! It will revolutionize travel, it will open up whole new experiences, it will . . .'

'The hell it will!' shrieked Homo Texus.

'Did you hear the goddam noise?' screamed Homo Oklahomus.

'My God!' yelled Homo Arkansus, pointing a trembling finger, 'look at its damn droppings!'

'The environment!' howled the Americans, 'The environment!'

Whereupon, brushing aside the enfeebled European bonebags, they fell upon the hapless pterosaur, and beat it to death.

A WHITE HORSE WITH WINGS

Anthea Davis

In this re-telling of the ancient Greek myth the hero, Bellerophon, has been ordered by the king to kill the Chimaera, a monster which has been ravaging the land. He seeks out the beautiful winged horse Pegasus, and tames him with a magic bridle. Together they spend a week training for the battle with the monster, using a cabbage stuck on a stake for target practice.

In the cool of the day Bellerophon waded out into the bay and rescued the target, and moved it on to a ledge below which the slabs of rock jutted out like fangs. He lit his fire, taking an armful of smelly seaweed up there on Pegasus's back, which annoyed the horse considerably. Then they flew at the target from about three, four and five hundred feet in succession, and cut off its cabbage head all three times. Each dive was perfect.

That was the end of the training, and Pegasus was so pleased with himself that he did one of his most hair-raising tricks—scrambling up the steep side of the inlet on his feet, with the loose rocks shifting and toppling as he gripped them, only opening his wings when he slipped down, or fell backwards from the overhanging boulders.

'Absurd creature,' said Bellerophon happily. 'Now fly along and play while I sharpen the sword, and then we'll both have an early night.'

Half an hour later he found himself sitting on the cliff-edge shouting: 'Pegasus! Bedtime!' to the horse weaving in the air like a bat. Pegasus at once went and hid in a cloud, and Bellerophon lay back on the dewy grass and laughed.

'You make me feel such a fool sometimes,' he chuckled. Pegasus finally flew down to him, pretending to try to knock him off the cliff.

Next morning before daybreak Bellerophon schooled Pegasus for the last time on the shore. The tide was coming in, and Pegasus minced along with his head tucked demurely in and his ears nicely forward, swishing his tail and giving little bucks and snorts. Once he raised his wings and clapped them, and shook them into place again, like a game little merlin on the falconer's wrist.

'Up,' said Bellerophon, eventually, and the horse took off as lightly as if he hadn't been working harder during the past week than he had at any time in his life since he was a fledgling.

They flew inland, towards the east. The journey took two days. On the morning of the third day they drew near to a lonely mountain that reared up in the eye of the rising sun, above a richly cultivated plain. On the ground below them they saw as they flew several large burnt patches, some still smoking, and a smouldering farmhouse where grimfaced men and women were trying to save their belongings from the flames. As Pegasus's shadow fell across them they scattered like sparrows from a hawk, but Bellerophon coaxed the horse down to the fire and looked in at all the windows to make sure there was no one trapped inside.

'Did the Chimaera do this?' he called, and the people came out of cover, staring and dazed, and answered that he had, and that he had also carried off a child. They were too griefstricken to be amazed at the winged horse. They told Bellerophon that the monster was three times as big as Pegasus, with enormous wings of naked skin. They did not hold out much hope, but they cheered the horse and rider revengefully and hoarsely on their way. Bellerophon thought he would never forget their smoke-blackened faces.

'Only people who have seen the Chimaera will take *you* for granted also,' he said to Pegasus as they flew on. 'But I also have seen the monster—in my dreams. Oh, horrible!'

They went over the last village, which was just waking up, so that the cocks crowed at Pegasus from the housetops and the beasts, brought into the streets every night for safety, stamped and jostled each other, and started the dogs barking.

Beyond that was a great swath of desolate and darkened ground.

357

Then they flew up to the inaccessible cave in the mountain that only wings could reach, where the monster had its den. Bellerophon had known that he could have no hope of killing the monster unless he too had wings, and could take it unawares in the place where it thought it was unassailable. To this purpose he had had the magic bridle made, and then sought for the legendary Pegasus over half the kingdom.

He had hoped that the Chimaera would be lying gorged and half-sleeping in the cave-mouth, but when Pegasus swayed past the dark hole as silently as an owl, there was nothing to be seen. However, the reek of the monster's fumes blew out of the opening, and Bellerophon, his heart drumming, took a deep breath and shouted:

'Come on, Chimaera, let's see you then!'

On the heels of his shout Pegasus neighed fiercely. The tunnel echoed, and then there was silence, while Pegasus hovered, waiting.

'It can't be as big as they said, unless it's long and thin,' said Bellerophon, shakily, 'or it'd never get in through that crevice.'

They heard suddenly the scraping of claws and hoofs on rock, and the Chimaera slowly appeared. It was no bigger than Pegasus, and with a shorter spread of wing. It had three deformed heads, those of a lion, a goat and a serpent. Its forefeet were those of a lion, and its hindfeet those of a goat, and its body was long and scaly with a sinuous tail. It breathed flame from its six nostrils. It looked grotesque, ridiculous even, with all the unreasonable horror of a nightmare. Bellerophon, who had once or twice had the tears brought to his eyes by Pegasus's unfathomable beauty, had the crazy feeling that if he laughed long enough at this incomprehensible chaos it would vanish into nothing.

There could be no mistaking the malice in the Chimaera's three pairs of eyes as its heads stopped squabbling and slavering over a mangled hand, and turned their brooding regard on Bellerophon and Pegasus. Pegasus stared with enormous eyes and ears tensely pricked, and then spun round as speedily as a dragonfly to get out of range. The monster threatened them with jets of fire.

'We can outfly it, at least,' said Bellerophon, keeping his voice calm and practical, and measuring the ungainly body with his eye. 'But we must tempt it to the edge of the opening, or it'll dodge into the cave every time we attack. Let's tease it a bit.'

The monster breathed jets of fire at Bellerophon and Pegasus.

By now Pegasus was quaking and sweating, and each time he was set at the cave-mouth he sheered off-course long before the shooting flames could touch him, while Bellerophon menaced the Chimaera with his sword. But the monster stayed well within its lair, crouched to strike.

'I know,' said Bellerophon at last, and sent Pegasus scrabbling up the side of the mountain above the cave. The horse went willingly enough, loosening the scree with his hoofs as Bellerophon had intended, and sending it tumbling and ringing down the slope. Before they reached the mountain top the Chimaera had been forced out of its den, for the noise not only brought it to the edge of the cliff-face to glare wrathfully up at its enemies, but the sliding shale lodged itself across the cave-mouth and blocked it up, with a great commotion of dust and flying chips. In fact, the Chimaera narrowly missed being trapped inside. As it was, it was caught by the tail for nearly a minute, and had to burrow with its talons to get free.

But although Bellerophon's plan had succeeded far better than he could have hoped, he and Pegasus did not take advantage of the minute's grace they might have had. They were at the top of the mountain, and Pegasus, his head up and laid sidelong into his neck, his ears flattened, his eyes showing bloodshot, and his heels anchored like crowbars, was refusing to go down again. At each attempt Bellerophon made to fly him, he half-opened his wings and then jibbed, backing away from the edge. It was evident that had it not been for his love for Bellerophon he would have flown away altogether.

After a time Bellerophon got off his back, and rubbed the horse's throat and shoulders while he thought. The hide was dank and chill. Pegasus hung his head distressfully over his rider's bent back. Bellerophon wound his arm over Pegasus's neck, and leant forward to look over the steep drop to the cave.

'He's out there all right.' He straightened up. 'All right, Pegasus, my beauty, you've brought me far enough. You stay here and I'll climb down the way you came up, and see if I can take him unawares.'

This was complete nonsense, and he knew it, and he dropped his voice despairingly at the end in spite of himself.

He kissed the horse's face between the eyes, and then let himself down over the edge of the precipice, before he could start to feel as panic-stricken as Pegasus.

Immediately, his feet began to slip, and then his handholds gave way. As he lost his grip and went bumping down his held breath came out in a scream, and Pegasus neighed furiously from above him. The monster answered with a bellow.

Then Pegasus leapt over the cliff after Bellerophon, and caught the swordbelt in his teeth. Bellerophon, winded and badly grazed, hauled himself up as best he could with Pegasus's help, while the horse's wings lashed round him and his steamy breath blew into his hair.

Pegasus dumped him at the top, and waited impatiently for him to recover himself. Bellerophon stopped gasping, and adjusted the swordbelt over his chafed belly. Then he eyed the horse that loomed over him and grinned. Pegasus's eyes were still huge with fright, but his ears were flicking to and fro naturally, and his neck was curved so that the skin puckered into wrinkles behind his cheek. He scraped the ground with his forefeet and fluttered his wings nervously but urgently. Not for nothing had Bellerophon praised his courage.

Bellerophon climbed on his back, and the horse sailed unhesitatingly out over the Chimaera's vantage point. Bellerophon drew his sword with a flash in the sun. The monster gathered itself together to pounce. Pegasus circled upwards and then idled, turning in the light wind and choosing his moment. Not for nothing had Bellerophon praised his intelligence also, for he put the sun behind him so that it shone straight into the Chimaera's eyes as they focused on him. When he dropped Bellerophon for once was not taken by surprise and was with the horse all the way. They hurtled downwards. The monster stayed motionless. The attack was accurate and deadly. At the turning-point of the dive Bellerophon struck cleanly, and although the shock of the impact made him reel, they were out of danger before the lion's head hit the rock and fell from there into the gulf. The Chimaera howled after it, and the head howled back. Bellerophon shuddered, and held his dripping sword clear of himself and his horse.

Pegasus, on the other hand, pranced and sidled in the air, behaving like himself again.

'Don't be frivolous,' said Bellerophon gently, checking him. 'Two more heads yet.' Pegasus, familiar with this reproof, was duly chastened, and started to gain height for the next dive. The Chimaera, realizing its peril, pressed itself against the mountainside. When it heard the air booming in Pegasus's wings as he dived the second time, it shrank back still further. This made everything more difficult. As the sword cut through the goat's neck it hit the rock behind and broke off a foot from the point. Pegasus's right wing and his tail were scorched by the fire that welled out of the stump of neck as he pivoted on the ledge, but they didn't catch alight. He swung clear as the second head followed the first.

The Chimaera now appeared smaller still, but more venomous. It wreathed itself in smoke.

'One more,' said Bellerophon jubilantly. 'We'll have to go in a bit closer next time, though.'

He and Pegasus had grown very sure of themselves, but the Chimaera was desperate. It turned at bay, and on the third dive it was ready for them. As they levelled out beside it for the last attack, it lunged off the solid rock, uncoiling and springing towards them ponderously but fluidly. Bellerophon was leaning over recklessly, and Pegasus dared not fling himself out of range. For a moment both creatures hung in space, and it seemed as if the air would not support the Chimaera, and that it would fall down between Pegasus and the ledge it had left, and hit the rocks far below. Then it jack-knifed in its own length, as a worm doubles up on itself when you touch it, straightened out and stretched itself with a jerk, and reached out to take a stranglehold with its forepaws on the flying horse. The three of them sank together through the gulf in a whirlwind of struggling and blows. Pegasus, lurching and foundering, flew hopelessly towards a little tarn about half a mile away, though he knew that they would all either have gone up in flames or crashed to the ground before they got anywhere near so safe a landing. He kicked like a catapult at the wriggling body of the Chimaera, and with a savage snap fixed his teeth in its neck, just behind the one remaining head. Bellerophon, snatching his feet out of the way of its fiery breath, found himself kneeling between Pegasus's wings, staring into the lidless eyes and open mouth of the snake's head, held fast as it was in Pegasus's jaws as if in a clamp. He seized his sword with both hands and drove the broken blade with all his strength down between the snake's fangs into its gullet. He leant back just in time as a blast of fire shot skywards. I should have struck through both sides of its mouth, he thought, and pinned them together. Too late now, the sword's stuck for good. Still, at least we'll take the brute with us, when we hit the ground and break ourselves in pieces.

But the monster was dead. Less than the height of a house roof from the earth its grip loosened, Pegasus unclenched his teeth, and the carcase fell away, the sword between its lips. It turned over once before it smashed down on a solitary boulder and lay humped over it, with its spine splintered and its limbs collapsed round it.

Pegasus bounced in the air as the weight left him, and then glided on for nearly a mile with Bellerophon sprawled across his back, until he came to rest in a meadow full of cows and sheep.

★　　★　　★　　★

The grazing beasts showed no signs of alarm, but came quietly up and gathered in a circle round the winged horse and his rider, and bowed their heads. Then they spread out and wandered off again. At least, that was how it seemed to Bellerophon. He dismounted, and walked unsteadily round Pegasus to see if he had any injuries. Pegasus started to follow him, so they walked drunkenly round each other a couple of times before Pegasus stopped, and shook himself stiffly. A few burnt plumes floated down, his tail was ragged, and he had some claw-marks in his neck, but that was all. Bellerophon's hands were torn from slipping on the rocks, and his feet were singed. Both of them were smeared with oily soot.

'I think, between us, we've done a really good day's work,' Bellerophon said muzzily, as he sat down on the grass.

'So do I,' said a girl's voice. Pegasus snorted. It was the daughter at the nearby farmstead. She had seen the final part of the battle, and had followed on foot to offer the victors her own breakfast. Where there has been a Chimaera, people wisely take everything for granted—or else, foolishly, take nothing on trust.

'Good day's work! It isn't even breakfast time yet,' she said, but her eyes shone. She gave Bellerophon a hunk of bread and cheese and an apple. 'Here's a piece of honeycomb for your horse.' She was accustomed to animals, but she looked cautiously at Pegasus. Even in weariness and grime his beauty was startling and his aspect full of glory. But he came hopefully up for his titbit, and sucked it out of her palm like a foal.

'You'll get toothache, you pampered jade,' said Bellerophon tenderly. Pegasus bent his head, took Bellerophon's apple out of his hand, and crunched it up.

'I think you're both heroes,' said the girl, laughing. 'I'll make you both garlands after I've done the milking. How is the king going to reward you?'

'His daughter's hand, I think,' said Bellerophon, with his mouth full. 'He didn't think I'd do it, you see. He didn't believe in Pegasus. I don't think he was too sure about the Chimaera either.' The girl didn't understand this. 'He just wanted to get rid of me. I wasn't in love with his daughter anyway, though I think I thought I was at the time.' She understood this. 'I'd forgotten all about her till now. It all seems so remote. I don't think I'll go back to the capital. The king will hear the news in his own good time, and the main thing is, the Chimaera's dead.' The girl, who had better reason than Bellerophon to know the importance of this, since she had lived for a long time under the shadow of the monster, nodded gravely. 'Anyway, I doubt if Pegasus would fancy a triumphal procession. He doesn't need telling how brave and clever he is—do you, greedy?' Pegasus put his head over Bellerophon's shoulder, took away his last mouthful of bread and cheese, mumbled it for a moment, and then dropped it back in his lap.

'Thank you!' said Bellerophon. 'I say, is there a stream nearby? I'm awfully thirsty.'

'Yes, but if you'd rather have milk there'll be some shortly. Lie still a minute, and I'll fetch my favourite cow and milk her into your mouth.'

She went off to collect a wooden pail and stool from under the hedge, and returned followed by a pretty little brindled cow, who stood quietly while her milkmaid settled herself with her head in her flank and milked one teat into the pail, and the other into Bellerophon's mouth, until he had had enough. Pegasus watched solemnly while he spluttered.

'Don't let him near the bucket,' Bellerophon warned, 'or he'll blow into it and spray the milk all over you.' But Pegasus trotted off to take his turn at the water trough.

'What are you going to do about him?' the girl asked quietly, changing on to the other two teats.

'Well, we'll probably go back to Helicon—the place where we met,' said Bellerophon, puzzled first by the question and then by the answer, which suddenly seemed to be not quite what he wanted. 'Actually, I'd rather stay here, but I expect he'd like to go back. It's his home, I think, if he has one. You know—I hadn't thought about it—he loves me, well, I love him just as much—but we'll have to part some day, I suppose.'

'You will,' the girl agreed. 'He's immortal.'

'So he is. Of course. I hadn't taken it in properly. Oh, Pegasus,' he said, softly and sorrowfully.

'Where's *your* home?' the girl asked quickly, hating to see him look so heartbroken at the thought of the parting.

'Nowhere, really. I've been wandering about most of my life. Now I've had one real adventure, I'd like to settle down, for good.'

'Doing what?'

'Oh, I don't know.' He watched her stripping the udders for the last drops, and grinned as an idea struck him. 'Is it easy to milk?'

She grinned back.

'It comes naturally to some. I'll bring the old white cow over to you and you can try and see.'

✶ ✶ ✶ ✶

When the milking was over and all the milk taken down to the farm, Bellerophon and the girl went back to the meadow and groomed Pegasus, for he hated feeling scruffy; and Bellerophon washed himself in the stream while the girl made garlands for the man and the horse, which they wore until the noonday sun withered them. Then the two humans lay and talked and talked in the shade until the evening, while Pegasus browsed round them. As the sun began to set the winged horse sprang into the air, and drifted among the darting swallows like a great white moth. Then he rose higher and set off westwards.

'Goodbye!' shouted Bellerophon suddenly. A distant, unmistakable neigh came back to him. The girl put her arms round him to comfort him.

'Was he jealous?' he said unhappily.

'No!' said the girl. 'But he must be given all your heart or nothing.'

'I'm afraid he'll be lonely,' said Bellerophon.

★   ★   ★   ★

For years Bellerophon would never ride an ordinary horse, even when he had married the girl, and had a son of his own, and the farmstead had prospered exceedingly under his hands, after the setbacks it had received while the Chimaera was alive. Then, one day, he saw his son gazing up at the sky, listening, with a white plume in his hand. Later he noticed grass-stains on the boy's tunic, and hoofprints that came and went in the dew. His wife remarked that honeycomb was always going from the larder.

'I think I'll get myself a little cob to ride round the pastures, instead of walking,' he thought. 'I'm not as young as I was, after all.'

There would always be someone who would find in Pegasus the companion he needed in adventure, after the winged horse had first learned, by making a friend of Bellerophon, to bestow his friendship among mortal men.

Acknowledgements

THE MIRACLE CLIMB, an extract from *Two in the Bush* by Gerald Durrell. Copyright © Gerald Durrell 1966. All rights reserved. Published by William Collins, Sons and Company Limited and Viking Penguin, Inc.

THE GREAT FEAR, an extract from *Wild Lone* by 'BB'. Published by Methuen Limited. Reprinted by kind permission of the publisher and David Higham Associates Limited.

THE WILD GOOSE CHASE AT THE KINGDOM OF BIRDS, by G. K. Chesterton. Reprinted by kind permission of A. P. Watt, Ltd and the estate of the late G. K. Chesterton.

THE CHIMPS COME TO CAMP, an extract from *In the Shadow of Man* by Jane Goodall. Published by William Collins. Reprinted by kind permission of the publishers. Copyright © Jane Goodall.

TYTO AND BRILA, an extract from *Tyto, the Odyssey of an Owl* by Glyn Frewer. Published by J. M. Dent and Sons Ltd. Reprinted by kind permission of Bolt & Watson and Lothrop, Lee & Shepherd Co.

PEPINO AND VIOLETTO, an extract from *The Small Miracle* by Paul Gallico. Reprinted by kind permission of Hughes Massie Limited. Copyright © the estate of the late Paul Gallico.

THE PIPER AT THE GATES OF DAWN, an extract from *The Wind in the Willows* by Kenneth Grahame. Published by kind permission of Methuen Children's Books. Copyright © University Chest, Oxford.

THE WHITE SEAL, an extract from *The Jungle Book*. Reprinted by kind permission of A. P. Watt and Doubleday & Co Inc. Copyright © The National Trust and Macmillan and Company.

WILLIAM AND THE PRIZE CAT, from *William the Bad* by Richmal Crompton. Published by William Collins, Sons and Company Limited. Reprinted by kind permission of the publishers and the estate of the late Richmal Crompton. Copyright © the estate of the late Richmal Crompton.

ADOLF, an extract from *The Mortal Coil and Other Stories* by D. H. Lawrence, published by William Heinemann Ltd. and *The Posthumous Papers of D. H. Lawrence* edited by Edward MacDonald, published by Viking Press. Reprinted by kind permission of the publishers and Laurence Pollinger. Copyright © 1964 the estate of the late Mrs Frieda Lawrence Ravagli.

THE ELEPHANT HUNT, an extract from *The Curve and the Tusk* by Stuart Cloete. Published by William Collins, Sons and Company Limited and Houghton Mifflin. Reprinted by kind permission of the publishers, Curtis Brown and Jane Wislon. Copyright © 1942 Stuart Cloete.

MAXWELL'S OTTER, an extract from *Ring of Bright Water* by Gavin Maxwell. Published by Penguin Books Ltd. and E. P. Dutton. Reprinted by kind permission of the publishers. Copyright © 1960 Gavin Maxwell.

THE LITTLE LEARNED MILITARY HORSE, an extract from *The First Circus* by Joan Selby-Lowndes. Published by Lutterworth Press. Reprinted by kind permission of the publisher.

CHIA AND HER KITS by Joyce Stranger. Reprinted by kind permission of Hughes Massie.

SREDNI VASHTAR by 'Saki' from The Short Stories of 'Saki'. Copyright © 1930 by The Viking Press Inc. Copyright © renewed 1958 The Viking Press Inc. Reprinted by kind permission of The Viking Press, Inc.

THE TRIUMPH OF BILL BROCK, an extract from *Bambi* by Felix Salten. Published by Jonathan Cape and Simon and Schuster (a division of Gulf and Western). Reprinted by kind permission of the publisher. Copyright © 1928 and 1956 the executors of the Felix Salten Estate.

THE DEATH OF WAHB by Ernest Thompson Seton. Reprinted by kind permission of Tony Sheel Associates.

FRIEND MONKEY HELPS THE SAILORS, an extract from *Friend Monkey* by P. L. Travers. Published by William Collins. Reprinted by kind permission of the publishers and David Higham Associates Limited.

FOUR SAINTS, an extract from *Beasts and Saints* by Helen Waddell. Published by Constable Publishers. Reprinted by kind permission of the publishers.

ON A WING AND A PRAYER by Alan Coren. Copyright © Alan Coren.

A WHITE HORSE WITH WINGS by Anthea Davis. Reprinted by permission of Faber and Faber and Macmillan, New York. Copyright © Anthea Davis 1968.

THE HAPPY FAMILY EXHIBITOR, an extract from *Mayhew's Characters* by Henry Mayhew (edited by Peter Quennel). Reprinted by kind permission of William Kimber & Co Ltd.

THE WART'S LESSON, an extract from *The Once and Future King* by T. H. White. Published by William Collins Sons and Company Limited. Copyright © the estate of T. H. White. Reprinted by kind permission of the publishers and David Higham Associates.